Mistres

GW00391817

Lance Horner

Mistress of Falconhurst

Pan Books Ltd
London and Sydney

First published in Great Britain 1973 by
W. H. Allen & Co Ltd
This edition published 1975 by
Pan Books Ltd, Cavaye Place, London SW10 9PG
ISBN 0 330 24137 0
© Lance Horner 1973

Printed in Great Britain by
Richard Clay (The Chaucer Press) Ltd, Bungay, Suffolk

PART ONE

CHAPTER ONE

It was quiet in Elm Grove's big kitchen which, like those of most Southern plantations, was separated from the main house by a covered passageway. There was only the ticking of the old wag-on-the-wall clock; the occasional lifting of the lid of the heavy iron teakettle to let the steam escape; and the mumble of words that came from Lucretia Borgia's dark lips.

'Work, work, work all day. Tha's all I do. Wishin' I was a field hand instead of a cook. Field hand, he stop work at sundown 'n his day over; but me, I git the supper at night 'n my work jes' a-startin'. Where that worthless Delilah? Where that shiftless Emmy? They supposed to help, 'n neither o' 'em here. Delilah, she still simperin' round in the dinin' room, clearin' off the table when she should be out here helpin' me. 'N Emmy? Who knows? Dishes to wash 'n dry, kitchen to clean up 'n everything. Goin' to *clobber* that Emmy when she git here; jes' goin' to clobber her good.'

She bustled about, carrying on her scathing denunciations as she poured water into the two big pans that sat on the deal table in the middle of the room, piled high with dirty dishes.

'Here I am, a-scurryin' to git through afore it gits real dark so's I kin meet Jem down by the springhouse, and lookin' like that Emmy 'n that Delilah ain' goin' to come out in the kitchen at *all*. She probably crumbin' the table with a silver tray and crumber.' Lucretia Borgia paused and made a most elegant motion with her hands, little fingers lifted as though she were delicately performing some gentlewoman's function. 'Anyone think that she cook the dinner 'n all. Jes' cain' stand these uppity light-skins like that Delilah. She 'n her crumbin' the table 'n battin' her eyes at Mista Macklin. If'n the pore man wan't so sickly she'd shore

7

try to git into his bed when Miz Macklin not around, but he ain' no way able to take a bed wench, he ailin' so. One thing though, even if'n he well, he ain' a-goin' to bed me. No suh! I too big 'n black for him! But he shore do 'preciate my cookin'. Best cookin' in the world, if I do say so myself. Learn from old Aunt Jenny 'n learned myself too. Ain' *none* better'n me. Why, them biscuits tonight so light they almost float off'n the table.'

She looked up from her rambling monologue to see Delilah come into the kitchen with a big japanned tray of dirty dishes.

'Well, 'bout time yo' got here. Whereat that goddamn Emmy? Suppose yo' 'spects me to do all the work out here myself. Yo' knows it for yo' to wash the glasses 'n the silver 'n put 'em away, and it up to Emmy to do the rest. I ain' no parlour maid, but I ain' no cook 'n dishwasher 'n scullery maid too. Le's git started. I'll wash 'em 'n yo' rinse 'n dry 'em. Wants to git out'n the house afore it gits dark, I do.'

Delilah shook her dark curls over her shoulder. 'Suppose yo' a meetin' Big Jem somewhere. Yo' better be careful. He one right randy nigger, 'n he a-goin' to git yo' knocked up.'

'So, if'n he do?' Lucretia Borgia shrugged her shoulders and smiled with one corner of her mouth. 'He gits me knocked up 'n Mista Macklin gives me a silver dollar. Makes him no neverminds who does it jes' so long's I give him a sucker. Jem right good when it comes to pesterin' – 'n that something every wench got to have. Don' yo'?'

Delilah looked at Lucretia Borgia with a withering glance. 'Ain' so crazy 'bout pesterin' as yo'. Don' make me no neverminds. When Miz Macklin she a-sayin' that she want me to git her a sucker, she a-goin' to wait till a white man o' some bright skin come along so's mine won't be black. I ain' aimin' to roll 'round in the weeds with any black nigger like Jem. 'Sides, he too big 'n powerful for me. Look at me. I'm li'l, 'n light, 'n pretty. Ain' like yo', Lucretia Borgia. I do declare, for a gal who's eighteen or so, I never *saw* one so titted out like yo'. Yo' the biggest gal on the whole plantation.'

8

Lucretia Borgia drew herself up to her full height. She was indeed impressive. 'That's why Jem like me. He a-sayin' that he got somethin' to hold onto with me. 'N he ain' too big for me neither.' She giggled. 'He ain' big 'nuff for me! Why yo' talkin', Delilah? Le's get these dishes done. I do declare, don' know where that Emmy is who supposed to help me. Cain' cook 'n everything 'thout'n a kitchen slut. Miz Macklin done sent her up to straighten out her button box 'n she bin gone all afternoon, like they was a thousand buttons there. She a-thinkin' she a parlour maid too. If'n I was a-runnin' this place, run it different. Ain' sendin' no scullery maid up to straighten out no button box. That really yore job.'

'But I bin busy a-sewin' for Miz Macklin. Cain' do everything.'

' 'N neither can I.' Lucretia Borgia leaned against the table and sloshed the soapy cloth over the plates. She was a tall girl, about five feet ten. Her light tobacco-brown skin showed either that she had some white blood or that she was from one of the North African tribes, possibly Jaloff with a touch of Mandingo or Hausa. Despite her size – and she was not corpulent but merely large – she was good-looking, with flashing brown eyes shaded by long, thick lashes. Her nose was only slightly flattened and her lips, not overbroad, were the colour of raisins. A tight-fitting calico dress, splitting at the seams, strained to cover her ample breasts, the big nipples of which showed through the cloth. She had a narrow waist, immensely broad hips, and stalwart legs. A complete Amazon of a woman – yet strikingly attractive.

She listened to approaching footsteps. 'Here come that Emmy now.' She peered through the open door that led to the passageway to the house. 'Anyone think she got nary a thing in this world to do but mince so ladylike 'cause she bin workin' for Miz Macklin! I'll take it out'n her.' She waited while Emmy, an awkward teen-age girl, entered the kitchen, and when she came near enough, Lucretia Borgia clouted her in the face with the soapy dishrag.

'Git to washin' 'n dryin' them dishes, gal! It ain' Delilah's

9

job 'n it ain' mine neither. Jes' cause Miz Macklin ask yo' to tidy up a few buttons for her ain' no reason yo' actin' like no upstairs house servant. Yo're here to help me in the kitchen, 'n damn lucky yo' are that yo're not choppin' cotton wid the rest o' the burrheads!'

She wiped her face with the folds of the cotton fichu around her neck. 'God, it hotter'n hell in here. Hope when evenin' comes it cool off a bit.'

With Emmy installed at the dishpan, Lucretia Borgia began tidying up the kitchen, wiping the broad shelf free of crumbs and putting back the spices and things she had used in preparing the meal. Nobody spoke, and if there was one thing Lucretia Borgia disliked it was silence.

'How Mista Macklin a-feelin' today?' she asked of Delilah, more to make conversation than anything else because she, like everyone else on the plantation, knew of her master's poor health.

'He still coughin' somethin' awful. Miz Macklin she think he got gallopin' consumption, the way he takin' on. Day comin' soon when he ain' goin' be able to manage this place with all the niggers 'n everythin'. Mista Macklin, he a sick man if'n yo' ask me.'

'Didn' ask yo'. Knows it myself.'

Emmy was getting the dishes done in good order. Delilah was counting the silver and putting it away in a special drawer. Lucretia Borgia gave one last wipe to the broad shelf and sighed with the completion of work well done. Whenever she had someone to boss around, things began to fly. Not that she was lazy herself; she was full of work and ambition, but her special faculty was getting work out of others.

'Katie git the supper ready for the hands?' she asked again, knowing the answer but wanting to hear the sound of her own voice.

Delilah nodded. 'She got it ready an' Big Jem he tooken it down to them. They a-talkin' at table tonight 'n Miz Macklin says that she a-goin' to change all that. Them that lives in cabins don' git slopped no more. Goin' to have all the cookin' done in the cabins when the hands git back from the fields. Any extra men a-goin' to eat in somebody's cabin. Say it easier that way. Mista Macklin, he say he order the vittles for 'em, 'n they cook it themselves. Ain' got 'nuff niggers on this plantation to do all the work, 'n those we got all a-gittin' older.'

For a long moment nobody spoke, then Lucretia Borgia asked, 'Whereat Miz Macklin now?'

'She a-settin' out on the front gallery, a-keepin' Mista Macklin company. He a-sayin' that he cain' do no more work, got to take it easy-like the rest o' the day. He wantin' to ask yo' if'n yo'll go down to the barns after yo' git through the dishes 'n see that everything 'tended to.'

'What he think I am, the overseer? That's what we need here. Mister Macklin ain' able; we needs us a good overseer.'

'He always dependin' on yo',' Delilah answered. 'Yo' know how yo' are, Lucretia Borgia. Yo' make everyone toe the line when yo' around. He say when you finish reddin' up the kitchen, yo' come out to see him on the gallery for a minute.'

'Jes' one damn thing after another.' Lucretia Borgia was fond of complaining, but she was secretly flattered to think that Mr Macklin wanted her to oversee things. She was aware that he looked to her for many tasks besides getting his three meals a day.

'Yo' know he always dependin' on yo',' Delilah answered, placidly smoothing her black calico and adjusting her little white apron. It was not flattery, but a statement of fact.

'Goin' now.' She turned to poor Emmy. 'If'n when I comes back everything not spick 'n span, goin' to clout yo' good. Yo' be sure to scrub that kettle with sand. Some nice clean sand in the keg out'n the back entry. Ain' wantin' no grease on that kettle when I gits back.' Lucretia Borgia wiped her hands on her apron, looked at it critically, went to a long cupboard off the kitchen and took out a new, stiffly starched apron. Behind the open door of the closet, so that nobody could see, she unwound the strip of plain madras that she wore on her head and rewound it again more neatly. She was ashamed of her hair; it was her one defect. It was short and no amount of combing could make it any longer. She never appeared without a headcloth.

With a nod to Delilah and a final admonition to Emmy, she walked across the gallery that led from the kitchen to the dining room, testing the surfaces of the furniture as she passed to see if they were dusty. Some of them were, and she frowned. If she was in charge of the house there wouldn't be a speck of dust anywhere. From the dining room, she progressed through the parlour or 'settin'room', through the wide hall and out onto the front gallery where Mr and Mrs Macklin were sitting.

The Elm Grove plantation had once had some pretension to having a fine and important big house, but things had long since begun to deteriorate. Of the two tall pillars that flanked the entranceway to the front gallery, one still supported its Ionic capital, but the other was nothing but the trunk of a tree, smoothly rounded to be sure, put up to take the place of the column which had rotted away. Both had once been painted white, but the paint was scaling and discoloured. The house itself was of a soft red brick which badly needed painting up, and the white trim of windows and doors was in as poor condition as the pillars. A line of trees, not elms despite the name of the plantation, but rather sweet gums, made a long lane from the big house to the main road.

Mr Macklin, a thin man, rocked placidly in a homemade rush-bottomed rocking chair. His high colour and thin cheeks contrasted oddly with the luxuriant moustache that seemed to have drained all the strength from his body. His thin waxen hands were hardly able to wield the broken palm-leaf with which he was fanning himself. Mrs Macklin, in direct contrast, was a plump, healthy-looking woman, filling the grey and white calico of her dress without a wrinkle.

'Yo' wantin' to see me, Masta Macklin suh?' Lucretia Borgia's voice was an octave lower and always respectful when she talked to white people.

'Shore do. Whar yo' bin all this time?'

12

'Had to git the supper dishes finished, Masta Macklin suh. That Emmy, she right slothful, 'n takes a lot to git her started.'

'Bet yo' got her started though. Things always happen when yo' round, Lucretia Borgia.'

'Yas suh, Masta Macklin suh. Shore ain' slothful myself.'

'Well, what I want is that yo' go down to the horsebarn 'n see that Djoubo have it all cleaned out. Ain' felt like goin' down today, 'n that boy mighty lazy. If'n he ain' done his work, set him to it; tell him I'm comin' down first thing in the mornin' to see how things are. Ain' jes' feelin' like it tonight, so Mrs Macklin 'n I a-settin' here on the gallery for the evenin'. When you finished with Djoubo in the barn, go to Bedelia's cottage 'n see if'n that Letty wench a-beddin' herself with Dade. Bin over a year since she had a sucker for me. 'Bout time somethin' happen. Ain' keepin' no more wenches round here less'n they produce for me. Trouble is, wenches is gittin' too old, 'n ain' got 'nuff good studs for 'em all. Goin' to git yo' covered pretty soon, Lucretia Borgia. High time I got a sucker out'n yo'. Jes' wonder who I a-goin' to mate yo' up with.'

'Shore would admire to be mated up with Big Jem. He ain' so handsome, but like him, I do.'

Mr Macklin levelled an accusing finger at her. 'Don' make a damn bit o' difference who yo' like or who yo' don'! Thinkin' maybe I'll put yo' to Albert. He ain' so old, 'n he right potent. Gits a sucker every time.'

'But he *is* old, Masta Macklin suh. Albert he mus' be 'bout thirty, 'n kinda puny like, too. Ain' got no more sap in him.'

'Lucretia Borgia.' Mrs Macklin spoke for the first time. 'Yo' inclined to argufy, 'n if'n there's anything I hate in a servant it's one what argufies. If'n Mista Macklin say Albert, then Albert it is. He kin bed down with yo' on yore quilt in the kitchen. What yo' wants, what yo' don' want – my land! Now jump, 'n don't stand there argufyin'. Go 'tend to those things Mr Macklin tell yo' 'bout, 'n when yo' come back, want yo' should knead up some bread. We mos'

13

out. I'll come out to unlock the larder when yo' gits back. Now hurry!'

Lucretia Borgia walked away, muttering to herself. 'Set bread, do the cookin', wash the dishes, oversee for Mista Macklin. A body don' have a minute to theyself! But don' make me no neverminds. Goin' to stop down by the springhouse where Big Jem said he'd be. Hope they-all don't think I ain' bin busted yet. Plantation like'n this with all the bucks and wenches, a gal reaches my age she always busted. Just hope I cotches with Big Jem so that Mista Macklin he git a good sucker out'n me. Don' want none by that puny ol' Albert. Why, Djoubo's better'n him. Might make a play for Djoubo. Only trouble, he a real bozal what jes' came over from Africy, 'n he ain' too good-lookin'. Hate to have my sucker look like him. Djoubo he right powerful, 'course, but not so powerful's Big Jem.'

She switched the skirts of her starched white apron off towards the barn. Djoubo was lolling on the barn floor.

'Yo' all cleaned up, Lucretia Borgia.' He rose and came over to stand by her. 'My, but yo' a pretty wench.' He grabbed for her hand but she pulled it away.

Her eyes took in the barn. 'Floor ain' bin swept all day 'n they's spilt oats over by that bin. Manure all out'n the horse stalls?'

'Well . . .'

'Better be. Mista Macklin he a'comin' down here later, 'n wants it all clean 'n nice. Yo' better step lively if'n yo' don' want him givin' yo' hell. He jes' might tie yo' up 'n strip yo' down.'

'Cain'! I the whopper here. Ain' no one kin lay it on like'n I do.'

'Want me to try?' she asked. 'Kin whop as well as yo' kin. Yo' damned lazy, Djoubo. Settin' here all day 'thout doin' a thing jes' 'cause Mista Macklin he a-ailin'. Now git started, or I'll draw off 'n wallop yo'.' She doubled up a fist that would have felled an ox.

'Now, Lucretia Borgia, le's yo' 'n me not git all out o' sorts.' His voice was filled with complaisant sweetness.

14

'Likes yo' I do. Bin thinkin' 'bout yo' all day. Thinkin' it right nice to pester yo', Lucretia Borgia. M-m-m! Yo' shore are titted out nice. Look,' he pointed down to the thin osnaburg trousers he was wearing, 'see what jes' thinkin' 'bout it do to me.'

She followed his glance to the rigid lump in his trousers. Her smile was almost an invitation. She walked over to him and let her hand glide smoothly over the projection and linger there a moment, pressing it with her fingers. 'Yo' a right nice boy, Djoubo, 'n someday I a-goin' to let yo' pleasure me. Yes, indeedy, some day. But jes' now yo' hop to it 'n git the barn redded up. I got a lot o' things to do an' ain' got no time now.'

He pressed closer to her, holding her hand, but she pulled away from him. 'Got to go, boy!' She gave a final squeeze and slipped away from him with a swish of her aproned skirts. 'Yo' start right in now 'n git this place all cleaned up, 'n I ain' forgittin' what I tol' yo'.'

She left him staring after her and started down the line of slave cabins to where Bedelia lived near the end of the street. The door was open and she went in. She addressed an ancient black woman sitting before the empty fireplace, smoking a corncob pipe.

'Evenin', Bedelia.'

'Evenin', Lucretia Borgia.'

'Whereat that Letty wench?'

'She out in the fiel' yet,' Bedelia answered. 'Still a-choppin' cotton. Ain' come home yet.'

' 'N Dade?'

'He still out too. Comin' in soon.' She pointed to the fireplace, the fire was out. 'Got to eat a col' supper, both o' 'em. Too hot to keep a fire goin'.'

'Dade a-coverin' Letty?'

Bedelia removed the corncob pipe and gazed up at Lucretia Borgia with rheumy eyes. 'Bed rope a-squeakin' so's I cain' git a wink o' sleep. Shore, he a-coverin' her, but he taken with that Hattie wench 'n I a-thinkin' she gittin' his strong sap first. He bin here three months now, a-goin' it

15

every night; Letty she ain' cotched yet but Hattie she already cotched, so she say. Don' think it Letty's fault 'cause she already had two suckers for Masta Macklin. Jes' think Dade all dreaned out when he git to her. Now that Hattie's knocked up, maybe Letty'll git some fresh sap.'

'Yo' give him 'nuff to eat?'

'He eatin' like'n a hoss.'

'Give him plenty o' clabber. Say that puts sap in a man.'

'He git plenty,' said the crone.

With a warning to Bedelia to see to it that things kept happening in her cabin, Lucretia Borgia left. Now that her errands were all accomplished she would have time for herself. She quickened her steps towards the springhouse.

CHAPTER TWO

The springhouse near the barn was low, its roof flush with the ground, on one side; but it became on the other a one-storied building of rough stone with steps leading down to an open door. Inside, a cold spring flowed over flat stones and it was here that perishable foods were kept cool: butter, milk, cream, lard and other things that would spoil in the heat. Because of the dampness around the springhouse, the ground was covered with high lush weeds, except for the path that led to its door. Nobody ever made an effort to cut down the weeds, which were now a veritable jungle.

Lucretia Borgia quickened her step along the path. She was late, but hoped against hope that Jem would be waiting for her. That was almost too much to ask, because Big Jem was popular with all the wenches on the plantation. He shared a cabin with a middle-aged woman called Muncie, but rarely stayed there except to sleep and eat. His lust for women was so strong that he often visited other plantations, sometimes being gone for several days, hidden in some cabin by a wench who was loath to let him go. When he returned to Elm Grove, as he always did, he was severely whipped with Djoubo's lash; but no matter how hard Djoubo laid it on or how many times Jem was whipped, it never cured him of running away if he had taken a notion for a wench on some other plantation. Just now, fortunately, he was interested in Lucretia Borgia, so he was willing to stay at home; but she, like all his other wenches, knew that the infatuation would be a short one and that he would be off and away as soon as he had tired of her. However, Lucretia Borgia, again like all the others, was hoping that he would stay infatuated with her. She was determined to keep him for her own for a while. He was not her first man. She had been initiated when she was not more than sixteen, but Big Jem was her first lover.

It was almost dark by the time she reached the spring-house and she halted at the entrance, listening for some sound other than the running of the water. Straining her ears, she could hear nothing. Finally she went to the corner where the weeds grew highest and whispered, 'Jem.'

The weeds slowly parted and a face, almost invisible in the darkness, appeared. Jem was a tall, good-looking fellow, rakish, well muscled and strong, but with a back that was corded with welts as large as blacksnakes, each one thick and well-rounded. His white teeth gleamed in the darkness as he grinned at her.

'Well, if'n it ain' Lucretia Borgia. My, my, but yo' shore look pretty tonight, li'l darlin'. Ol' Jem he bin a-waitin' 'n a-waitin', jes' hopin' yo' be comin'.'

'Busy up to the big house tonight, Jem.' Lucretia parted the weeds and went inside to where Jem had flattened them out. 'Jes' never did think I'd git away; ain' got much time neither. Miz Macklin, she a-waitin' for me to set some bread, so got to hurry 'n git back.'

His hands clasped her breasts and squeezed them. 'We ain' needin' much time tonight, Lucretia Borgia. Bin thinkin' 'bout yo' for so long, jes' about ready to pop, I am. See.' He

17

pushed her hand down to his crotch. 'Whyn't yo' lie down here beside me 'n jes' les' play around for a minute jes' to git things started.' He waited for her to take off her apron and undo the button of the linen blouse she wore underneath. Her breasts came free, pear-shaped and upstanding, and his fingers tweaked the nipples, making them hard and erect. With his other hand, he laid the flat part of his palm against the satin smoothness of her skin and let his hand creep up her thigh, exploring and reaching for the tender parts, making her squeal with delight.

'Ain' yo' goin' to play a little too?' he begged her, loosing the fly of his trousers which was held together by one wooden button. 'Yo' play around a little but be damn careful. Swear I 'bout ready to pop, cain' take much fondlin'.'

Her hand reached for the tumescent flesh and stroked lightly at first and then vigorously.

'Whoa, there, baby! *Tol'* yo' I cain' take much. How about a li'l kiss? They say kissin' is for white folks, and I know wenches ain' much for it, but once Big Jem kisses yo', yo' a-goin' to be hungry for it all yore life.' He placed his thick lips against hers and let the point of his tongue pass between her teeth. She responded.

'Likes kissin' with yo, Big Jem, but wouldn't like it with Mista Macklin with all that hair on his lip.'

'Sh-h-h! Don't talk about white folks now. They don' know nothin' 'bout pesterin'. That something white ladies never do less'n they wants to birth a sucker. Forget about white folks.'

For a few moments they lay there enraptured, their hands and tongues busy exploring, finding, satisfying. Finally with a 'Cain' stand it no longer,' he rolled her over on her back. 'Cain' take no more, Lucretia Borgia. Don' want to waste it on yore nice white apron.' She opened her legs in invitation. He mounted her quickly and without any preliminaries. For a second she moaned, and then pulled him to her. He plunged again, then gasped, sucked in a lungful of air and made a final thrust, dropping inertly on her, his limbs

18

twitching. 'M-m-m-m! That was wonderful.' He remained without withdrawing. She took his weight for a long moment and then slowly pushed him off. There was a note of exasperation in her voice. 'Yo' too quick tonight, Big Jem,' she complained. 'Ain' no fun in it for me when yo' come so quick-like. Kin yo' make it a second time if'n yo' hurries?'

He rolled away from her. 'Cain' make it again tonight, Lucretia Borgia. I plenty dreaned. Waited for yo' too long tonight 'n jes' couldn't hold it in. 'Sides, yo' said yo' in a hurry, so tried to do it quick-like for yo'.'

'But don' *like* it when yo' hurries too fast.'

'Lookin' like I won't be seeing yo' for a couple o' days. Found me a new wench over to Roundtree Plantation 'n she jes' a-dyin' for it. Thinkin' I may go over 'n visit her. She live with her mama in a cabin all alone 'n her mama, she a-likin' it as well as the gal. Shore dreans me a-keepin' 'em both satisfied.' There was bragging in his voice. 'Ain' none but Big Jem kin do it either.'

She sat up, buttoning her blouse and skirt and then slipping the apron on over her head. 'Yo' ain' goin' to run again, Big Jem?'

'Ain' runnin', li'l gal. I always come back. Jes' visitin' for a couple days. Masta Macklin git mighty mad at me 'n he have Djoubo give me some wales with a lash, but that don' make me no neverminds. Hurt like hell for a day or two but it wear off, 'n havin' all that pesterin' is worth it. Ain' 'nuff wenches on this plantation to keep a real man satisfied.'

'I'm here.' Lucretia Borgia stroked his face. 'Ain' I 'nuff for yo', Big Jem?'

'Ain' no one woman 'nuff for me. Shore would like to be a stud on some big plantation where they plenty o' wenches. What we got here? Only got 'bout three wenches what is young 'n pretty. All the rest ol'. Likes that gal what's Miz Macklin's body servant up at the big house, she that's bright-skinned, but Masta Macklin won' let me touch her. Shore is a misery when a buck don' have a wench. Look at pore Djoubo – he ain' got nobody 'tall. Djoubo a nice boy;

19

don' hol' it 'gainst him 'cause he wales me. Does it 'cause Masta Macklin say so, so ain' his fault. Whyn't yo' try Djoubo while I'm over to Roundtree? Know he mighty anxious for yo', Lucretia Borgia. He a-tellin' me so.'

She remembered her short contact with Djoubo in the barn that night. Certainly he was a lot more potent than anyone else on the plantation except Big Jem. 'Djoubo, he not bad,' she admitted, 'but he such a bozal 'n all. Don' know if'n he know how to pester or not. They must do it in Africy, Jem?'

'Better'n here, I've heard say.'

'May think about Djoubo then. Hopin' yo' planted a sucker in me tonight, Big Jem. Yo' so quick 'n powerful, mayhap I cotch tonight.'

'Mayhap. Who knows? Hear tell that Masta Macklin he a-goin' to give yo' to Albert.'

Lucretia Borgia made a face, screwing her lips together and popping her eyes. 'Don' want him, he so old 'n puny-like. Djoubo better'n him, 'cept Djoubo he so everlastin' homely. Never *see* such big lips on a boy, or such a flat squashed-out nose.'

'He be mighty potent once he git a chance at a wench, I bet. Masta Macklin he ain' bred him 'cause they ain' 'nuff wenches to go round at Elm Grove, 'n Masta Macklin a-sayin' too that he don' want no sucker what look like Djoubo.'

'Might jes' make up to him if'n yo' go, but hopin' yo' come back soon. Don' want yo' to stay away too long 'n git a lot more wales on yore back.'

'What's a few wales, gal, when it comes to some nice pesterin'?'

She stood up, arranging the folds of her madras and smoothing down her apron. Even in the darkness a spot stood out against the pure white. 'Oh, Jem, got me a grass stain on my nice clean apron! Whatever am I going to say to Miz Macklin?'

He laughed loud. 'Tell her yo' bin with Big Jem 'n she know how yo' git grass stains all over.'

20

'Oh, yo'!' She slapped him lightly across the face. 'Gotta run now, Big Jem.'

'Gimme a kiss afore yo' go. Seein' yo' when I git back from Roundtree. But remember! Not a word to anyone where I gone. Don' think Masta Macklin git the blood-hounds out 'cause he used to my runnin' 'n he knows I come back in a couple days or so.'

'Not a word,' she promised.

She freed herself from his lengthy kiss and ran along the well-beaten path, glad that she knew it so well; even in the darkness, she would not stumble. She came into the kitchen through the back door. Emmy had left one tallow candle burning in an iron candlestick on the table. One look assured Lucretia Borgia that everything was in order, and she took only a second to rub her fingers inside the big iron pot to see that it was clean. Quickly she went through the house and onto the front gallery where Mr and Mrs Macklin were waiting.

'Took yo' a powerful lot o' time to do a few errands, Lucretia Borgia.' Mrs Macklin was querulous.

Lucretia Borgia looked down at the green stain on her white apron. 'Had an accident, Miz Macklin. Was takin' a pan o' milk down to the springhouse to set for breakfast cream, slipped 'n fell. Lost the milk, I did, and had to go back to the dairy for more. All in all it took a lot o' time.'

Mr Macklin stopped rocking to point the fan at her. 'Yo' always bin right truthful to me, Lucretia Borgia, but if'n it any other wench I'd say she'd bin pesterin' with some buck out in the weeds. Shore yo' ain'?'

'No suh, Masta Macklin suh. 'Sides, they ain' no bucks here.'

Mrs Macklin gave her a look of strong disapproval, pushed back her chair and stood up, producing a large bundle of keys from her pocket. 'Well, Lucretia Borgia, if'n we're going to have bread tomorrow, we'd better get started. I'll go out in the buttery with yo' 'n get out the flour 'n sugar 'n such. Better make up a big batch, then we won't have to make it again so soon in this hot weather.'

21

'Oven shore do heat up the kitchen, ma'am.'

Mrs Macklin, with Lucretia Borgia following her, crossed the gallery. Just as they were about to open the door to go inside, Mr Macklin halted them.

'One minute, Lucretia Borgia! Yo' say yo' ain' particular 'bout Albert. Yo' a-sayin' that he kinda old. But he still gitting suckers.'

'Yas suh, Masta Macklin suh. Ain' got nothin' 'gainst Albert, he a right nice boy; but a trifle old for a wench like me.'

'Bin a-thinking. How yo' like that Djoubo boy out'n the barn? He a right nice boy too, but pretty awful niggery with them big lips o' his 'n all. Ain' never mated him up yet, but it no good for a buck not to be mated up. Gits ornery, he does, although ain' seen nothin' ornery 'bout Djoubo.' His mind went off on another track. 'But if'n they's one thing we need here at Elm Grove it's more wenches – young ones what kin bring in a good crop o'suckers every year. Thinkin' I better buy me some. Reckon I'll go over to Mr Oliver's at Spring Branch 'n see kin I git some from him. He a-sayin' as how he got some fresh ones. Ain' goin' to cost too much?' It was a question which he looked to Mrs Macklin to answer.

She nodded her head in agreement. 'Shore needs 'em, we do. Ain' got any here 'ceptin' those we had a long time, 'n most o' 'em ain' got a sucker left in 'em. We got Lucretia Borgia, we got Delilah, we got Letty 'n that li'l runt Emmy if'n she old 'nuff – and reckon she is. Why'nt yo' give Lucretia Borgia to Djoubo?'

'He awful black for Lucretia Borgia. Want to get some light-coloured suckers. They the ones that bring the money soon. Everyone a-lookin' for them.'

'Dade he a-coverin' Letty 'n Big Jem kin cover some of the new ones. Ain' anxious for him to cover Delilah. She bright-skinned with a lot o' human blood in her 'n like to git some real bright-skin suckers out'n her. Wishin' some nice young white fellow come along and spend the night here so's we could offer him Delilah for a bed wench. Ain' goin' to mate her up till I kin git some light blood for her.'

Mr Macklin rocked back and forth several times, pondering. 'If'n Mr Oliver sell me five wenches for five hundred dollars apiece, kin git more money on the mortgage. Worth it to have some good suckers comin' along. Slave dealers payin' high money now for niggers. Think I'll do it. No use in havin' niggers unless yo' can raise more. We sort of peterin' out here at Elm Grove. Should of sold off a lot of the hands a few years ago 'n got new ones. Pretty soon, if'n we don' do nothin', all we have will be a lot of ol' folks to take care of.' He nodded to himself in confirmation of his words and looked at his wife. She nodded back. Mortgaging the plantation to buy more niggers sounded like good judgment to her.

'Yo' talkin' few minutes back 'bout Djoubo 'n Lucretia Borgia here. Yo' a-goin' to do anything about it?'

Again Mr Macklin pondered the question.

'Ain' likin' for him to sleep in the kitchen with Lucretia Borgia; that Djoubo he mighty stenchy, being a bozal and all. 'N ain' wantin' Lucretia Borgia to sleep out in the barn, 'cause then she git stenchy too.'

'Masta Macklin suh?' Lucretia Borgia's question was for permission to speak.

'What yo' want now?' He was impatient with her.

'It warm weather. I kin give Djoubo a tin o' soft soap 'n he kin go down to the creek 'n wash himself all over good. Ain' musky after an all-over wash. I do it, 'n yo' knows I ain' musky.'

'If'n he'll do it,' said the owner dubiously.

'He'll do it if'n I tell him!' Lucretia Borgia was emphatic.

Mr Macklin looked up and smiled, his lips parting so that his teeth showed under his big moustache. 'Reckon he will, Lucretia Borgia. Sooner or later everyone seem to do as yo' tell 'em. Don' need me no overseer on this place so long's I got yo'.'

'Argufyin', always argufyin',' Mrs Macklin snapped. She

23

opened the front door and beckoned Lucretia Borgia to follow her. Out in the kitchen, Mrs Macklin looked around to see that everything was in order. She lit another tallow dip and placed it on the table. Taking the keys from her pocket, she unlocked the buttery door and measured out flour, sugar, and salt; then instructed Lucretia Borgia to go to the springhouse for lard. 'Yo' got the can o' yeast?' she asked.

Lucretia Borgia nodded.

'Then start in on the bread.' She turned with another quick look of inspection to see if there was anything she could criticize in the kitchen. There was nothing. Without a word, she left.

Lucretia Borgia started once again for the springhouse to get the can of lard. 'Bread!' she sniffed. 'White bread. Maybe it all pore Mista Macklin kin eat, but bread not so good as pone. Lots more work an' ain' nothin' when yo' git through. Ain' like pone. Now pone is somethin' that sticks to yore ribs. Kin do a day's work on pone. But bread! Pshaw!'

She started down the path to the springhouse, but without the light and expectant step she had taken over the same route before.

On the way back to the kitchen, she thought of stopping off at the barn and waking Djoubo to tell him the news. But it was too late, and there was the bread to make. Somehow she was not too sorry that it was Djoubo who had been chosen for her; he was better than Albert. Mr Macklin would tell him tomorrow. Well, this would be the last night she would have to take the quilt out of the closet and curl up on the floor of the kitchen alone. That was something to look forward to.

CHAPTER THREE

As soon as Big Jem had kissed Lucretia Borgia good-bye and watched her depart up the path to the big house, he separated the weeds and peered out to be sure there was nobody around. Nothing was stirring and he stepped out of the weeds and up the path, but when he came near the big house, he circled it, through a pecan grove at one side, and, avoiding its avenue of trees, came out on the main road. This led to Marysburg, the nearest settlement to Elm Grove. Big Jem did not fear travelling the roads at night. There were no patrollers in the vicinity, for the plantation owners in the area (none of them very large owners) had not yet banded together to hire men to patrol the roads at night on the watch for runaway slaves. Runners were uncommon in the neighbourhood and it seemed a waste of money to hire people to watch out for what few there were.

The moon was bright enough for him to see the road and he stepped along at a vigorous pace. Ordinarily he might have yielded to Lucretia Borgia and satisfied her twice, but he had a walk of some ten miles ahead of him and a welcome at the other end that would amply satisfy him.

Big Jem had been to Roundtree Plantation before; in fact, there was not a plantation within twenty miles that he had not visited at one time or another, or where he hadn't at least one wench anxiously awaiting his services. Actually Big Jem blamed Mr Macklin for his wanderings away from home. Every plantation owner should have a suitable wench for every buck. Raising children was a profitable sideline for any plantation owner. But of course Mr Macklin was not a big owner. Elm Grove was small and not over prosperous and he had not added to his stock of slaves since taking it over, with the result that most of them were around his own age, the women too old to produce offspring or to appeal to a boy of Big Jem's capabilities.

When he neared Marysburg, he took to the back roads

and fields until he had made a complete circuit of the village. He was about halfway to Roundtree and didn't want to arrive until after midnight so that he would not be seen by any of the other servants there. Effie, his present light-of-love, and her mother Amanda were expecting him. His knock would be a signal for them to open the door quietly and let him in. He had not made any plans as to how long he would stay – probably not more than a couple of days.

He well realized the punishment that was awaiting him when he returned but, although he dreaded the pain of the thrashing, it could not deter him from going out into the world to seek a little variety from the everyday monotony of Elm Grove. It had been his habit since he was a young man of twenty and Mr Macklin, although always angry at him for skipping out, knew that he was not really a runner and had never branded him on the cheek with the 'R' which signified that he was a habitual runner.

His long legs carried him along at a good pace and the moon was still up when he came to the stone gateposts and the avenue of trees that led to the big house at Roundtree. There were no lights in the big house or the slave cabins. People went to bed early on these Southern plantations, to arise early the next day and get out in the fields to work.

Circling the big house, noiseless as a cat, he came to the line of slave cabins. He was not exactly sure which cabin he wanted, but knew it was towards the end of the street. He carefully tiptoed to the one he thought it might be and listened at the opened shutter. He could hear the sound of a man snoring inside and decided that this was not it. He crept to the next one and listened. Surely there was no man here – only the sounds of women breathing.

The front door was ajar and he tiptoed inside, seeing only two dark forms, wrapped in blankets, on the floor. Cautiously he walked over to them, knelt down and placed his fingers on the smooth skin of a woman's neck. She stirred in her sleep and he touched her face lightly. Yes, he was sure that this was Effie, and the woman beside her must be her mother. With his hand over her mouth to stifle any scream, he spoke her name: 'Effie.'

She woke, frightened by the pressure of the hand over her mouth.

'It Big Jem, baby,' he whispered soothingly. 'Big Jem he come to stay with yo' for a coupla days.' Her hands reached up to encircle his neck. Her movements had awakened her mother and she too sat up.

'It Big Jem, Amanda.' She too made him welcome with an affectionate gesture.

'Shuck off yore clothes, Big Jem,' the mother said. 'It late and we-uns got to be up at sunrise. Ain' got us much time for pleasurin'. Effie she bin a-takin' on for days a-wonderin' where yo' were. Yo' promised to come soon as yo' could git away.'

Big Jem started to strip off his clothes. 'Couldn't git away until now.' He pulled down the blanket and crept in between them.

Roundtree Plantation was completely different from Elm Grove. Here there were plenty of wenches but only a few young bucks. So Big Jem was doubly welcome, for the wenches at Roundtree rarely had a chance to sleep with a man. It was a welcome change to them and although Big Jem's presence would be cunningly hidden so that neither owner nor overseer would know of it, it is doubtful if either would have objected except on the grounds of Big Jem's defection without permission from his master. Although children were a valuable crop, most plantation owners could not afford to keep a supply of fruitful young bucks and wenches on hand. Usually the population of most of the smaller plantations were slaves who had been young when the owners were young and who had grown old along with them.

Effie claimed Big Jem first, although her mother assisted in getting Big Jem aroused. Now that he was inside a cabin, comfortably naked and stretched out on the floor and not in so much of a hurry as he had been with Lucretia Borgia, he took longer, both with Effie and with Amanda.

27

The moon was down and it was near dawn when the three finally went to sleep. At daybreak, Amanda made up a packet of cold pone for Big Jem and he left the cabin to hide through the day in a grove of pines near the big house. They promised to have a good supper awaiting him when he returned after dark.

Big Jem's visit lasted for three days, at the end of which he thought it wise to start back home. Big Jem was not considered missing until he had been gone a week, and at that time a general alarm would be sounded for him. Now he began to dread the punishment he would receive, and felt that he had extended his visit long enough. Shortly after dark on the evening of the third day, he regretfully bade farewell to Effie and Amanda and set out for home. He followed the same route as previously.

Before circling the village of Marysburg, he hastened his steps, hoping that he would arrive and get into his own cabin without anyone seeing him. He was only a couple of miles from the village when he saw a light alongside the road. As he approached he could see that it was the remnants of a fire, nearly burned out. He could see the silhouette of a buckboard and a horse, and dark forms sleeping around the fire. As he passed the group, which he recognized as that of one of the itinerant slave traders who were a common sight around the plantations, he was accosted by a white man's voice. 'Where yo' a-goin'? What yo' out at this time o' night for, nigger?'

It was a white man, Jem could see, who stood up and walked over to him. The strange fear and need to show proper respect which was inherent in every slave compelled Big Jem to answer the man truthfully. It never paid to be caught in a lie by a white man – there was always a punishment.

'Goin' home,' Big Jem answered, 'back to my own home at Elm Grove Plantation.'

'That quite a few miles down the road, ain' it?'

'A goodly piece, Masta suh.'

'Well, where yo' bin at this time o' night?'

28

'Bin visitin' over to Roundtree Plantation.'

'Yo' have yore master's permission?'

'He don' care.'

The white man was incredulous. 'Yo' mean to say a masta don' care if'n his boy a-wanderin' the roads at night? Don' tell me that! I knows better. Yo're runnin'; that's what yo're doing. Got a good min' to take yo' back where yo' belong 'n git a reward for bringin' yo' in.' The man went over to the fire and threw on a few more sticks of pine so that the fire blazed up. It wakened the seven or eight slaves who were sleeping, huddled together around the fire.

'Masta knows I a-comin' back.' Big Jem was frightened. 'He ain' goin' to pay no money for me.'

'Then why yo' out runnin' at this time of night?'

'Tol' yo', Masta suh. Got me a wench over to Roundtree who likes to have me come over and spend a few days with her.'

'A few days?' The man's voice rose higher both with surprise and a glimmer of understanding.

Big Jem nodded.

'Then yo' bin gone more'n a day?'

'Yes suh, Masta suh, I bin gone three days.'

' 'N yore masta ain' bin lookin' for yo' yet?'

'No suh, Masta suh. He knows I always come back.'

The man's voice changed. It was now unctuous and pleasing. 'What's yore name, boy?'

'Calls me Big Jem.'

'Now that a good name for a boy like yo' – good-lookin', big, well-featured. Jes' how come yore masta ain' sendin' out bloodhounds for yo'?'

'Like'n I said, he used to my runnin' for a few days. Gits whopped when I gits back, but runs the next time jes' the same if'n I'm needin' a wench bad.'

'Ain' yo' got 'nuff wenches on your own plantation for all the pesterin' yo' need?'

'Ain' got more'n two or three. Mighty short o' wenches, my masta is. That's why I have to walk miles to git my pesterin'.'

29

'Now that's a shame, Big Jem. A miserable shame! Big fellow like'n yo' must have lots o' sap in him 'n takes a lot o' wenches to drean it out.'

'Yes suh, Masta suh, shore takes a lot to drean me.'

The white man bit his lower lip in thought for a moment, then came over and placed one arm affectionately around Big Jem's back.

'Shore wish yo' were my boy. Knows a man what has a big plantation down Clarksburg way. He got lots of wenches but he ain' got no buck what kin give him a sucker. None of his bucks potent. Askin' me to look out for a mighty big potent buck for him what kin cover all his wenches all day 'n all night and bring him in a lot o' suckers. Yes sir, askin' me jes' that.'

Jem rolled his eyes in astonishment. That such a place could exist was too good to be true.

The man became more confidential, his words more honeyed. 'He ain' askin' that this buck do any work in the field. Jes' want him for a stud. He got a big place with some thirty–forty wenches on it, all of 'em jes' waitin' to be studded. Too bad yo' ain' on his place. He keep yo' busy all the time.'

'Wishin' I was on a place like'n that. Jes' a wishin' I was. No need to run away and then git whopped when I git back.'

'No need at all.' The man led Big Jem over nearer to the fire.

'Seems to me that that's jes' the place for yo'. Tell yo' what I kin do. Kin take yo' along with me 'n make a deal with this man. He willing to buy yo' at a good price, I kin turn 'round 'n send the money to your present owner. What yo' say yore masta's name is?'

'Masta Macklin o' Elm Grove Plantation, suh.'

'Yes, that's just the right thing to do,' the man patted Jem affectionately on his shoulder. 'Yo' come right along with me. Yo' got my permission and I'll write a letter to your Masta Macklin 'n tell him all about it; tell him that yo' ain' runned but that I sol' yo' 'm sending him the money. Now how's that?'

30

'Don' seem right, suh, that I goes 'thout 'n speakin' to Masta Macklin first. That is, suh, *yo'* a-speakin' with him.'

'Pshaw, now! Yo' don' think I'm goin' to drive way over there and wake him up in the middle of the night 'n tell him all about such a fine place as I have for yo'! He'll git the letter 'n he'll tell you it's all right. He'll be right happy. You should bring him around a thousand dollars.'

Big Jem stood still, thinking. The word of a white man was law and if this man told him to do such and such a thing, it was up to him to do it without question. It really did not seem right to him, but if a white man said it was right it surely must be so. Besides, he dreaded the whipping that was in store for him when he returned to Elm Grove. Masta Macklin would have Djoubo lay it on good this time, he was sure.

'Yo' say that if'n I go to this new place, ain' no work to do, jes' studdin' wenches, tha's all?'

'And right pretty ones too. This man got a lot o' light-skinned wenches if'n that the kind yo' like.'

'Like 'em all,' Big Jem grinned.

'Then yo' come along with me. Yo' kin call me Masta Baxter. Known far and wide I am as an honest nigger-dealer. Ask anyone 'bout Honest Tom Baxter. They'll tell yo' I'm a right fine man.' He walked over to the sleeping forms and kicked them awake. 'Come on now, we all got to git up 'n git started. Got a long way to go today.'

Still friendly, Mr Baxter turned to Big Jem. 'Yo' mus' be all-fired tired out, walkin' so far. Whyn't yo' ride in the buckboard with me? The rest o' the coffle kin follow on foot.'

'Yo' shore it all right 'bout Masta Macklin?' Jem was still dubious. Naturally he had never done anything, except run away, without his master's approval. And yet, here was a white man telling him to do something which he assured him would please Mr Macklin. Naturally the man must be right. White folks always were.

31

'Yo' got Honest Tom Baxter's word for it. If'n Mista Macklin here now, he be tickled to death to sell yo' for a goodly amount o' money.'

'Nigger-dealer offered him eight hundred dollars for me once not so very long ago.' Jem remembered how fearful he was that he might be sold.

'Eight hundred dollars? Pshaw! That's nothing. I'm going to get Mr Macklin a thousand dollars for yo'. Jes' think o' that – a thousand dollars!'

'Then I better go along with yo'.'

'Shore. See to it that you git the best of everything 'n when yo' git to yore new place, yo' a-goin' to thank me every day.'

The two horses were soon hitched up to the buckboard; the coffle of slaves, which amounted to twelve, ranging in age from about fourteen to forty, were spancelled together behind the buckboard. Jem got up on the seat beside his new master and they started off in the direction from which Jem had come. Baxter figured they'd have put twenty miles behind them by dusk the next night. He'd be too far away for Macklin or anyone else to find Big Jem, and blood-hounds would do no good. He congratulated himself on getting such a fine slave for nothing.

The horses started. Big Jem was tempted, at the last moment, to jump from the buckboard and head back to Elm Grove. After all, it was his home; but he dreaded the punishment and of one thing he was very certain, he could not disobey the white man who was sitting beside him. This man's word was law, just the same as Masta Macklin's. Well, studding wenches would be a lot better than being whipped. He looked forward to the prospect. Little did he know that he was being taken to The Forks-in-the-Road near Natchez where he would be sold to a Louisiana cane planter and be worked so hard every day that he would not even have any desire for a wench at night.

But he did not know that, and was already anticipating the promises of this Honest Tom Baxter who was so good to him. Why, he wasn't even spancelled, and all the other servants were. He sat back on the uncomfortable seat and

32

smiled to himself. Mr Macklin sure would be surprised when he got all that money. Jem had never realized he was worth that much.

CHAPTER FOUR

The morning after Big Jem had absconded from Elm Grove, Mr Macklin missed him at early morning roll call. He was angry, as always when Jem disappeared, but not worried. Big Jem had been doing this same thing for five years or so and Mr Macklin knew that eventually he would return. But . . . he did not like to think that any Negro would question his authority, would act on his own impulses. Had Big Jem come to Mr Macklin and asked permission to leave for a couple of days, it might even have been granted. But running without permission was contrary to all discipline and set a bad example for the other slaves, who were already aware that Big Jem was gone once more.

'Big Jem runned again.'

'He, he! Big Jem, he got a wench somewheres else.'

'Mus' be a damned good wench to take him away.'

'Masta Macklin, he goin' to whop him when he git back.'

'Djoubo strip the meat right off'n his bones, he will.'

'Big Jem, he don' mind.'

'That nigger he wench-crazy. He shore is.'

Up at the big house Lucretia Borgia, standing before the fireplace frying ham in a big iron skillet and boiling coffee in the tin coffee pot, heard the news when Emmy came up from the quarters.

'Big Jem runned.' She was out of breath from hurrying. It was so seldom that anything unusual happened on a small plantation that the least bit of news was important and was talked about for days.

'Runned, did he?' Lucretia Borgia was not too surprised. 'Well, he's runned before 'n he come back 'n git whopped, 'n suppose this time he runs 'n comes back 'n gits whopped again. Djoubo do the whoppin', I reckon. Mista Macklin he ain' got the strength to whop like'n he useter, but Djoubo he mighty strong.' She turned the ham in the skillet and swung back the crane that held the coffee pot. More to herself than Emmy she asked, 'What yo' think 'bout that Djoubo boy?'

The girl sighed. She had been an admirer of his for a long time and was secretly in love with him. 'Think he right handsome, I do. So fine 'n tall 'n upstandin'. 'N gentle too. Djoubo he one nice boy.'

'Ain' yo' goin' to git no work done?' Lucretia Borgia could not bear to see anyone standing idle. 'Git those plates down so Delilah kin be settin' the table in the dinin' room; git the cutlery out; git pepper 'n salt; git some butter; git started doing somethin'! Don' jes' stand there with yore mouth open a-gawkin'. Kin talk whilst yo' work, cain' yo'?'

'Yes, Lucretia Borgia.'

Lucretia Borgia turned quickly and slapped Emmy a resounding thwack on the cheek. ' 'N 'nother thing. When yo' and I here in the kitchen alone, I wants yo' should call me Miz Lucretia Borgia *ma'am*. Understand? I over yo'. I like yore head man 'n it up to yo' to show me respect.'

'Yes ma'am, Miz Lucretia Borgia ma'am.'

'That more like it. Don' have to do it in front o' Masta Macklin o' the Missus but jes' here when we alone. 'Member? Now what were yo' sayin' 'bout that Djoubo boy?'

Emmy was stepping from one side of the kitchen to the other, doing the chores that Lucretia Borgia had laid out for her. She stood in awe of Lucretia's big hand, always ready to slap her across the face, sometimes when Emmy least expected it. It was a good thing to keep in with Lucretia Borgia.

'Was jes' sayin',' she took the knives and forks from the cutlery drawer, 'that Djoubo he a right fine-lookin' boy.'

Lucretia Borgia slipped the slices of ham from the skillet

34

on to a warmed platter and broke several eggs into the sizzling fat. 'Go on with yo'! He nothin' but an ugly bozal from Africy. Comed when he a baby, I guess, 'cause he talk good; but he not handsome, not like Big Jem.'

'Djoubo right good-lookin' tho', Miz Lucretia Borgia ma'am. He tall 'n broad 'n right well set up. Mayhap he ain' so pretty in the face as Big Jem but he right good-lookin'.'

'Awful niggery, tho'.'

'Shore ain' got no human blood in him,' Emmy was forced to admit. 'I ain' neither but yo' have, Miz Lucretia Borgia, ma'am.'

' 'Course I have. My mama she a quadroon. She brought me with her from Mount Airy Plantation where Miz Macklin lived before she got married up. Mount Airy a quality place; mos' o' the house servants had human blood, so my mama said. She a *mos'* handsome woman, my mama was. Kin 'member her well.'

'I reckon so. Yo' mos' handsome too, ma'am.' Emmy fully realized what side her bread should be buttered on.

Delilah entered the kitchen through the passageway door. 'Miz Macklin jes' came downstairs. Where's my table settin's?'

Lucretia Borgia pointed to the plates and utensils on the big scrubbed deal table. Delilah picked them up and carried them into the dining room.

'Quick, gal,' Lucretia Borgia pointed a long iron fork at Emmy. 'Skip down to the springhouse 'n skim off a pitcher o' cream for coffee. Done forgot to have yo' do it, 'n of course yo' never remember to do it yo'self. I do declare, Emmy, I think yo're gettin' more slothful every day.'

Emmy left, running with the cream pitcher in one hand. Delilah returned from the dining room.

'Masta Macklin he right put out this morning,' she observed. 'He so mad he had a fit o' coughin' 'n thought he like to die.'

' 'Cause Jem runned?' Lucretia Borgia knew the answer without asking the question.

'He shore mad at that boy. Goin' to drive over to Mista

Allen at the next plantation to see if'n he there. Seems that sometimes Jem run over there for a day.'

'Ain' goin' to do him no good. Jes' wastin' his time. Big Jem ain' at the Allen place.'

Delilah snickered and looked questioningly at Lucretia Borgia. 'How come yo' know all about Big Jem?'

'Ain' knowin' nothin'.' Lucretia Borgia poured the coffee from the tin pot into a silver urn, grabbed the cream pitcher from Emmy who had just come in the door, put it on the tray with the sugar bowl, and handed it to Delilah.

'If'n Masta Macklin mad, a cup o' coffee a-goin' to make him feel better. Better git it to him fas'.' She took the eggs from the skillet and placed them on the platter with the ham, then opened the big iron door of the brick oven and took out a small loaf of bread.

'This too hot to cut. Tell Miz Macklin jes' to break it in pieces.'

When Delilah had departed, Lucretia Borgia sat down on a chair beside the table. Her part of getting the breakfast was over. She had a few moments in which to relax. She even allowed Emmy to stop her work.

'Got news for yo'.' Lucretia Borgia spoke solemnly. 'From now on Djoubo a-goin' to be my man. He comin' in here to bed down with me every night. Mr Macklin a-sayin' so.'

Poor Emmy's envy showed in her face. 'My, but yo' a lucky woman, Lucretia Borgia ma'am, a-gittin' Djoubo.'

'I don' know.' Lucretia Borgia waved a disparaging hand in the air. 'Would of liked Big Jem better'n Djoubo, but cain' depend on Big Jem. Here he gone away again. Bet he gits the daylight whopped out'n him when he gits back.'

Delilah appeared. 'Masta Macklin, he a-sayin' he want to talk with yo' when he finish his breakfast.'

'Yes suh, Masta Macklin he always wantin' to tell me how good his breakfast is.'

'Ain' that,' Delilah said. 'Somethin' more 'portant.'

'How yo' know?'

'Ain' a-sayin'. Don' repeat things in the kitchen what I

36

hear in the dinin' room. I a house servant, I is,' Delilah drew herself up, 'not jes' kitchen help. Masta Macklin tell yo' when he git good 'n ready.'

Lucretia Borgia's temper flared up and she felt like clouting Delilah, but she had to restrain herself. Delilah was *house*, Lucretia Borgia was *kitchen*; however good a cook she might be, Delilah was one step higher on the complicated ladder of servant hierarchy. Lucretia Borgia knew her place. She slipped into a clean apron and headcloth and stood by the door until Delilah came to tell her that Mr Macklin would see her.

She walked in, her body proudly poised, breasts thrust out, made a little bow to Mrs Macklin, and stood beside her master. 'Yes suh, Masta Macklin suh, Delilah a-tellin' me yo' want to see me.'

'Oh yes.' Anger over Big Jem's disappearance, resentment that he had been disobeyed, made his voice hoarse and weak. 'Lucretia Borgia, think yo' better have Djoubo start beddin' down with yo'. I'll tell him, 'n give him that tin of soft soap too. Djoubo mighty stenchy.'

'Yes suh, thank yo' Masta Macklin suh. Kin save yo' a few steps though. Kin take the soft soap down 'n tell Djoubo myself. That way, won' be a botheration to yo'.'

'Why don' yo' do that, Lucretia Borgia?' Mr Macklin smiled to himself at his own willingness to accept and be influenced by Lucretia Borgia's way of thinking. It would be difficult to outwit her, he decided. She seemed always to have the other person's best interest in mind; yet somehow it invariably coincided with hers, so it was always *her* best interest that was served.

'Kin I go now?' He nodded and with another, 'Thank yo', Masta Macklin,' she was off to the kitchen.

'Masta Macklin he sendin' me to the barn on an errand,' she announced officiously. 'Emmy, go out in the back room 'n scoop a tinful o' soft soap out'n the barrel, while I finds myself an old towel. Yo' got one in the linen press upstairs, Delilah?'

'Mayhap has 'n mayhap hasn't.'

37

Lucretia Borgia became a suppliant, a role that did not fit her well because she was unaccustomed to playing it. 'Will do something for yo' someday, Delilah. I have Emmy wash all the glass 'n silver for yo' for a week, huh?'

'Thinkin' I kin find an old towel that worn out 'n ragged. It for Djoubo?' Delilah's curiosity was getting the better of her.

Lucretia Borgia nodded her head and Delilah sped up the back stairs to return in a moment with a worn and frayed towel. Proudly, Lucretia Borgia took the can in her hand, slung the towel over her arm, and started for the barn. There she called for Djoubo, who answered from one of the big empty box stalls at the rear of the barn.

'Yo' a-callin' me, Lucretia Borgia?'

She walked to where the voice came from. Djoubo was listlessly sweeping the floor of the stall with a twig broom. Lucretia Borgia offered him the tin of soap and the towel.

'Whaffor yo' a-givin' me these things? What I do with 'em?'

'Tha's soap to wash yo' all over in the creek, 'n tha's a towel to dry yo'self with. Yo' 'n me, we a-goin' to bed together.' She came closer to him and placed one hand affectionately on his cheek. The satin of his skin surprised her. 'Yo' smooth like that all over, boy?' she asked.

He took the soft soap and the towel and laid them on the floor of the stall. 'I ain' got no hair,' he admitted, clasping her wrist and placing her hand down into the opened neck of his shirt. 'I smooth all over 'cept for here.' He indicated his crotch. 'Got me a li'l hair there tho'.'

'That's where yo' should have it.' Her hand wandered over his chest, marvelling at the firmness of his muscles and tweaking his paps so that he winced. 'Tonight yo' gits yore barn chores done early 'n go down to the creek 'n wash all over. Then don' bed down in the barn, but come up to the kitchen where yo' beds with me. Be sure to wash good. Cain' have no musky-smellin' bozal in my kitchen. Masta Macklin he don' want it.'

38

'Masta Macklin say I kin?'

'Don't think I'm a-tellin' yo' if'n he didn'! Shore ! e say yo' kin. Ain' yo' a-wantin' to?'

His pink-palmed hand sought out the fullness of Lucretia Borgia's breasts under the thin cloth of her apron.

'My, my, Masta Macklin he shore good to me.' Djoubo's words were so softly spoken as to be hardly distinguishable and his eyes were closed, his body pressed close to Lucretia Borgia's. 'Ain' had me no wench since I bin here. Not for regular-like anyway. Jes' a few times I stole out in the weeds with some o' the old women, but didn't have me no real good time. 'N now Masta Macklin a-sayin' I kin bed with yo', right in the kitchen, huh?'

She nodded her head. There was an irresistible invitation about Djoubo's smooth skin and hard musculature which impelled her to explore further. She let her hand slide down under his shirt to the ridged hardness of his belly, then under the waistband of his trousers until her fingers encountered the patch of wiry hair. He pulled her closer. She placed her lips against his and although he did not seem familiar with the gesture he did not pull away but pressed his lips even closer. Her tongue darted into his open mouth while her fingers searched lower.

'My oh my, but yo' a mighty potent boy, Djoubo,' she whispered, taking her lips from his. 'If'n I know yo' so potent, would of met yo' out in the weeds before; but it better this way, now Masta Macklin a-sayin' we kin.'

He paid no attention to her words, but undid the wooden button that held up his pants and they slipped down to his ankles. His body arched as Lucretia Borgia continued her soft caress.

'Go ahead, Lucretia Borgia,' he was panting, 'faster. Make it faster.'

She stopped immediately.

'Please,' he begged. 'Cain' stand it no longer.'

'Ain' wastin' no sap o' your'n on the barn floor,' she said. 'Savin' it for tonight. Masta Macklin he right anxious that I get a sucker, but know I ain' goin' to if'n yo' dreans yo'self

39

all over the floor. Jes' hike up yore pants 'n wait until tonight.'

Reluctantly he did as she told him.

She pointed to the tin of soap and the towel on the floor. 'Want yo' all nice 'n sweet-smellin' tonight, Djoubo. We a-goin' to git a good sucker for Masta Macklin. Only hopin' that it look like me 'n not like yo'. Yo're special, Djoubo, all 'cept that face o' your'n. It mighty niggery.'

'Don' make me no neverminds, Lucretia Borgia. Masta Macklin a-knowin' I don' get suckers with my face.'

' 'N I a-knowin' it too.' She watched him pull his pants up over his thighs and fasten the button.

'My oh my, jes' a-waitin' for tonight!' Her laughter reached a high falsetto giggle as she left the barn. 'Don' min' now so much that Jem he gone. Goin' to have Djoubo regular-like, 'n cain' see his face in the dark anyway. M-m-m! Masta Macklin he shore good to me.'

She walked on a few steps and added, 'But I mighty good to him too. I'm a good servant to him, I am. None better!'

CHAPTER FIVE

The fourth day after Big Jem's disappearance, Mr Macklin was not only angry but beginning to worry. He called everyone in earshot to witness that he would dole out such a whipping on Jem's return as no nigger had ever received before. He'd have Djoubo lay it on so hard that it would be a week before Big Jem could even stand up, let alone walk. It would cure him once and for all of running. He passed the fifth and sixth day even more worried, and on the seventh had Djoubo harness the team of driving horses to the buckboard and started on a round of nearby plantations to ascertain if anyone had seen Big Jem. At each place, even

Roundtree, he met with failure. Jem had entirely disappeared. His trail was so old that bloodhounds could not cover it, and there was nothing to do but admit that he was gone, probably for ever.

On the way back he stopped off at Bannion's crossroad store and told Bannion and a young blond fellow, one Ransom Lightfoot, that he would pay a reward of one hundred dollars for news of Jem's whereabouts or for his return to Elm Grove. He asked Bannion to tell all his customers, who came in of an evening for a drink of Bannion's corn whisky, about the reward. Both Bannion and Lightfoot vowed they would do all they could to earn the hundred dollars – a generous reward in those days – although both declared that they had neither seen nor heard anything about Big Jem.

'How yo' a-doin' these days a-raisin' light-skinned suckers, Mista Macklin?' Bannion asked, glancing at Ransom Lightfoot who was standing by the zinc-covered counter.

Macklin shook his head. 'Ain' doin' so well as I might. I a-goin' to git me some new wenches from Oliver over to Spring Branch. He got some nice light-skin wenches but trouble is, I ain' got nary a decent buck to cover 'em now that Big Jem he gone. That Djoubo what drivin' me is a purentee bozal. Got me another boy called Dade, but he black too. Don' know how I'm going to get any brighter skins out'n those wenches I a-goin' to buy.'

'Well now, Mr Macklin, yo' jes' stopped by here at the right time. Young Lightfoot here he more'n willing to oblige yo'. He a good-lookin', well-set-up boy, 'n hung like'n a stallion. He bin coverin' wenches for some owners 'round here who wantin' to git light-skins. Don' charge much, he don' 'n always gits his wenches knocked up. Bes' way I know o' lightenin' up yore breed. Lightfoot's got good blood in him 'n yo' got to admit he good-lookin' with that curly yellow hair 'n all. Want him to stud for yo' over to Elm Grove?'

'Good idea.' It might solve Macklin's problem. 'I git in

41

touch with him when the time come, 'n have him over to stay a month or so. Should have my wenches from Oliver pretty soon, 'n got one or two already there. Should have six or seven for him to cover, come the time.'

'Thank yo', Mr Macklin,' said Lightfoot. 'Won't forget yore kindness. Jes' let me know when yo' ready for me 'n I'll come over. Do a good job for yo' too, I will.'

Macklin didn't particularly care for the fellow, but he accepted his words with grace. At least he was good-looking, and if his progeny inherited his looks, they would be right valuable.

'Funny how bright-skins a-bringin' the high prices today. Time was when they not worth much.' Bannion felt he was backing up Lightfoot by his opinion. 'Time was when all anyone wanted was a good black nigger what could work all day long 'n not get tired. Now seems everyone wants light-skins for house servants. Wants 'em pretty if'n they gals, handsome if'n they boys. Hears tell that on some plantations they nut all the boys so's the women won't git interested in 'em.'

'Well, they ain' never nutted me,' Lightfoot bragged. 'I gits 'em knocked up every time. Mighty potent sap I got.'

Rather than continue the conversation, Mr Macklin got in the buckboard and told Djoubo to drive him to Marysburg, where he stopped at the office of the local weekly. 'Put in an ad 'bout a nigger runnin',' he said, ' 'n use that picture yo' got of a nigger runnin'.' The clerk showed him the woodcut of the boy with a pole on his shoulder, a bundle of clothes at the end of it. 'That the one,' Macklin agreed. 'Offer a reward o' a hundred dollars. It for my boy Big Jem what runned a week ago from Elm Grove Plantation. Valuable nigger, Big Jem was. Anxious to git him back.'

More even than his loss of Big Jem, Mr Macklin regretted the fact that he had not accepted the offer of eight hundred dollars, which had been made for Jem by an itinerant slave dealer some months previously. Macklin had not sold him, because of all the slaves at Elm Grove, Big Jem was the most valuable; even more so than Djoubo, despite the weals on his back which usually lowered the value of a Negro. And now he was gone! Eight hundred dollars right out of his pocket!

After another week had passed he became sceptical about Big Jem's ever returning. He had never been gone as long as this before and surely something must have happened to keep him away. Possibly this time he had really run. If so, he'd probably headed for one of the cities like Mobile, New Orleans, or Natchez, where he could pass himself off as a free coloured man. But, as Mr Macklin thought it over, that did not seem like Jem. He was a country boy, not a city boy, and he had always been fond of his home at Elm Grove. He was a willing worker, not lazy, and his only fault was the periodic wanderings.

Life progressed as usual at Elm Grove. The subject of Big Jem's disappearance finally settled into an occasional desultory conversation about him, and after a few weeks it was as though he had never been. The two who missed him most were his cabin wench and Lucretia Borgia. Not that she wasn't entirely satisfied with Djoubo, who regularly slept on a pallet alongside her in the back room off the kitchen. No, she was almost contented with Djoubo; but Big Jem had had a magnetic quality which had satisfied her more than physically. It was thrilling in a special way to be with Big Jem.

Lucretia Borgia did, however, have important news for Mr Macklin, which she announced one morning after breakfast when Mrs Macklin had retired to the sitting room.

'I'se cotched, Masta Macklin suh,' she beamed. 'Goin' to give yo' a good sucker, I am. That Djoubo boy, he shore potent.' Secretly Lucretia Borgia wondered if it were Djoubo or that last quick session with Big Jem which had made her pregnant. But whether it was one or the other, she was proud of the news she gave her master. It increased her value in his estimation.

'So Djoubo finally got yo' knocked up, did he?' He tried to laugh, but was taken with such a fit of coughing that he had to get up and leave the table. He went into the sitting room where Mrs Macklin made him lie down on the couch. She was worried over the clots of blood staining the torn piece of sheet he used for a handkerchief.

'It's all that worryin' about Big Jem what's brought it on,' she informed Lucretia Borgia and Delilah. 'That boy cost Mista Macklin eight hundred dollars. Could of sold him for that, 'n now we ain' got nothin'. Good thing he wasn't mortgaged,' she added.

After lying on the couch for some time, Mr Macklin felt sufficiently recovered to get up. There was work to be done and he must be out overseeing it or nothing would be accomplished. It needed a white man to see that things were kept going, and he was the only one on the place.

Lucretia Borgia's advancing pregnancy did not interfere with her work. She was up early every morning with three meals to prepare. But as her body grew larger and more cumbersome, it became difficult for her to work. Her disposition did not improve with the swelling of her belly and poor Emmy, who was now doing twice as much as before, often felt the back of Lucretia Borgia's hand. Djoubo had now been relegated to his bed in the barn, and Lucretia missed his nearness in the night. All she could do was wait until her baby was born and hope that she could have Djoubo back again. She thought there might be a good chance of it. After all, Letty, who had finally become pregnant by Dade and given birth to a sucker, was now back with Dade again.

Mr Macklin, although pleased that Lucretia Borgia was about to add to the population of Elm Grove, had not forgotten his former intention of visiting Mr Oliver of Spring Branch Plantation to see about purchasing some new wenches. At present Letty and Lucretia Borgia were the only ones who could increase and multiply. There should be at least another four or five wenches to give birth frequently, and Mr Macklin regretted his negligence. The gradual petering out of his stock had already begun.

True, he did not have Big Jem to stud for him now and that was going to hamper things somewhat. He did, how-

44

ever, have Dade and Djoubo as well as Albert, and he had not forgotten about young Lightfoot. Must be poorer than Job's turkey, Macklin thought, any white fellow who hired out to stud nigger wenches. Still, the fellow didn't look like poor white trash; he was right good-looking. Well, it was one way to make a living, and probably Lightfoot enjoyed it.

However, just at that time some unexpected help arrived: a letter from the family solicitor in Marysburg was delivered by a slave on horseback and informed Mrs Macklin that a maiden aunt had died and left her a tidy little legacy. This she was willing to invest in five wenches from Mr Oliver's herd. She had always been in favour of the idea, even if it meant placing a mortgage on Elm Grove; now that would not be necessary. The worst thing that could happen to a plantation was for its slaves to age and die out. There should be a constant infusion of new blood to keep a herd fresh and workable.

Lucretia Borgia's baby was born about a month after Letty's, on a morning in early winter when frost lay on the ground. When the pains started in the night, she abandoned her warm pallet in the kitchen storeroom and made her way in the gathering dawn light to old Aunt Carrie's cabin down in the quarters. Aunt Carrie had been a midwife back when the plantation was producing suckers as regularly as it produced crops of cotton. Lucretia Borgia's knock on the weatherbeaten cabin door awakened Aunt Carrie, and she had Lucretia Borgia take her place on her own shakedown in the cabin. She stirred up the fire, adding more pine knots, and heated up a kettleful of water on the crane. But her ministrations were scarcely needed. Lucretia Borgia was young and strong as a plough horse, and her baby was born easily and quickly.

'Jes' popped out, he did,' Aunt Carrie said as she lifted the infant by the heels and slapped him till he emitted loud wails. 'Fine bouncin' boy. My, won' Masta Macklin be happy.'

Lucretia Borgia spent the rest of the morning in Aunt Carrie's cabin, but was back at the big house in time to superintend the midday meal. Although she was a bit unsteady on her feet, she was there to see that everything went all right, accepting more help from Emmy and Delilah than was usual. However, she was able after the meal to go in and tell Mr and Mrs Macklin that she had a fine new baby boy, strong and healthy and even lighter in colour than she had anticipated. Secretly she was sure that Big Jem was his father.

Both the Macklins congratulated her and Mr Macklin reached in his pocket and gave her a silver dollar, promising that he would give her another for each sucker she produced.

'Had a pretty hard mornin'. How yo' feelin' now, Lucretia Borgia?'

'Right fine, Masta Macklin. Have to nurse that little sucker o' mine, so got to keep up my strength.'

Mr Macklin pointed his fork at her. 'Yo' kin nurse him for a li'l while, Lucretia Borgia, but then I'm goin' to have Letty nurse him. Have her keep him in her cabin. Cain' have no squallin' sucker in the kitchen.'

'Yes suh, Masta Macklin suh.' Lucretia Borgia, although not wholly lacking in maternal feelings, did not care too greatly that her child would soon be taken away. She was already looking forward to resuming her affair with Djoubo, and hoped that Mr Macklin would give her his nod of approval shortly.

'Why I askin' yo' if y' feelin' pretty scrumptious is that I want to git two cabins all cleared out. Double up some of the folks that are here. Want yo' to see to it that those cabins all cleaned out, newly whitewashed, spick 'n span. Ain' askin' yo' to *do* the work, mind, jes' to oversee it and make sure it done, tha's all. Gettin' me four or five new wenches from Mista Oliver over at Spring Branch Plantation, goin' to have me a few more suckers around here.'

'Yes suh, Masta Macklin suh.' She beamed at him, proud of her own accomplishment. 'Shore could use more suckers at Elm Grove. Letty's 'n mine the first ones we had in quite a spell.'

'Reckon I kin git me some bright-skins out'n those

46

wenches. It's goin' to be bright-skins what bring the money from now on.'

Lucretia Borgia was puzzled. 'Bright-skins, Masta Macklin suh? Shore don' know how yo' a-goin' to git 'em here. Djoubo he blacker'n midnight, 'n Dade he not much lighter. Albert he pretty black too. Big Jem the lightest nigger we had, but he long gone.'

Mr Macklin coughed and spat blood into his handkerchief, then regarded Lucretia Borgia, who stood between Mrs Macklin and himself.

'Set down, Lucretia Borgia.' It was almost unheard-of for a master to tell a slave to sit in his presence. 'Yo' jes' gave birth to a sucker this mornin' 'n ain' feelin' too scrumptious, I know.'

She was aghast at the suggestion, but nevertheless drew up a straight chair and sat on its very edge.

'Don' know why I talk these things over with you,' Mr Macklin continued, 'but Miz Macklin she always a-sayin' if yo' want to git anythin' done, git Lucretia Borgia to do it.'

Lucretia Borgia looked towards her mistress and smiled her thanks.

'Well, the truth is I ain' feelin' too spruce these days, and I need someone to kinda look after things. Reckon yo' kin do it. Reckon no one else kin. Now here's what I want to talk to yo' about. These wenches I'm gettin', they all bright-skins. All got human blood in 'em. Thinkin' mayhap Mista Oliver's three sons may be the reason for it. So, I want to git even brighter skins.'

Lucretia Borgia shook her head in complete ignorance of how Mr Macklin would accomplish this unless he sired them himself, and she knew he was incapable of that. Besides, Mrs Macklin was sitting right there and he certainly would not suggest such a thing in her presence.

Mr Macklin had to wait until he quelled another paroxysm of coughing. 'Seems there's a young feller down at Bannion's store what hirin' himself out to stud nigger wenches to git bright-skins. Name o' Ransom Lightfoot. Ain' nothin' but white trash, but he a right good-lookin' boy with curly yaller

47

hair. Been thinkin' I'd git him to stud these new wenches o' mine and then we git some real bright-skins. Wantin' to know if'n yo'll look after things when I gits me the wenches, and we have this Lightfoot feller come over to stud 'em. Think yo' kin oversee it?'

'Shore kin, Masta Macklin suh.' She started to speak, then hesitated.

'Well, what is it? Go on, Lucretia Borgia!' Macklin was impatient.

'Was yo' thinkin' also o' havin' him cover me? Ain' never had no bright-skin and it look real good to have one.'

'We'll think about it, Lucretia Borgia, we'll jes' think about it. Might not be a bad idea. This new sucker o' yourn probably pretty niggery, comin' from Djoubo 'n all. Shore admire to git a nice light-skin out'n yo'. We'll think about it.'

My oh my, that was something to look forward to. Things were picking up at Elm Grove Plantation. 'Yes suh, Masta Macklin suh!' she said.

'Now, if'n yo'll go down to the barn – no, don' yo' go y'self, want that yo' should take it easy today. Send Emmy down to the barn 'n tell Djoubo to hitch the horses to the spring wagon. I'm going over to see if Mista Oliver's got anything I want. So yo' git all the hands started 'n git those cabins cleaned up. Kin yo' do that for me?'

'Shore kin, Masta Macklin suh.'

She stood up but waited, hesitating, and he knew that she had something more to ask.

'Well, what is it, Lucretia Borgia?'

'Jes' a-wondering what we a-goin' to name this new sucker of mine. He a fine strong boy.'

'Well, why don't we name him after Jem? Jem was a good strong boy. But let's hope this one won't turn out to be no runner. Wonder what in tarnation happened to Jem?'

'We calls him Jem, then?'

'No, Lucretia Borgia, we calls him Jeremiah; but Jem is short for Jeremiah.'

She bobbed her head in a thank-you. 'Have Emmy go to the barn and tell Djoubo 'bout the wagon; then have a gang of wenches which ain' doin' nothin' else clean up two cabins 'n git them ready for the wenches yo' a-bringin' home. That all, Masta Macklin?' She stopped, still looking at him expectantly.

'What is it now, Lucretia Borgia?'

'Yo' thinkin' that after a week or so Djoubo he kin come back in the kitchen with me?'

Mr Macklin shook his head. 'Not if'n I'm going to turn you over to this Lightfoot. See about all that when the time comes. Like to git me a good bright-skin out'n yo' this time. Let Djoubo handle someone else. These new wenches 'n yo' *specially* for Lightfoot, Lucretia Borgia.'

Her face fell. Perhaps it wasn't going to be such a good idea after all. She'd never bedded herself with a white man and she didn't know what it was going to be like. But then, why worry about that yet? She had plenty to do today and she would much rather crawl into her shakedown in the back room and rest. She heard a wail from the kitchen.

'Time to nurse that little brat,' she said to herself. 'Jeremiah! That a right fine name. Glad he goin' to have that name, 'cause I *shore* he Big Jem's 'n not Djoubo's.'

CHAPTER SIX

By the time she had attended to her several chores that evening, Lucretia Borgia was exhausted – so much so that she could not superintend the evening meal; for the first time since she had been at Elm Grove, poor Emmy had to prepare the food for Delilah to serve. It was not much of a meal because Emmy did not know much about cooking, but it did not seem to disturb Mr Macklin, who was so elated over having purchased four wenches from Mr Oliver that he could think or talk of little else. But as much as Lucretia Borgia wanted to see them, for once in her life her physical

49

condition overruled her desires and she went to bed on her shakedown in the back room, cuddling the baby in her arms.

Next morning it took all her strength to make the trip to the cabins, but she was determined to pass judgment on them. As always, she was determined that nothing must go on at Elm Grove that she did not have a finger in.

There were only four of them, but their colour was lighter by far than that of anyone at Elm Grove, with the possible exception of Delilah. Lucretia Borgia supposed them to be mulattos, and a certain look-alikeness among them confirmed in her own mind the fact that the Oliver sons must have sired all of them.

The youngest, Pansy, was about fourteen or fifteen. Lucretia looked her over with a practised eye, appraising her.

'Yo' ever bin busted?' Lucretia Borgia inquired, willing to take the girl's word, for she did not feel up to examining her.

Pansy shook her head in tearful denial. 'Masta Oliver he never let me be with a man, say he a-savin' me up for somethin' special 'cause I so light-coloured. 'Fraid of a man, I am. Say a man does *awful* things to a wench.' She started to cry again with a combination of fright and homesickness.

'Pshaw! Ain' nothin' to be skeered 'bout.' Lucretia Borgia was disdainful at this outburst of tears. 'Imagine! Any wench being afraid of a man. This little fool don' know what she's bin a-missin'. Once she git started there'll be no stopping her. High time she startin' in too, all titted out like'n she is. Soon she goin' to be jes' another man-hungry wench around here.'

In the same cabin with Pansy was an older, somewhat darker girl by the name of May-Ann. She informed Lucretia Borgia she had already birthed two suckers, so there was no question about her productivity. She too had a woebegone expression and Lucretia Borgia imagined that she must be homesick. All wenches did have a few days of sorrow for the place where they had lived and for their friends. Lucretia Borgia knew that this would soon wear off, particularly if Mr Macklin got that white boy to stud them. That would be

50

something for the girls to be proud of. To be covered by a white man was an honour – a most unusual one.

In the next cabin there were two more girls, Pearl and Agnes, both of medium light colour. Pearl was the prettier of the two, Agnes apparently the more intelligent. Lucretia Borgia approved of them as far as looks were concerned, and both seemed amiable. Neither indulged in tears like Pansy and May-Ann; Lucretia Borgia found this most sensible. In response to her questions they stated that they had both had children. Well, that was good. Pansy was the only unknown quantity and Lucretia Borgia did not believe that any girl as well developed as she was could possibly be barren.

She went to the door and shouted for Pansy and May-Ann to come into the second cabin. She had made up her mind that there was going to be no question of her own position at Elm Grove, and it would be just as well to let them know right now where they stood.

'My name's Lucretia Borgia,' she stated unequivocally. 'It a right long name, but yo' always calls me by my full name. Ain' got no use for being called Lou or Creetia or anything else, 'n if'n I am, I clobber the first wench what does it. Masta 'n Miz Macklin they always call me Lucretia Borgia and it up to yo' gals to do the same. Kin yo' 'member it?'

'Loo-cree-sha Borja,' they answered in unison.

' 'N another thing.' Lucretia Borgia waggled an admonitory finger at them to emphasize the importance of this. 'When they ain' no white folks around, yo' calls me *Miz* Lucretia Borgia *ma'am*. We ain' got no overseer here 'cause Masta Macklin do all the overseein', mostly by way o' me. 'Course I ain' no overseer, but I gives the orders round here. Masta Macklin he tell me do thus-'n-so, 'n I do it. Want yo-all to remember that. When I says do somethin', yo' jump to it.'

'Yes ma'am, Miz Lucretia Borgia ma'am.'

'That's better.' Lucretia Borgia pulled out a straight chair and sat on it, allowing the others to stand. It was another way to show her authority, most of which was self-assumed. 'Now yo' gals goin' to be livin' here in these two cabins for

51

a while till we gets yo' covered. Ain' goin' to let yo' to bed yo'selves with no niggers what we got here. Ain' got many anyway what young 'nuff to do anything. We got Djoubo what's in the barn, 'n he mighty black, so don' want yo' to git friendly with him 'n invite him in here. We got Dade too, but *he* mighty black. Masta Macklin a-havin' a white man come over here to cover yo' gals, 'n want yo' to wait till he comes. Don' rightly know when he a-comin', but yo' gals got to wait.'

'Yes ma'am, Miz Lucretia Borgia ma'am.'

'Yo' catchin' on good.' She relaxed a little more. 'Jes' remember who I am. I may jes' be the cook at the big house but I'm Masta Macklin's head man too. 'Course he got a nigger what's a driver in the fields, but round here he give the orders to me. Yo' gals kin cook yore own meals in the cabins. Come up to the big house 'n Miz Macklin she give yo' the vittles 'n stuff for cookin'. You kin cook, cain' yo'?'

'Yes ma'am, Miz Lucretia Borgia ma'am.'

'Time come for yo' to git pestered, yo' won' have to cook for no man. He goin' to be a white man and he a-livin' in the big house, so Masta Macklin say. But 'member, yo' wait till he comes. Don't want to hear nothin' 'bout no pesterin' in the weeds; 'n if'n anything like that happen, I shore to hear 'bout it. Knows everything that goes on round here, I do.'

'Ain' wantin' to anyway, Miz Lucretia Borgia ma'am.' Pansy was weeping again. 'Ain' wantin' to never. Don' want no man a-pushin' that big thing in me. I don'. They say it hurt somethin' awful.'

Lucretia Borgia guffawed at her, laughing so she had to hold her sides. 'That only the first time when yo' gits busted. After that it don' hurt none at all. 'Sides, this being a white man, he probably ain' very big or potent 'n he won' hurt yo'. White men ain' like niggers – ain' hung so heavy an' ain' so big. Nigger bust a gal, it right painful. We had a nigger here by the name o' Big Jem what runned. My, my, he shore a big boy 'n shore liked his pesterin'. Couldn't git 'nuff of it. Tha's why he always a-runnin', but last time he didn't come back. Nobody cain' tell what happened to him.'

52

Had she known it, the mystery of Jem's disappearance was about to be solved. It was only a few days later that two men rode up on horseback to Elm Grove and stopped at the big house to inquire of Mrs Macklin where her husband was.

'He down in the south field with the hands. Kin send a nigger down 'n fetch him if'n yo' gentlemen want to take yore ease on the gallery. Be right here, won' take but a minute.'

No, they informed her, as they were already riding it would be easier for them to go to Mr Macklin. They'd kindly ride down and talk with him.

Mrs Macklin saw that the elder of the men carried a croker sack with something in it under one arm. 'Yo' kindly wait a minute.' She yelled from the front door. 'Lucretia Borgia! These men a-goin' down to the south field to see Mr Macklin. Mayhap it a little hard for them to find their way. Whyn't yo' go along with them 'n show them how to git there.'

Lucretia Borgia emerged from the kitchen, wiping her hands on her apron. She was tickled to death to have the opportunity of being with Mr Macklin when the two white men were present. In particular, she wanted to be with the tall handsome young stranger with the yellow hair. He was, she thought, the handsomest white man she had ever seen.

'If'n yo-all will follow me,' she was obsequious and polite, 'I'll go ahead 'n show yo' the way. Ain' far.' She strode off down the quarters street, behind a barn and then down a narrow lane bordered on both sides by high brush. This led into another lane and from it into a fairly large field where a gang of Negroes, mostly elderly men and middle-aged women, were clearing away the brush.

'That there man on the horse,' she pointed, 'he Masta Macklin.'

Macklin had seen the two men riding towards him and with a word to his Negro driver to continue with the work, he rode over to meet them about halfway across the field. He looked sharply at the elder, trying to recognize him. 'Well, if'n it ain' Mista Allen. Welcome, sir, 'n right proud to see yo' here at Elm Grove. Ain' often yo' favours us with a visit. Come right down to the barn 'n let me offer yo' a drink o' corn. Miz Macklin she temp'rance, so have to keep my corn out in the barn.'

Allen declined the invitation. 'I'm sorry to say I ain' so happy to come today, Mista Macklin. Got bad news for yo', I'm 'fraid: Jem is found.'

'He found? Where he at? Don' see him. Ain' he here with yo'?'

'Sorry, Mr Macklin, but I guess you'll never see Jem again. We got bad news for yo'. This is all that's left.' He handed Mr Macklin the croker sack.

Lucretia Borgia edged closer to see what it was that Mr Macklin was about to draw out of the sack. She shrank back a little when she saw that it was a human skull. The sight of it jolted Macklin into a fit of coughing. When he had recovered, he asked, 'What yo' reckon I want o' this?'

' 'Cause it's Jem, that's why,' Mr Allen announced. 'Or at least it's all that's left of him.'

'Jem? How we a-goin' to know that it Jem? Cain' tell if'n it a human skull o' a nigger skull. Could be, though. Jem had all his teeth, 'n so's this one.'

'Jem the only person what disappeared around here for a year or so. Must be him. Panther musta got him. Some saplin's o' mine a-playin' in a ravine not far from my place 'n they found this with a lot o' bones. Lookin' like he bin all pulled apart by a panther. Boys brought this to the house 'n were a-playin' with it, 'n Mr Lightfoot he thought it might be yore Jem. Took time off, we did, to ride over with it, thinkin' yo'd like to know 'bout it.'

'Right kindly o' yo' gentlemen.' Macklin looked at the skull dubiously. 'Ain' no way to tell if'n it nigger o' human. But shore look like it might be Big Jem with all those teeth.' He called to his Negro driver, who came running over. 'Yo' thinkin' this jes' might be Big Jem?' Mr Macklin asked.

The man looked up at him. He did not know whether to say yes or no until he knew his master's pleasure. It was always best to give the answer expected of one. Something

54

seemed to tell him that Mr Macklin expected him to give an affirmative answer, so he nodded his head vigorously.

'Jes' could be, jes' could be. Shore got a fine set o' teeth like Big Jem had. 'N another thing, head ain' too big. 'Member Jem he always had kinda small head for so big a body? I'd shore say it was Jem if'n yo' ask me.'

Macklin sighed and coughed again, spitting out bloody phlegm. 'Guess then it must be him. Thought it funny he never come back. Panther musta got him 'n ripped him all to hell. Knew Jem would of come back if'n he could. Jem wasn't no real runner. Jes' lef' home every once in a while 'cause he wanted a change o' screwin'. Goddamndest buck for screwin' what ever was. Kept all my wenches knocked up 'n most of those for twenty miles round. Seemed like'n he could never git enough o' it. Tol' me once he took on ten wenches in one night 'n had jes' as much sap left for the last as he did for the first. Don' believe it tho'. Jem he an awful one for braggin'.' Macklin looked up. 'Beggin' yore pardon, suh, but ain' yo' that Mista Ransom Lightfoot what live over by Bannion's store? Shore kin recognize yo' by that yaller hair. Ain' never seen a man afore with such curly yaller hair.'

'That's me,' Ransom answered. 'Don' you 'member talkin' to me once before? Mr Bannion a-tellin' yo' I good at coverin' wenches 'n gittin' light-skinned suckers. Yo' askin' me if'n I'd like to come here 'n cover some o' yore wenches. Bin covering for Mista Allen. He kin recommend me.'

'This Ransom boy, he shore good, he is.' Allen indicated Ransom with a congratulatory wave of his hand. 'He bin studdin' my wenches 'n he got six knocked up already. Goin' to have me a nice crop of bright-skins. He mighty full o' sap, this boy, 'n mighty damn potent. Bet yo' he better than that Jem o' yourn. Never saw a white fellow take to studdin' like'n this Ransom boy.'

Macklin smiled wanly. 'Well, he got here at jes' the right time. Had it in mind to ride over to Bannion's store to inquire 'bout him. Needin' him, I am. Jes' bought me four light-skinned wenches from Mista Oliver over at Spring

55

Branch.' He turned to Lightfoot. 'Now that yo're here, whyn't yo' stay a spell? It too far to go back 'n forth every day.'

'Kin right well do that.' Ransom was pleased that Macklin had brought up the subject rather than himself. Not that he was in any way ashamed of studding Negro wenches, but he preferred that the other mention it first. 'Kindly like to know how many yo' got 'n how much yo' a-payin' for the studdin'?'

'Got me about five or six. Got me a young 'un called Pansy, ain' never bin busted.'

'Kin do that; I a champion at bustin' wenches.'

'Then I got me a dark-skin called Emmy what ain' bin busted neither. She about thirteen–fourteen. I say she never bin busted, but ain' *real* sure, what with Big Jem a'takin' all the wenches in the weeds. Anyhow, she ain' knocked up.' He turned suddenly as if he had noticed Lucretia Borgia for the first time. 'What in hell yo' a-doin' here, Lucretia Borgia? How come yo' down here?'

'Miz Macklin she asked me if'n I'd show these gentlemen the way.'

'Well,' Macklin pointed to her, 'Lucretia Borgia here, she ain' no light-skin, but I rather special about gittin' me a good sucker out'n her. Jes' birthed one and high time she started another.'

'Thank yo', Masta Macklin suh.'

He ignored her. 'Then I got three more light-skins 'sides Pansy that I bought from Mista Oliver. Also got Jem's woman Muncie, and Miz Macklin's Delilah. She a quadroon more or less; want to git a good sucker out'n her. Then I got another dark wench called Letty but a boy named Dade he a-coverin' her regular so don' know if'n it do any good to cover her. She probably knocked up by Dade already.'

Ransom nodded. 'To do a good job on all o' 'em 'n be sure each one cotches, should stay here 'bout a month. Easier if'n I could go home days but like'n yo' say, it too far to ride every day. Right tirin' it is, pesterin' wenches every night, need my days to git rested up in. Whereat yo' a-wantin' me to stud 'em?'

'Got four o' 'em in cabins, two to each one.'

'That good,' Ransom said enthusiastically. 'Wench always enjoy gittin' pestered after she hearin' another one git it. Sort o' sets 'em up, it do.'

'Lucretia Borgia she a-beddin' herself off'n the kitchen, yo' kin take her there. Delilah she a-beddin' herself in the little room next to Miz Macklin, so mayhap it be a good idea if'n yo' bed her in one o' the cabins, so's Miz Macklin she not have to hear what's a-goin' on. 'Course she knows about all this but somehow a white woman's funny. Don' like to hear 'bout studdin' even when they know it necessary. We got a spare bedroom in the house where yo' kin sleep.'

Ransom hesitated a moment, striking his boot with a switch which he had broken off along the way.

'Wonderin' how much yo' a-payin' me for all this studdin'.'

Macklin stroked his luxuriant moustache for several moments, pondering.

'Tell yo' what. I'll do better'n pay yo'. Yo' studs all these wenches 'n I give yo' one o' the pups. That worth more'n money. Yo' probably got a nigger at home what kin take care o' it.'

Ransom didn't answer, but kept switching his boot.

'Yo' kin take yore choice of anyone exceptin' Delilah's or Lucretia Borgia's. Miz Macklin right fond o' Delilah and wantin' to keep her sucker; 'n if'n I do say so right in front o' her, Lucretia Borgia the smartest wench I ever had 'n want to keep her git too.'

Ransom still considered the matter. The last thing in the world he wanted was a squalling black baby, but he could not admit that his family was so poor they had no nigger wench to care for it. After it was weaned, of course, his mother could manage. True, he had anticipated cash and preferred it, but as he considered the matter, he realized that the prestige of owning a slave would far exceed any amount of money he could earn.

He finally replied, 'If'n its dam keep it a-suckin' for 'bout six months, I'll be glad to take it over. All our wenches at home got their tits taken up with their own suckers. Once it's weaned, I'll take it, but it *got* to be a wench. Don' want no buck baby.' He envisioned what it would be like, fourteen or fifteen years from now, to have a slut of his own to do exactly as he liked with. He wouldn't have to go around the country studding any more unless he wanted to. He'd have one right there at his house. His very own! And added to that would be the prestige of owning a slave.

'Then yo' better come up to the house, seein' as how yo're going to stay a spell. 'N yo' too, Mista Allen, stay 'n have supper with us. Yo', Lucretia Borgia, git to hell back to the house 'n git a company supper started.'

She backed away but she was glad that she had been present to hear all the conversation.

'Yes suh, Masta Macklin suh, real company supper.'

Mr Allen shook his head. 'Thank yo' kindly, but I have to git back; got a lot o' work to do and want to be there to oversee it. Jes' rode over to bring yo' Jem's skull 'n set yore mind at rest 'bout him.' With a formal bow to Macklin and Lightfoot, Allen rode away.

Lucretia Borgia, hurrying back to the house on foot was passed by the two horsemen. She arrived just as Mr Macklin was leaving the horses with Djoubo.

'Djoubo,' he was saying, 'want yo' to go out in the wood lot 'n cut down a nice straight pine 'bout twice as high as yo' are. Take off all the branches 'n bark and make it into a nice smooth tall pole. Goin' to put this up on top of it.' He took the skull from the sack. 'This yere's Big Jem's head. Panther got him whilst he was a-runnin'. Want everyone on the place to see what happens to runners.'

'Yes suh, Mista Macklin suh. Jes' soon's I take care o' the horses, I go. Git it done right now.'

' 'N set it out in front o' the barn so's everyone kin see it.'

'Yes suh, Masta Macklin suh.'

Lucretia Borgia stared at the bleached white object in Djoubo's black hands. So that was all that was left of Jem!

It made a shiver go up her back to see his teeth. How often her tongue had felt them, how warm and thrilled it had made her to kiss him. And now this was all that was left. She'd never see him again. Certainly no other man could ever be as thrilling as Big Jem. She glanced from under her eyelashes at Ransom Lightfoot. Being a white man, she didn't imagine he would be very potent, but it would be an experience to bed with him.

Many, many miles from Elm Grove Plantation, Big Jem himself was returning from the Louisiana fields where he had been cutting cane all day. He was so tired that he could hardly place one foot in front of the other. Little did he realize that the skull which would stand atop a pole at Elm Grove Plantation would be pointed out as his. Given the choice, he'd willingly change places with it. He'd never believe a white man again. Stud on a big plantation? He was nothing but a field hand, he'd never had a wench since he'd been here. There was no chance of running either. All the bucks were spancelled every night. With all his heart he wished he was back at Elm Grove. Those had been the happiest days of his life, despite the welts on his back.

Lucretia Borgia took a long look at the skull and then ran to the kitchen. Company dinner tonight for the good-looking young fellow with the yellow hair. M-m-m! She missed Big Jem a lot but she'd had Djoubo and now she was going to have a white man.

CHAPTER SEVEN

Ransom Lightfoot spent his first night at the Macklin plantation as a sort of vacation. He admitted to Mr Macklin that he had been working hard for Mr Allen and that he was too tired from the long ride over from the Allen place to really do justice to any wench. Delilah had made the guest chamber ready for him and he slept comfortably all night and far into the morning. When he arose, Lucretia Borgia had a special breakfast for him, which Delilah served to him alone in the dining room. He was satisfied about one thing: there would be plenty to eat at the Macklin place, and if it was all as well prepared as this breakfast, he'd want for nothing. Lucretia Borgia was a fine cook.

After eating he inspected the plantation, paying particular notice to the slave cabins, especially the two that had so recently been spruced up. He was tempted to go in and see the girls; but thought it better to be presented to them officially, which he imagined Macklin would do that evening.

After dinner, Mr Macklin confessed to Ransom that he was not feeling too well. 'This damned cough o' mine wracks me 'n gives me pains in the chest too. Some days I kin hardly drag one foot after t'other, 'n don' sleep well of nights neither. Coughin' all night 'n keepin' Miz Macklin awake.'

'Right worried 'bout him, I am.' She sighed and shook her head. 'He jes' a-pinin' away to nothin'. Used to be a strong man, could do more work 'n any field hand, but look at him now. Could lift him with one hand almost.'

Ransom expressed the proper words of consolation and optimism, saying that he was sure it was only a passing illness and Mr Macklin would soon improve; but Macklin negated this with a shake of his head.

'It gittin' worser 'stead of better. Coughin' more 'n harder. Jes' don' think I'll take yo' down to the cabins tonight. Wantin' yo' to git started on them four new wenches, but Lucretia Borgia she kin help yo'.' He turned in his chair and called out, 'Delilah.'

She appeared at the front door.

'That Lucretia Borgia out in the kitchen?'

'Yes suh, Masta Macklin suh. She a-finishin' up the kitchen chores afta supper.'

'Ask her to come out here. Want to talk to her.'

Lucretia Borgia was a little out of breath from hurrying

60

when she appeared on the gallery, but stood before Mr Macklin, all attention.

'Lucretia Borgia,' he commenced, but was interrupted by a fit of coughing. He was finally able to go on. 'Ain' feelin' right peart this evenin' 'n thinkin' mayhap yo' better take Mista Lightfoot down to those wenches which he a-goin' to cover. My idea is that he start on that Pansy first. Think yo' can do this for me?'

'Shore kin, Masta Macklin suh.' Nothing would have pleased her more. She hated to miss anything, and had been hoping that she might be present at the scene.

'Well, after yo' finish yore supper chores, yo' take Masta Lightfoot down to the cabins where the new wenches are. Don' know how many he want to take on in one night, but they's the most important 'n want him to git started. He anxious to do it too, ain' yo', Mista Lightfoot?'

'Sooner I start, sooner it's over with,' he answered.

Lucretia Borgia turned to face Mrs Macklin, a question on her face.

'Yes, Lucretia Borgia, what is it?' Mrs Macklin rocked several times before the tall black girl answered.

'Well, it like this, Miz Macklin ma'am. We put some good corn-shuck mattresses in them two cabins, 'n quilts too, but I wonderin', seein' as how Mr Lightfoot he a white man, if'n I better not take a sheet along too. White folks used to sleepin' on a sheet.'

Mrs Macklin nodded her head in time to the rocking of her chair. 'Right thoughtful o' yo', Lucretia Borgia. Delilah'll git a sheet for yo' from the linen press.' She turned to Delilah, who was still standing in the doorway. 'Git one o' them old ones from the bottom shelf what has been mended.' She waited until she heard Delilah's footsteps going up the stairs. 'Ain' a-needin' pillers, I hope?'

Ransom Lightfoot shook his head. 'Don' need 'em, Miz Macklin, thanks just the same.'

Lucretia Borgia waited until Delilah came back with the ironed and folded sheet on her arm. She straightened up, thrusting out her ample breasts, head held high. She had never been happier. Now she had something over even Delilah the house servant. It was *she* Mr Macklin had chosen to go to the cabins. It was *she* that Mr Macklin trusted to see that things were done. He had put *her* in charge. He depended on her. She was proud of her place and of his confidence, for it not only gave her added prestige among the new wenches, but by tomorrow it would have travelled the grapevine and be all over the plantation. She retraced her footsteps to the kitchen to await her master's call.

In the gathering dusk, Mr and Mrs Macklin with Ransom Lightfoot sat out on the gallery until the woman excused herself, saying she had things to do in the house. As soon as she left, Ransom had much to relate about his prowess and his good luck on other plantations. He bragged about his successes and vowed that he was the only white stud in the neighbourhood. 'My brother,' he said, 'he tried it, but he couldn't keep it up. It too much for him but it ain' for me. Stronger'n him, I am.'

Mr Macklin listened, interrupting from time to time with severe paroxysms of coughing. After it became dark, he sent Delilah to the kitchen to fetch Lucretia Borgia, who had been regaling Emmy with details of the terrible thing that was in store for her. She had the poor girl frightened nearly to death over the approaching ordeal with Ransom Lightfoot. Poor Emmy was easily frightened and Lucretia Borgia took a sadistic delight in adding to her fears. But Emmy's trials would come later. Just now it was up to Lucretia Borgia to superintend the covering of the four new wenches. She changed her apron, wound on a clean scarlet head cloth, and reported to Mr Macklin on the front gallery.

'Lookin' like it dark 'nuff for me to take Masta Lightfoot down to the cabins, Masta Macklin suh.'

'Jes' what I was wantin' yo' for; yo' jes' see that things git started. If'n Mr Lightfoot he a-wantin' anything, yo' kin git it for him.' He noted the clean sheet folded over her arm.

'Cain' think o' anythin' I need, Mista Macklin.' Ransom stood up from his chair. 'In my business they's only two things needed – a man 'n a wench. Usually better if'n the

62

wench is willin', but even if'n she ain', it don' make much difference. She git it anyway, willin' or no.'

'This way, Masta Lightfoot suh.' Lucretia Borgia preceded him down the steps from the gallery and to the path that led to the barn and the quarters. She went first to the cabin where Pansy and May-Ann lived. Without knocking she opened the door and bade him come inside. The two girls were sitting in straight-backed, rush-bottomed chairs on either side of a scrubbed table that supported one tallow dip in a rusty iron candlestick. They both looked up as Lucretia Borgia and Ransom entered, Pansy with fear on her pretty face and May-Ann with expectation.

'This yere's Pansy,' Lucretia Borgia indicated the youngest of the two girls, ' 'n t'other one she called May-Ann. In the next cabin we got two more what named Pearl 'n Agnes. All o' them 'ceptin' Pansy bin busted, 'n Mista Macklin be a-thinkin' mayhap yo' start first with Pansy.'

Ransom glanced around the cabin, satisfied that it was neat and clean and newly whitewashed. He would not mind staying here. Some of the cabins he had been forced to work in had been dirty and in poor condition. He noticed a corn-shuck mattress in one corner, covered with a ragged but clean pieced quilt. With a flourish, Lucretia Borgia swept the quilt from the bed and shook out the clean sheet. 'If'n this git bloody from Pansy's gittin' busted, want it all washed out clean tomorrow mornin'. Beddin' with a white man, he used to a sheet.'

'Blood?' Pansy started to weep. 'He a-goin' to hurt me that much?'

'Whaffor yo' a-cryin', li'l gal?' Ransom asked, his voice honey-sweet, 'Yo' ain' afeard o' me, be yo'? I'm goin' to make yo' the happiest gal in the world.'

'By hurtin' me?' she wailed. 'That ain' no good time.'

'Shore is!' He grinned at her. 'This's one hurt yo' a-goin' to love.'

'Heard tell the first time it *bad*.'

'Hush yore mouth, Pansy. Masta Lightfoot, he a white man. He ain' no nigger what a-goin' to force yo' onto yore

63

back down in the bushes 'n ram yo' with something big 'n hard. Bein' a white man, he probably small, ain' yo', Masta Lightfoot?'

Ransom looked at Lucretia Borgia and laughed. He rubbed his hand along his groin and in a few seconds it bulged under his manipulation.

'All white men ain' small 'n puny, Lucretia Borgia. Reckon I got more'n any nigger on this plantation. If'n she never bin busted she shore goin' to git busted now good 'n plenty. Thinkin' I'll start on her first. Always a good thing to git it over with, then she be wantin' it more'n all the rest. 'Sides, it goin' to put May-Ann in a good mood 'n she a-goin' to enjoy herself more. Make her think o' the first time she was busted 'n how much she loved it.'

Lucretia Borgia looked longingly at the swelling bulge in Ransom's trousers. The cloth that covered it seemed to increase its size rather than hide it. True, she had never envisioned such a thing on a white man. Evidently the gossip she had heard was entirely untrue, for this man certainly could compare with Djoubo, even with Big Jem.

'Beggin' yore pardon, suh, but don't yo' think it might be a good idea if'n I went back to the big house 'n got some goose grease or a bacon rind? She such a small gal 'n yo' such a potent man.'

He shook his head in denial. 'Don' need no goose grease nor bacon rind neither. Always jes' use a li'l spit.'

'Spit, huh?' She laughed, remembering Big Jem and how that was what he always used. She turned to Pansy. 'Shuck yo'self down, gal, 'n lie flat. Masta Lightfoot, he ain' got all night, yo' know. Cain' spend his time a-foolin' round with yo'.'

But Pansy was truly frightened and the mention of blood had terrified her even more. Lucretia Borgia came over to her, yanked her out of the chair and unloosed the single button that held her thin osnaburg dress together. 'Is yo' a-goin' to shuck down or do I have to make yo'? Whaffor yo' think Masta Macklin he bought yo'? Whaffor yo' think Masta Lightfoot he here now? High time yo' found out!'

64

She tore the dress from the girl and pushed her towards the corn-husk mattress. Pansy fell on it and curled herself up, knees at her chin.

'That ain' no way to act.' Lucretia Borgia clouted her on the rump. 'Lie out flat on yore back 'n spread your legs. If'n yo' don', yo' goin' to git clobbered right smart.' She threatened the girl with an upraised hand. Pansy slowly and unwillingly did as she was told. ' 'N yo', May-Ann, yo' a-goin' to be here 'n I wants that yo' should tell me tomorrow how this Pansy act. She better quit her weepin' 'n wailin' 'n git down to business.'

Ransom Lightfoot removed his shoes and socks and then took off his shirt. Pansy lay on the corn-shuck mattress watching his every move. Lucretia Borgia would have given anything she possessed to stay, but she felt she had no adequate excuse to do so. She went over to the door. Regretfully she opened it, hoping that by the time she was ready to go, Lightfoot would have shucked off his trousers, but he waited while she stood in the doorway for several seconds.

'Well, Lucretia Borgia,' his voice was impatient, 'ain' yo' a-goin'? Don' need yore help no more. I kin handle this li'l gal.' He turned to the weeping Pansy. 'Now stop that. Ain' goin' to be no fun with yo' a-sobbin' like that. Mayhap I'm goin' to give yo' something to sob 'bout, but yo'll soon forget it.' He turned to May-Ann who was still sitting at the table. 'Whyn't yo' shuck yo'self down too? It more fun with two wenches than with one.'

She agreed. 'Mayhap Pansy she won't be so skeered if'n I'm there 'side her.'

There was no excuse for Lucretia Borgia to linger. Reluctantly she closed the door. The thin ray of candlelight that shone under the door now went out and blackness took its place. Well, if she couldn't see, she could at least listen. She walked softly around to the side of the cabin where the shutter directly over the bed stood open. Halting near it, she scarcely dared to breathe lest she be heard.

She heard Lightfoot's footsteps as he crossed the floor and

then the rustling of the corn-shuck mattress. He was trying to quiet the sobbing girl.

'Feel down here 'n see what Ransom got a-waitin' for yo', li'l gal. Ain' that somethin' wonderful for a nice li'l wench to play with?'

There was no response from the luckless Pansy.

'Here, gal,' Ransom's words were quiet and reassuring, 'whyn't yo' do like May-Ann doin'? Yo' likes it, don' yo', May-Ann?'

'It wonderful, Masta suh. Loves it. Don' be foolish, Pansy. Jes' put yore hand down here. See,' she waited a moment, 'ain' that nice?'

There was a rustling of the mattress, then Ransom spoke in anger. 'Goddammit, gal, git yore legs open. Better do it, 'cause if'n yo' don' I *pry* 'em open!'

There was a low moan from Pansy.

'Please, Masta Lightfoot suh, please don'.'

For a moment there was silence then a scream, quickly muffled by a hand over Pansy's mouth. She continued to moan but the action in the cabin increased. Lucretia Borgia could hear a continuous rustling of the mattress accompanied by Pansy's moans and sobbing. At last the sobbing quieted and there was complete silence. Then she heard Pansy's voice.

'Is that all they is to it, Masta Lightfoot suh? Hurt awful it did, 'n still hurtin' with yo' in me. Cain' yo' take it out?'

'No. Pretty soon we a-goin' to git really started. That jes' the beginnin'. But it ain' goin' to hurt so much no more. Come over closer, May-Ann. Wants to feel yo', I do.'

Lucretia Borgia continued to listen. Within a few moments there was a regular movement which increased in intensity and then stopped abruptly.

'Whew!' Lightfoot gasped. 'Nearly popped! Want to save it a little longer.' The regular movement began again.

May-Ann's voice caressed Lightfoot. 'Ain' yo' nearly finished, Masta suh? Seems like'n I cain' wait much longer. Cain' yo' hurry, Masta suh?'

Lucretia Borgia, in the shadows heard a muffled gasp, a

shouted 'Goddammit', and Lightfoot's frenzied filling of his lungs with air. 'Goddammit, that was good. Ain' nothin' quite so good as bustin' a wench wide open, 'n this one's shore busted as much as she ever will be. Yo' jes' hold yore horses, May-Ann. Takes a man a minute to git his breath. How'd yo' like'n that, Pansy?'

'That special, Masta suh. Don' care if'n it did hurt somethin' awful. It worth it. Shore was.'

Lucretia Borgia's curiosity was satisfied. She had no desire to listen to the more practised to-do with May-Ann. Pansy's defloration had been the one thing that interested her. She tiptoed away from the cabin and out into the street. Walking up the quarters street in the moonlight, she dreaded to go back to the house. There was nobody in the kitchen for her to sleep with but little Jem, and her senses were so aroused by what she had heard and the mental images thus conjured up that she did not feel like sleeping alone, or even being alone. She needed male companionship.

Well, there was always Djoubo; he and she had been separated for some time. No, she didn't dare bed herself with Djoubo. Just once with him and he might implant another black sucker in her, and then what good would it do to have Lightfoot cover her? Damn it! She needed something. She must have something.

Keeping to the shadows of the quarters street, she came to the end of it, ducked into the broad doors of the horse-barn, and made her way to the empty box stall in the rear where Djoubo slept. She walked in, bending over and feeling in with her hand. Finally she encountered the warmth and hardness of Djoubo's body. Her hands fondled him in his sleep and he awoke.

'Who there?' he called out.

'Hush yore mouth, boy, it me, Lucretia Borgia.'

'Yo', Lucretia Borgia? Masta Macklin he done say I wasn't to touch you 'gain! Say he a-wantin' to git a light-skinned sucker out'n yo' by that yaller-haired fellow. 'N here yo' comes, a-fiddlin' roun' with me in the night 'n gittin' me all hard 'n hottened up. Don' yo' know better?'

67

'It all right, Djoubo.' She knelt beside him in the darkness, her hands increasing their embrace. 'Masta Macklin he did say yo' not to touch me. Well, yo' ain' touchin' me at all. But Masta Macklin he didn't say anythin' 'bout me touchin' yo', did he?'

'No, Lucretia Borgia. Oh, that's fine!'

'Ain' so good as pesterin', at least for me, but it the next best thing for yo'. 'N one thing for shore. I ain' goin' to git knocked up this way.'

'Faster, Lucretia Borgia, faster.'

She accommodated herself to his words. His body arched and he sucked in a lungful of air, then lay back on the straw, breathing hard.

'Thank yo', Lucretia Borgia.'

'Don' thank me; jes' had a feelin' I wanted to, tha's all. Yo'll sleep better tonight.'

'Thinkin' I will.'

' 'N I'll sleep better too.'

She turned at the door of the stall. 'Yo' know somethin', Djoubo?'

'No, what, Lucretia Borgia?'

'That ain' true 'bout white men being so small 'n puny. That Masta Lightfoot, he shore ain'. Bet he bigger'n yo', Djoubo.'

'Could be he bigger'n I am now,' he laughed back at her.

Lucretia Borgia made her way to the big house and out into the back room behind the kitchen. Little Jem was asleep on her shakedown. She pulled him to her and his mouth found her nipple. Lucretia Borgia nursed him till he went to sleep. She thought of Pansy and May-Ann and envied them. A white man! Imagine! But her turn would come. She anticipated it. In the meantime there was Djoubo, for what small comfort *that* was.

CHAPTER EIGHT

Ransom Lightfoot remained about a month at Elm Grove Plantation. He was not in residence there all the time, however, as he insisted on riding home on Friday afternoons after he had had his late breakfast and then would not return until Monday. This left him only four nights to work, but he figured that as he was not getting any cash payment for this job, he could take his time and do it as he wished.

After he had finished with Pansy and May-Ann, much to their regret – Pansy had now lost all fear and looked at Ransom only with anticipation – he moved in with Pearl and Agnes and stayed there even longer than he had stayed with Pansy and May-Ann, probably because he liked Pearl the best of all the wenches. He did cover Jem's woman but he did not cover Letty, because Dade was still with her. He did, however, break in poor Emmy, who declared to Lucretia Borgia that she wouldn't be able to work for a week. One good clout across the cheek from Lucretia Borgia's hand immediately set her to recuperating, although she dragged herself around the kitchen, moaning audibly whenever she had an audience. Mr Macklin, for some reason known only to himself, had saved Lucretia Borgia as the last one for Ransom to cover and both had been looking forward to the experience; Lucretia Borgia because she had never been touched by a white man and Ransom because Lucretia Borgia was such a statuesque woman that he, like Jem before him, knew he would have something to hang on to. He realized the fire that burned in Lucretia Borgia and was anxious to see if it would scorch him.

A cradle was brought in from one of the cabins for Little Jem and Lucretia Borgia entertained Ransom on her shakedown in the kitchen storeroom. Although he enjoyed the experience enough to stay several nights with her, she was forced to admit that she did not much care for a white man's pestering. In the first place, they had a strange odour which offended her, and as Ransom had not bathed since he had arrived at Elm Grove, he was more offensive than most. And then, Lucretia Borgia discovered that white men were hairy. She had been accustomed to the satin-smooth skins of black men and it seemed strange to find hair all over a person: on chest, arms, legs, wherever hair could grow. It was hot and uncomfortable and scratched her skin, and she didn't like it. It was a far cry from the smooth darkness of Big Jem's or Djoubo's body.

Furthermore, both Big Jem and Djoubo had made some effort to please her. There were little fondlings and kisses and pleasant words of love, and they had often delayed their ecstasies so that she could match them; but Ransom Lightfoot thought of nobody but himself. When he was through, he was through, and that was it. It made no difference to him whether Lucretia Borgia was satisfied or not. He had done his job and that was all he was expected to do. In his business, there was no time for making love or for any words or gestures of endearment. There was only one reason for him to be there and as soon as that was accomplished, he was through. Sentiment and pretty words did not get a wench knocked up – there was only one thing that would do it, and that was what he did.

Being in the big house, he did not stay the whole night with Lucretia Borgia but got up, went into the main house to his own room, and slept. Often during those nights Lucretia Borgia would leave the house after Ransom had departed and go to the barn to seek what solace she could from Djoubo's dry embraces.

About a month after his departure, Lucretia Borgia reported her second pregnancy to Mr Macklin and the certainty that Ransom Lightfoot was the father; she then begged her master to let Djoubo come back into the kitchen and stay with her. Her reputation was at stake. He had, being one of only two young males on the plantation, suddenly become very popular, and Lucretia Borgia had discovered that he had stayed in both cabins with the new girls. Lucretia Borgia felt that she had a prior claim on him and that he was hers. She was unwilling to share him just to pleasure some other pregnant wenches. Once back in the kitchen, his wanderings would be over. Mr Macklin agreed, and Djoubo's philanderings ceased. He was marked as Lucretia Borgia's and no other wench had a right to him.

As to whose child would go to Ransom as payment for his services, that depended to a great extent on which baby would be female, since Ransom had declined to accept a buck; but it was generally conceded that if Agnes, the least attractive of the new girls, should have a girl, that one would be given to Ransom in payment.

Ransom rode over once to see the results of his work and receive congratulations from Mr Macklin, who admitted that it was even better than he had expected. There was only one failure: Emmy had failed to conceive. This Ransom blamed on her rather than on himself. He assured Mr Macklin with his usual braggadocio that he certainly was not sterile – look at all the wenches he had already knocked up – so it must be Emmy's fault. Besides, Ransom admitted, she was too small to do a proper piece of work on.

All through the fall and winter, Mr Macklin continued to ail, and the colder the weather got the more he suffered. His wife tried all the well-known home remedies. She put applications of goose grease on his chest; she fried onions, and made poultices, and sewed up red flannel bibs as chest protectors. Each neighbour woman who gave her a new remedy (which, she declared, had worked wonders in her own family) along with the 'yarbs' to prepare it, meant another bitter dose for Mr Macklin; though he swallowed them all without complaining, none seemed to help. He gradually became weaker and weaker until he was finally confined to bed, getting up occasionally to sit in a padded chair by his bedroom fireplace. Here he held a daily conference with Lucretia Borgia.

In addition to her duties as cook, Lucretia Borgia was now practically the overseer of the plantation, issuing Macklin's orders to his various drivers and then often inspecting the work herself to see that it was satisfactory. If it were, she was never lavish with her praise; that was the way it was supposed to be and there was no reason to praise a person who had merely done his job. But if the least little thing was undone or poorly done, she raised hell – with the hand that had done it, with his driver, and finally with Mr Macklin. Her palm was always ready to slap some luckless cheek, and all the hands moved more quickly when 'Miz' Lucretia Borgia made her appearance on the scene. During Macklin's illness, Elm Grove was actually run more efficiently than ever before.

Lucretia Borgia was a hard worker herself. She was not afraid of toil, though if she could get somebody to do it for her, she was delighted. But it had to be done as well as she would have done it. She never forgot. Woe to him or her who did not perform a job to her satisfaction.

'Best servant I ever had,' Mr Macklin often said to his wife. 'Don' know how we'd git along without her.' To which Mrs Macklin agreed. She depended more and more on Lucretia Borgia, as did everyone at Elm Grove.

As her outside duties took more and more time, she attempted to teach Emmy to cook and eventually, after a multitude of slaps across the face, Emmy learned to cook acceptably. Of course, *nobody* could cook quite as well as Lucretia Borgia. She didn't intend that they should. Although she taught Emmy the rudiments she did not impart the fine points which only she herself knew.

Lucretia Borgia did, however, prepare many things to tempt poor Mr Macklin's appetite. She made custards and porridges, chicken and beef broths, calf's-foot jelly and fine white bread. She even sat beside his bed and fed him, dipping the bread into the broth and putting it in his mouth. There was nothing he seemed to relish. It was Lucretia Borgia who first suggested a doctor.

'Whyn't yo' have that Doctor Bennett come look at Mista Macklin?' she asked one day.

Mrs Macklin looked at her aghast. 'Dr Bennett is a vet'narian; he only treats niggers 'n animals. He couldn't help Mista Macklin.'

72

'Don' seem to me that the innards o' a white man much different than the innards o' a nigger, 'n if'n a man know how to treat one, he know how to treat t'other.' Lucretia Borgia was emphatic. 'Then whereat a doctor what kin treat a white man?'

Mrs Macklin shrugged helplessly. There was no doctor in Marysburg; the only doctor she knew of was a Dr Eldredge in Emporia, which was too far away for Mrs Macklin to drive and fetch him back. Lucretia Borgia, disgusted with the inabilities of white persons to do things, offered to go. She had never been away from Elm Grove Plantation since Mr Macklin had purchased her, but she felt that with a tongue in her head she would be able to find the way.

Mrs Macklin, now anxious to get medical advice, was willing to let her go, although she doubted Lucretia Borgia's abilities to get there, find the doctor and persuade him to make the long trip to Elm Grove.

Furthermore, Lucretia Borgia said, she preferred to go alone. Mrs Macklin offered to send Djoubo with her, but Lucretia Borgia scoffed at the idea.

'Him?' One would have thought that Djoubo was indeed the animal he was supposed to be. 'Djoubo he nothin' but an ignorant bozal. What he know 'bout gettin' to Emporia? He more a bother than he worth. Kin drive a team o' horses, kin, 'n don' need no Djoubo to tell me how. Dade? He ain' never been nowhere neither. Now if'n we had Big Jem here, he could show me the way; but all's we got left o' him is his bare head out on that pole. Every time I sees it, wid all the meat gone, it bring tears to my eyes.'

It was finally decided between the Macklins that Lucretia Borgia could go alone, and a day was set. She was up early, before the dawn. It was fifteen miles to Emporia, and no telling how long it would take her to get there. Mr Macklin instructed her as best he could and Mrs Macklin wrote a note for her saying that she was on her way to Emporia to fetch a doctor for Mr Macklin of Elm Grove, who was severely ailing. This was to be shown to anyone of whom Lucretia Borgia would ask directions or assistance.

She packed a lunch for herself, folding it up in a red-and-white fringed napkin and tucking it into a small basket which she put under the seat of the buckboard with the oats for the horses' midday meal. Djoubo was at the barn to see her off and she turned several times to wave to him as she drove down the avenue of trees to the main road. She had no trouble until she got to the little village of Marysburg. Here she became confused; there was a fork in the road and another lane which crossed them both. She stopped her rig and with proper deference (for Lucretia Borgia was always respectful to white people) she asked a man the directions to Emporia, at the same time showing him Mrs Macklin's note. He was a kindly person and most explicit in his directions. He told her, pointing with his finger, to turn to the right and then to the right again, keeping on the same road until she came to a crossroads where there was a place called Bannion's. This Lucretia Borgia had heard about from Ransom Lightfoot.

She had no difficulty in keeping on the road until she came to what she thought might be Bannion's store. At least it looked like a store, and had a lettered board over the doorway which, although she could not read it, appeared to be a sign such as a store might have. Here there was a choice of two roads; she drove her buckboard up to the steps and, seeing nobody on the sloping veranda, got down and went inside. It took her a moment to adjust her eyes to the gloom, then she recognized Ransom Lightfoot, who was talking to another stouter man.

'Lucretia Borgia,' he called out, his eyes making out the fullness of her body in silhouette against the open door. 'Yo' stayed cotched, then.'

'Shore did, Masta Lightfoot suh. Goin' to have a nice yaller-haired sucker from yo'.'

'Well, what brings yo' in this direction?' the other man, who was Bannion, asked. 'Bin a-hearin' 'bout yo' from Ransom 'n it 'pears that yo' 'bout run Elm Grove Plantation. Got some more wenches yo' want Ransom to cover for yo'? He do a right good job, don' he?'

'Right good,' Lucretia Borgia agreed, 'but ain' searchin' for Masta Lightfoot this time. Goin' to Emporia to fetch the doctor; Mista Macklin he a-gittin' worser every day.'

'Waste o' time and money,' Lightfoot said, his palms raised in a gesture of helplessness. 'Ain' no doctor kin help him. He got the gallopin' consumption like'n I tol' yo', Mista Bannion. Lung fever, that what he got. Jes' skin 'n bones, a-coughin' up blood all day. Yo' might jes' as well turn round 'n go back, Lucretia Borgia.'

She shook her head. 'Cain',' she answered. 'Miz Macklin she possessed to see a doctor 'n so I got to go. Which road take me to Emporia, Mista Lightfoot suh?'

'Take the one on your left. The other go to Clarksburg, 'n that a right long piece down the road to Mobile; yo' don' want to go there.' He eyed her speculatively. He had an aversion to pregnant women, otherwise he would have prevailed on her to stop for a while. In fact, had she not been pregnant he would have been willing to accompany her to Emporia. It would have been a welcome break from the monotony of his daily existence, but her swollen body held no attraction for him.

She bade them both good-day with grace and thanked them for their directions. As she was leaving the store, she met a particularly light-skinned girl, coming along the path that led from a cabin behind the store. She was carrying a naked baby in her arms. It was a handsome baby, with no indication that it carried any coloured blood save for some dark blotches on its chest and stomach.

'Cute li'l sucker.' Lucretia Borgia chucked the baby under its chin. She hoped that her own, coming from Ransom Lightfoot, would be as white; but she realized that this was doubtful, as the girl herself was most probably an octaroon.

'He mine,' the girl said proudly. She could scarcely be more than fifteen, Lucretia Borgia thought.

'Want to see something funny?' the girl asked.

'Them spots on his belly?'

The girl shook her head. 'No, that ain't it, but that why we

75

calls him Calico. That's his name. Look.' She held up his right hand.

Lucretia Borgia stared in amazement at six perfect fingers.

'Well, I do declare.' She took the baby's hand and examined it carefully. 'That something I never in my life did see afore.' She was still thinking about how strange it was when she got into the buckboard, clucked to the horses, and drove away. 'Wonder if'n that one's Ransom's git too. Mos' white, that sucker is. Probably Ransom's. Imagine he's sired most o' the light suckers for miles around.'

She stopped when the sun was high and ate her lunch alongside a little spring edged with mint and ferns, then was on her way again. It was early afternoon when she arrived in Emporia and although it was only a small town, it was so much larger than Marysburg that it frightened Lucretia Borgia. She had never seen so many white people at one time before. Teams of horses were hitched along the main street; there were stores with glass windows; and people walking up and down the plank sidewalks – such a bustle of activity as Lucretia Borgia never had known existed.

She tied her horses to a hitching rail and got out, waiting for someone to pass to whom she might dare to speak. Soon a middle-aged woman, buxom and with a high, florid complexion, came along. She was followed by a well-dressed young Negress carrying a basket of vegetables and several bundles.

'Beggin' yore pardon, ma'am.' Lucretia unfolded the note and passed it to the white woman. 'Can yo' be tellin' me whereat Dr Eldredge lives? I come all the way from beyond Marysburg to fetch him, 'n don' know his house.'

The woman took the note and read it. 'Why, yo' pore thing! 'N yore poor mistress! Let me tell yo' now. This street yo' on is Main Street, understand?'

Lucretia Borgia nodded.

'Well, yo' keep right on a-goin' until yo' come to a sign what says Magnolia Street.'

'Cain' read, Mistress ma'am.'

'Well, you'll know it. They's a big white house on the corner which has a little cast-iron nigger out in front, all painted up with a red coat for a hitchin' post. Yo' turn right there and Dr Eldredge's house is the next house 'side that'n. It a white house with a big oak tree in the yard.'

Lucretia Borgia thanked the woman most graciously – as only she knew how to do – and moved on. Sure enough, there was the big white house with the little red-coated cast-iron figure in front. She turned the corner and stopped at the next house, going around the big oak tree to the back door, which was opened for her by a stout black woman who, noting Lucretia Borgia's country clothes, greeted her with a scowl.

'What yo' want, nigger?'

'This yere where Dr Eldredge live?'

'Shore is. What that mean to yo', nigger?'

'Got a note for him, I have.'

'Yo' don' think Dr Eldredge he have time to read notes what every nigger woman a-bringin' round to de back door? He a busy man. Go long with yo'.'

Lucretia Borgia measured the woman in the doorway. She was bigger but she was mostly fat. Lucretia Borgia had no qualms. 'I asks yo' once more nice-like. Is yo' goin' to take this note to him?'

' 'N I tells yo' like'n I tells any nigger wench what comes in from the country with cowshit all over her shoes that I ain' a-botherin' the doctor with no notes.'

Lucretia Borgia lost her patience. '*I* tell *yo*', I bin up afore dawn, drivin' them horses 'n tryin' to fin' the doctor. Found him, I have, 'n ain' goin' to be stopped by no ignorant wench what think jes' 'cause she a-livin' in de town, she know more'n me. Git out'n my way, fat gal, afore I clobbers yo' one.'

The woman did not move.

Lucretia Borgia doubled up her hand into a fist and let the girl have it, directly in the stomach. She doubled over with pain and sank to the floor. Lucretia Borgia strode over her and went through a door which she supposed led into a

77

dining room; it did, and then into a parlour. Across the hall there was another room in which a middle-aged man sat before a desk. Lucretia Borgia walked in and bowed. She had manners, Lucretia Borgia did, where white people were concerned.

'Beggin' yore pardon, suh, but be yo' Dr Eldredge?'

He glanced up at her, noting her dusty clothes and rather dishevelled appearance. 'Who let you in?' he asked.

'Ain' nobody let me in. Some nigger wench in the kitchen, she try to stop me so I clout her good 'n walks in here. Bin drivin' all day long to get this note to yo' 'n ain' lettin' no wench keep me out. Sorry to disturb yo', but kindly read the note which is from my mistress at Elm Grove Plantation, Miz Macklin, over Marysburg way.'

'So Rosalia couldn't keep you out.' The doctor laughed. 'First time she ever failed.' He took the note and read it. 'You go back and tell your mistress that I shall be over in a few days. It's a long way and I'll have to plan my calls to be sure and get there and back in one day. Tell her not to worry in the meantime.'

'Shore will, Dr Eldredge suh, 'n thankful I am that yo'll come. Masta Macklin he a mighty sick man.'

'So I judge.'

Lucretia Borgia started to retrace her steps, but Dr Eldredge held up a warning finger. 'It's just possible that Rosalia is laying for you with a rolling pin or some other weapon,' he said. 'I think it might be wise if I escorted you out the front door. In a match between you and Rosalia I don't know who'd win, but I'm in no mood this afternoon to find out.'

'Yes suh, Masta Doctor suh. 'N I thanks yo' for comin'. I'll tell Miz Macklin not to worry.'

It was late that night when Lucretia Borgia arrived back at Elm Grove. Djoubo took the horses and she hurried into the house.

'He a-comin', Miz Macklin. The doctor say he a-comin' in a few days, jes' as soon as he kin arrange it.'

Mrs Macklin, a white woman, born and reared in the

traditions of the Old South, did a strange thing. She went to Lucretia Borgia and laid her head on the black woman's capacious bosom and wept out her thanks. Lucretia Borgia quieted her as well as she could.

'Thank yo' for makin' that trip for me, Lucretia Borgia.' Mrs Macklin finally had control of herself. 'I don't hardly think Mr Macklin will last out till the doctor gits here, but I'll feel better if he kin see him.'

'Doctor said not to worry, Miz Macklin. He a-goin' to fix Masta Macklin up fine.' She walked through the sitting room, the dining room, out into the kitchen. Djoubo was sitting on a chair in the kitchen waiting for her.

'Yo' better go back to the barn tonight, Djoubo boy,' she said, sighing with fatigue. 'I dead tired. Too tired to even talk. Good night, Djoubo.'

CHAPTER NINE

Despite the nostrums and panaceas that Dr Eldredge left at Elm Grove, Mr Macklin did not improve; nor did Mrs Macklin expect him to, because the doctor had assured her as kindly as possible that her husband had but little time to live. Mr Macklin, as he diagnosed it, was the victim of lung fever and for this wasting disease there was no cure. He explained that the body would gradually waste away as the lungs became consumed until there would be nothing left to breathe with. He advised that in case of severe pain, Mrs Macklin could give her husband laudanum; and this did relieve him, although it could not cure him.

Nevertheless, even in his weakened condition, Mr Macklin was able to keep control over the plantation by using Lucretia Borgia as his good right hand. But as her pregnancy eventually distorted her lithe body into something so swollen and cumbersome that it was difficult for her to get around, she found it difficult to attend to all the duties he imposed upon her. She was forced to delegate many of them to others. Even her inspection of the field work was slighted, and she had to depend on the Negro drivers. However, she still managed to oversee the house, slave cabins and the barns.

With more temerity than seemed possible, Mr Macklin clung to life, awaiting the culmination of the pregnancies of his wenches. These would be particularly valuable light-skinned suckers, so he would not have them born in the usual haphazard way with a plantation midwife assisting. Instead, he went to the expense of having Dr Bennett the veterinarian attend to them. He didn't want to lose any; and it seemed better to spend a little money for professional service. So, when the time came, Dr Bennett was kept busy. May-Ann gave birth to the first, a boy. Then followed boys from Pearl and Agnes and Pansy. The last infant to be born was Lucretia Borgia's, the only girl in the lot.

Strangely enough, even with Dr Bennett's attendance, she had more difficulty with her second birth than with her first, and was forced to stay on her shakedown off the kitchen for two days and two nights. When she could finally get up, she brought the child to Mr Macklin to see, a fine, light-skinned child with wisps of blonde hair on its head. She knew without Mr Macklin's reminding her that this child must be forfeited to Ransom Lightfoot under the terms of their agreement.

The fact that she could not watch the child grow up was one of the saddest experiences she had ever endured. Somehow its light skin made it particularly dear to her. However, she consoled herself that she could at least keep it and enjoy it until it had been weaned. She was well aware that the child did not belong to her. It was Mr Macklin's and his alone. He could do with it as he wished. The Macklins sympathized with her, and Mr Macklin suggested that soon she turn the baby over to May-Ann, who had plenty of milk, and let her nurse it. In that way she would not become so attached to it.

'The longer you keep it 'n let it suck, Lucretia Borgia, the more attached yo' git to it. I know it' yourn, 'n goin' to be mighty hard for yo' to part with it, but that's the way it is 'n ain' nothin' what kin be done about it. Gentleman's agreement what I have with that Lightfoot fellow; I gotta keep it.'

Reluctantly she followed his orders and within a week the baby, yet unnamed, had been turned over to May-Ann to nurse along with her own. At first Lucretia Borgia was most solicitous after its welfare, enquiring of May-Ann daily how the mite was progressing, but gradually Lucretia Borgia got over the pain of parting with it, just as she had with little Jem who was now being cared for in one of the cabins. She had been a mother twice and both children were lost to her. There was nothing she could do but accept this with as good grace as possible; but she nourished an almost hopeless hope that someday she could keep and raise a child of her own.

However, she had been born black and black she must remain; she had been born a slave and slave she must remain, even though she was not called a slave, rather a servant for life. It made no difference how much white blood flowed in a person's veins, only a smidgeon of black blood could offset the white. One drop – just *one* drop – made all the difference in the world. One drop of white blood could not make a person white but oh, how one drop of black blood could make a person black! She belonged to Mr Macklin because she was black. That was that, and no matter how many children she produced, not one of them would ever be hers. And yet if she allowed herself to think about it, that was the one thing she wanted. A child of her own. A child to bring up, to raise to be like herself. She'd make certain that no child of hers ever turned out to be no-count nigger trash.

However, that was something she had to put out of her thoughts, for she must now attend to the ever-increasing tasks on the plantation. Mr Macklin was growing weaker and weaker, he was confined to his bed and unable to get up. Some days he was too feeble to speak more than a few words to her, but she knew what had to be done and went ahead and did it.

Things hummed around Elm Grove Plantation. It seemed to Lucretia Borgia that the plantation had never looked so prosperous as it had since she took over its management. The hands worked from sun-up to sun-down, accomplishing everything she intended them to do. The drivers – those petty tyrants who had authority delegated to them by their master – were now eating out of her hand and although they realized their own importance they were aware that she was in authority over them and that this authority had come from Mr Macklin, the omnipotent white man. To disobey Lucretia Borgia was to disobey their owner, and she would hand out whippings just as their master had done. In fact, she seemed to relish doing it, and Djoubo was kept busy with the lash.

Lucretia Borgia was everywhere. If she wasn't on her old grey mule, riding down the rows of cotton to see that the hands chopped out every single weed, she was in the kitchen at the big house, putting the fear of God into poor Emmy, or in one of the cabins, berating the luckless occupant because the yard was not swept clean or the cabin itself was dirty.

Most evenings she was too tired to enjoy Djoubo's company and although she did not entirely banish him to the barn, she often fell asleep before he could arouse himself sufficiently to mount her. She would drop into a dead sleep, devoid of dreams, until first light streaked into the kitchen and awoke her. Then she would direct the drowsy Emmy in the process of getting breakfast, although she always made the gruel, which was about all that Mr Macklin could keep on his stomach. She saw to it that Djoubo had a white folks' breakfast because even though she did not often copulate with him, she had some affection for the black brute.

This was her life's pattern: hard work all day and dying in sleep at night. One evening, feeling more exhausted than usual, she sent Djoubo back to the barn and fell on her pallet, fully clothed, wanting only to close her eyes and seek the blissful unconsciousness of sleep. Even before she had drifted off, however, she heard steps and saw a circle of light as the kitchen door opened. Mrs Macklin rushed over to her, running so fast that the flame of the candle she held was nearly blown out. She stooped over, her hand shaking so that some of the hot wax fell on Lucretia Borgia's face.

'He a-goin'!' She shook the girl hard. 'Mista Macklin he a-goin', Lucretia Borgia, and I want yo' upstairs with me. Ain' never seen no person die afore, 'n I afraid to be alone with him! Skeered, I am.'

In spite of her exhaustion, Lucretia Borgia came fully awake. She sat up, taking the candle from Mrs Macklin's trembling fingers. 'He worsened?' She heaved her huge body up, knowing that further sleep would be impossible.

'He a-dyin', I tell yo'!' Mrs Macklin was hysterical, sobbing so she could hardly speak. 'Nearly breathed his last, he has. Ain' fittin' I leave him to die alone, but want yo' with me. Know yo' ain' human, Lucretia Borgia, but yo' better'n nobody. He might be gone by the time we could fetch a white person.' Mrs Macklin leaned on Lucretia Borgia, glad of the monumental support she found in the other woman's strength.

Lucretia Borgia headed for the house and the stairs, pushing Mrs Macklin before her. Together they traversed the long hall to the bedroom. Mrs Macklin had left a lighted candle on the stand beside the bed, but it was not necessary to see to realize that the man on the bed was nearly gone. They could hear a horrible wheezing rattle as he expelled air from his tired lungs, and then another as he gasped to inhale his next breath.

'He a-dyin'?' whispered Mrs Macklin.

' 'Pears that way, ma'am. Shore havin' a time gittin' the breath into him. Even worse gittin' it out. Yo' give him the doctor's medicine when he went to bed?'

Mrs Macklin nodded her head. 'Don' never do no good tho'. He too far gone for medicine now. I tell yo' he a-dyin'!'

Lucretia Borgia bent over the bed, listening to the terrible forced breathing. 'Yes ma'am. He don' even know we here.

Mista Macklin suh?' She knelt beside the bed and shouted at the man, but there was at first no sign of recognition. Then his body shook convulsively and he opened his eyes, staring at her and then beyond her to his wife. In that instant she knew that he recognized them. Feebly one hand went up and he beckoned, uttering the word, 'Miranda'.

His wife knelt alongside the bed with Lucretia Borgia. 'Yes, dear.' She leaned over him. 'Yo' all right?'

He struggled to get out the words, slowly and almost inaudibly, one by one. 'Leavin' ... yo', Miranda. Sell ... everythin'. Go to ... yore sister in ... Atlanta. Plantation ... ain' ... no ... place for a lone ... woman.'

The effort of speaking exhausted him. He sank back on the pillow and closed his eyes. A slight shudder ran over his body, his breath rattled in his throat, and it was over.

'He's daid,' Mrs Macklin screamed. 'Oh, Lucretia Borgia, he's daid!'

Lucretia Borgia drew Mrs Macklin close to her and enfolded her in her arms. The woman laid her head on Lucretia Borgia's bosom and wept, while the Negress made little clucking noises to comfort her.

'There, there, ain' as if we didn' 'spect it, Miz Macklin. Mista Macklin, he done gone and left yo', but Lucretia Borgia she here with yo' 'n she'll protect yo', 'deed she will. But we better git someone started on making a coffin for him. Yo'll need to wash him 'n lay him out in some clothes. I'll skedaddle down to the barn, 'n wake Djoubo. He not bad with a hammer 'n nails 'n a saw, he kin make up a coffin. Kin cover the boards with a clean sheet, tack it right on.'

Mrs Macklin roused herself from Lucretia Borgia's embrace. 'Got us something better'n a sheet. Got some black cotton cloth left over when we mourned my mamma. Kin tack that on 'cause that's what we did with my mama's coffin.' She had stopped sobbing and stood up straight. 'Yo' go to the barn, Lucretia Borgia, 'n rouse Djoubo. Better rouse everybody. I'll fix po' Mista Macklin. Dress him in his Sunday-go-to-meeting clothes 'n Djoubo 'n one of the hands kin lift him into his coffin when it done. Better have

84

some of the hands ride round to all the plantations. Tell 'em that the funeral be tomorrow.'

'Yes ma'am, Miz Macklin ma'am. Do all that. Black cloth shore going to look nicer'n a sheet.' Lucretia knelt down again beside the bed, her arms outstretched alongside Mr Macklin's body.

'What yo' doin'?' her mistress asked.

'Measurin' him so's Djoubo git the coffin the right size. He's the length o' my arms 'cept for one hand.'

Mrs Macklin rummaged in the wardrobe and brought out a bolt of black cotton cloth, which had turned a little green over the years. She handed it to Lucretia Borgia and together the women went down the stairs.

'Emmy ain' here, I'll have to rouse her, but I'll het up some water so's yo' kin wash him.' Lucretia Borgia filled the big kettle and set it on the crane. The fire had burned down to a few embers; she added more wood, blowing with the bellows until it burst into flame.

She looked at her shakedown on the floor with longing eyes, realizing suddenly how tired she was. Then she turned towards the outside door. 'Goin' to the barn to get Djoubo started, 'n then I rouse the folks. Lots of work to be done for the funeral. House got to be cleaned 'n bakin' to do. Will get all the women here 'n will send three-four hands to tell t'other plantations.'

It was dark outside but she needed no lantern to find her way to the barn. Once inside, she could hear Djoubo's breathing and she went over to the stall where he was sleeping. In the darkness she reached out, her fingers encountering the warmth of his body. Slowly her hand slid down over his shirt to undo the single button that held up his pantaloons. Her fingers clutched the rigidity of his maleness.

Suddenly she did not feel tired any longer. She had been without a man too long. Her fingers slid back and forth with a firm but slow fondling. Djoubo sighed in his sleep, tensing his body, then woke up. Half asleep still, his arms enfolded her. 'Don' stop, Lucretia Borgia. Keep right on, it so wonderful. Glad yo' come.'

'Bin missin' yo' too, Djoubo,' she whispered, laying her body down beside him. 'But we ain' got much time. Po' Mista Macklin, he daid. Jes' died tonight 'n yo' got to heist yo'self up 'n start making a coffin for him. Lookin' like we got to work all night gittin' it ready for the funeral tomorrow.' Her hand continued to tantalize him.

'Ain' goin' to take much time for me to do a little pleasurin' tho'. I'm 'bout ready to pop now. Yo' better stop or I will.'

'Guess we kin spare the time,' she assured him, 'though it don' hardly seem right to be pleasurin' when we in a house o' sorrow.'

'This ain' no house; this a barn. 'N ain' no sorrow here neither, Lucretia Borgia. Jes' yo' 'n me.'

He rolled over and she felt the weight of his body on her. How welcome it was. Everything else was forgotten in the warmth and animal passion of his embrace. She sought his lips and felt them warm and wet pressed against her own.

It took him only a moment and he rolled away from her, spent. She got up on her knees and then to her feet.

'Hey yo', Djoubo boy,' her mood of tenderness had passed, 'don' yo' go off 'n go back to sleep.'

'Bin off once,' he giggled.

'Tha's 'nuff. Git up. Stir yore stumps. We got us a lot o' work to do. Git a lantern lighted 'n get out those boards. Got to make up a coffin for po' Mista Macklin and tack it all over with black cloth. I got to rouse all the folks 'n send some a-ridin' to the other plantations. Take the rest o' the night to git things ready for the funeral tomorrow. Stir yo'self. Cain' dawdle no mo'. Git stirrin'!'

Slowly he rose to his feet. 'Yes ma'am, Miz Lucretia Borgia ma'am. Goin' to do jes' that.'

CHAPTER TEN

It was long past first light when Lucretia Borgia and Djoubo finally drove the last tack through the black cloth that covered Mr Macklin's coffin. Lucretia Borgia stood back to admire the effect, which was rather skimpy in spots as they had had to patch the cloth to get enough to cover top and sides. She sighed at the completion of one job and then went to the door of the barn and called to a hand who was sweeping the drive with a twig broom. She ordered him to go along with Djoubo and carry the coffin to the upstairs room where Mr Macklin had died, and to help Mrs Macklin place him in it. She herself carried the two sawhorses from the barn, where they had been used in making the coffin, into the parlour and draped them with a white sheet to provide a suitable resting place for the coffin and poor Mr Macklin's remains.

This accomplished, she went out into the garden insisting that Mrs Macklin, after her late husband had been arranged in his coffin, accompany her. She knew that the woman needed some job to keep her mind occupied, so together they stripped the garden of all its flowers – heavy-scented tuberoses, pungent marigolds, bachelors' buttons and whatever late roses were blooming. These they laid on the coffin. Lucretia Borgia had to admit that Mr Macklin looked better now than when he was living. There was an expression of peace on his face which had not been there when he was struggling to catch one breath after another to keep alive. Once again, alongside the coffin, now strewn with flowers, Mrs Macklin broke down and wept on Lucretia Borgia's ample bosom, but the servant did not allow this paroxysm of grief to last long. Though she was perfectly willing to sympathize with the weeping widow, she had work to do that could not wait.

Djoubo, tired from his night's toil, had already been sent into town to fetch the parson for the funeral, which custom declared should be at two o'clock to give all the neighbours time to arrive. Riders had been dispatched to all the surrounding plantations and it was certain that their occupants would all be on hand, partly out of respect to Mr Macklin, whom all had considered a good neighbour, and perhaps even more because funerals, like weddings, were an opportunity for neighbours to meet and talk together.

Lucretia Borgia had assembled all the women of the slave cabins and they were attacking the big house with cloths, scrub brushes, brooms and beeswax until every corner gleamed with cleanliness. From time to time she abandoned her supervision of the cleaning women to go out into the kitchen where a bewildered Emmy, together with some of the more experienced women, directed the cooking of hams and side meats, the baking of bread and pastries. Plentiful as these were, Lucretia Borgia knew that they would be supplemented by various dishes brought by the neighbouring women, so that there would be enough for all to sit down to at the trestle tables out under the trees and have a feast after the interment. This was the social part of such occasions that relieved the lugubrious period of mourning which custom demanded precede it.

By noon, Lucretia Borgia was scarcely able to stand on her feet, but there was much more to do in the limited time left to her. The women who had cleaned the house and those who could be spared in the kitchen were sent to their own cabins because these too must be redded up and yards swept clean so that the whole plantation would have a spick-and-span appearance. It was not until after the minister had arrived and was praying with Mrs Macklin in the parlour, where Mr Macklin lay in the shadows of drawn shutters, that she had time to think of herself. She sniffed her armpits, then took a tin of soft soap and a towel, with clean clothes and a stiffly starched white apron, and made her way to the creek behind the barn. Here, under a screen of overhanging willows, she washed herself all over. She dried herself on the towel and donned her clean clothing just as the first wagons began arriving, filled with sympathizing neighbours. There was a large variety of conveyances, ranging from the shiny barouche with its liveried coachmen that belonged to the Courtney Hammonds – the most affluent neighbours in the vicinity – to the buckboards and mules which brought some of the rednecked farmers and their women. By one-thirty they had all assembled, the horses were hitched in the shade of the trees and the women had placed their food offerings proudly on the table.

Then the women, after embracing Mrs Macklin, who shed new and copious tears at each arrival, settled down in the house or on the veranda, where they rocked and chatted with each other. The men, uninterested in patchwork quilt patterns or the latest gossip of the neighbourhood, formed another group in the barn. Lucretia Borgia had had a keg of Mr Macklin's corn taken there with an odd assortment of tin cups, glass tumblers, and cracked china teacups so that the men could refresh themselves. Indeed, Lucretia Borgia had forgotten nothing and she, along with Djoubo, stayed in the barn waiting on the men, although from time to time she slipped out to oversee the other necessary preparations.

When one of the women came to the barn to inform the men that the services were about to start, Lucretia Borgia sped down through the street of cabins, assembling all the Negroes who, arrayed in their best, trooped up to the big house and stood around it in a semicircular group. One of them started to sing and the others took up the wordless, mournful cadence, while the white folks listened to the drone of the minister inside. His was a longer-than-necessary sermon; seldom did he have an opportunity to get so many people together to hear him, and he took advantage of it. This was followed by a glowing eulogy of the deceased and then an even longer prayer. At length they emerged from the house, the honorary pallbearers carrying the coffin whose cover had been nailed down at the close of the services. The procession of whites started across the fields to the small family burying ground, followed by the keening plantation slaves. When they arrived at the cemetery, where they had

89

some difficulty getting the coffin over the wooden stile, Lucretia Borgia realized to her regret that she had left one thing undone. The grave had been dug according to her instructions, but the high grass had not been mowed nor had the large holly trees at the corners of the plot been pruned. She was aghast and ashamed, but nobody else seemed to notice.

Now the coloured folk were quiet while the minister in his rusty black suit delivered another long and redundant prayer in which he again eulogized the dear departed and committed his soul to that divine province for which everyone present was ultimately destined – provided they attended his services regularly and were not backsliders. At the conclusion, which everyone, even Mrs Macklin, was eagerly awaiting, each of the white people filed past the grave, throwing a handful of dirt; then came the turn of the blacks who did likewise, weeping and wailing and keening their wordless tunes. Mr Macklin had been a good master. True, he had whipped more than occasionally, but then all masters did that. Now that he was gone they were concerned over what was going to happen to them. Lucretia Borgia, leading the straggling procession, was also concerned. She had no desire to leave this comfortable home where her rule had been definitely established and she recalled Mr Macklin's last words to his wife: to sell everything and go and live with her sister. Perhaps she could persuade her mistress not to sell. She could continue to oversee the plantation as she had during Mr Macklin's illness, getting the full quota of work out of each hand.

She had a fear of being sold. It was always a risk. No blacks ever knew what their lot would be once they stood on the auction block. She would have to use her powers of persuasion on Mrs Macklin. If the plantation were sold, perhaps she could convince Mrs Macklin that she should take her with her. Lucretia Borgia hoped so. Mrs Macklin was an easy woman to get along with and there had been few angry words between them.

Now the procession straggled back through the dusty

fields to the house. Custom demanded that Mrs Macklin should not preside at the table of funeral meats, but that she stay in the house in a darkened room, accompanied by one or two of the neighbouring women who clucked sympathy and from time to time dabbed camphor on her forehead and fanned her with a palm-leaf fan. But if the darkened room was a place of mourning, the tables on trestles under the trees were a scene of festivity. The men had begun to feel the copious draughts of corn whisky they had imbibed before the funeral and the women, released finally from the bondage of enforced mourning, were jovial and happy to indulge once more in small talk. The food was ample. Each woman had tried to outdo her neighbours in some speciality of her own, whether it was pecan pie or Dady Baltimore cake or, for the poorer women, merely a pan of corn pone. It was not until nearly sundown that the men started towards their several vehicles and while they were unhitching the horses the women made a mad scramble for their own plates and tins and platters. By early evening Elm Grove was empty of outsiders; its owner was secure in his six feet of soil under the spreading holly trees; and his widow, alone at last in the house, was the only white person left alive on the plantation.

Lucretia Borgia's work was far from done. She gazed out at the remnants of food and the dirty dishes on the trestle tables in the yard. The plantation folks had not eaten, so she portioned out the food and sent some to each cabin with strict instructions that after the food was eaten they should all tackle the enormous task of getting things back in shape. It was night before the last dish had been washed and put in the kitchen cupboards; before the trestle tables had once again turned into planks and saw-horses; before the soiled and stained sheets which had been used as tablecloths had been accumulated in a pile in the wash house; before Lucretia Borgia could find relief by sitting in her chair in the kitchen, her shapeless shoes kicked off and her tired feet hoisted up on a kitchen chair.

She dispatched the last few black women to their quarters;

91

all the candles were out now save one. She felt she should go to Mrs Macklin and see if there was anything needed, but Mrs Macklin had not summoned her and she was too exhausted to make the effort. She sat there, trying to make her mind a blank in her weariness, when the door of the kitchen opened and Djoubo came in. He too was dead tired and threw himself down on the floor on Lucretia Borgia's shakedown, welcoming the warmth of the dying embers in the fireplace. For a long time neither of them spoke, then Djoubo said, 'Now that Masta Macklin he daid, wonder what happen now? Miz Macklin she a-goin' to run the plantation with yo' to help her, Lucretia Borgia?'

She shook her head sadly. 'Cain' tell. Do all I can to make her believe things kin run jes' as well now's ever, but don' know. Don' want yo' a-shootin' off that big mouth o' yourn to t'other folks, but mayhap Miz Macklin she a-goin' to get shet o' the plantation, lock, stock, 'n all the niggers. Mista Macklin's las' words to her were jes' that.'

'Why yo' a-wantin' me to keep my mouth shet about it?'

'Yo' know how it goin' to upset the hands if'n they think things goin' to change. Niggers don' like changes. Gits used to one place 'n hate to git sol' off 'n go to another. Make *me* nervy too, jes' a-thinkin' 'bout it.'

Djoubo sat up, trying to digest what Lucretia Borgia had said. Idly, he played with his toes as his mental processes worked. 'Yo' mean it liable we git sold?'

She nodded. 'It more'n liable. Dreading it too, I am. Like it here. Mista Macklin he was a good masta and Miz Macklin she easy to git along with. Ain' never had no disputin' with neither o' them. But ain' no tellin' what sort of place any o' us got to go now.'

'Don' wan' to go nowhere else!' There was a tremor in Djoubo's voice, 'Jes' don' want to leave yo', Lucretia Borgia.'

'Ain' matterin' what yo' 'n I wants or don' wants. We ain' got nothin' to say 'bout it, but I glad o' one thing.'

'What that?' He perked up, hoping that there might be something that he too could be thankful for.

92

'Glad we both young 'n strong 'n good-lookin'. Course yo' pretty niggery 'n bozal-like in the face but yo' got a good strong body and anyone kin see that yo' make a good worker. I ain' handsome or pretty-like, but I'se strong 'n kin always take care o' myself. Ain' likely that we don' bring good prices if'n we sold. 'N yo' 'member this one thing, Djoubo boy.'

He slid over on the floor to be nearer to her. 'What that, Lucretia Borgia?'

'The more money a servant bring when he on the vendue table, the better he a-goin' to git treated by his new masta. New masta ain' goin' to mistreat a servant he pay a lot o' money for.'

'Course he ain',' Djoubo agreed, ' 'n yo' a-thinkin' we bring good money if'n we sol'?'

'Thinkin' mayhap we bring the highest prices o' any o' the folk here; but I'm not shore I'm goin' to be sol'. Mrs Macklin she 'pending a lot on me 'n it jes' possible she take me with her when she go.'

Djoubo's lower lip trembled. 'But that mean we a-goin' be separated!' He inched across the floor to lay his head on her lap. 'Don' want to leave yo', Lucretia Borgia. Know yo' don' like me so well's Big Jem, 'n don' know if'n yo' like me a-pesterin' yo' so well as yo' liked gittin' pestered by that yaller-haired white fellow, but I loves yo', Lucretia Borgia. Ain' never wantin' me no other woman in my life but yo'.'

Her hand caressed his head with tenderness.

'Shore admire to have yo' a-lovin' me, Djoubo. Wishin' too that we git sold together, but don' dare hope 'bout anything like'n that. Yo' a good boy. If'n we separated, I miss yo', but nobody kin tell what a-goin' to happen. Maybe the same man buy the two o' us – even though we pretty costive for one man to buy.'

He stood beside her, lifting her from the chair. Putting his arms around her, he kissed her and then led her towards the shakedown on the floor. While he stood there, his lips pressed against hers, his fingers unloosened the buttons of her dress.

'Too tired for pleasurin' tonight, Djoubo,' she protested.

'I too tired too, Lucretia Borgia, but want to be near yo'. Ain' got no hankerin' for goin' out to the barn 'n sleepin' 'lone in a stall.'

She sank to the floor, pulling him down beside her. 'Ain' complainin', Djoubo. Somehow I jes' don' want to be 'lone tonight neither. I said I too tired for pleasurin' tonight, but guess a body never too tired for that. Mayhap that what I'm a-needin'. Las' night I had yo' but in such a hurry that I nigh forgot 'bout it. Lovin' ain' a-goin' to hurt nobody, 'n if'n what yo' say is true that yo' love me, then I want yo' too, Djoubo.'

He released her long enough to blow out the tallow dip and then found his way across the floor to the warmth and tenderness of her body. Somehow there seemed to be a finality to their lovemaking that night. There was no frantic and sweaty struggle between them. Instead there was tenderness and quiet and a complete joining of hearts as well as bodies. It was as though they might never be together again. Perhaps that was why their love was so ardent and why they slept so soundly afterwards.

CHAPTER ELEVEN

For the time being, life at Elm Grove Plantation went on almost as usual. There was, of course, no more of the care and continuous fussing that had been such a part of the household during Mr Macklin's illness. There were no broths or pap to prepare, no continuous changing and washing of bed linen or long periods of attendance in the sickroom. Mrs Macklin seemed perfectly willing to let Lucretia Borgia take over the management of the plantation and, as always when given power, Lucretia Borgia was eager to accept it. Authority over others was her *métier* and she was never happier than when delegating. Now she put even more effort into her work, because she was trying very hard to convince Mrs Macklin that things could go along as efficiently at Elm Grove as when the master was alive.

One morning a few days after the funeral, Mrs Macklin summoned Lucretia Borgia and instructed her that Djoubo was to hitch the horses to the surrey and take them both into Marysburg. She said she needed Lucretia Borgia's company; she did not want to go alone and Delilah was occupied in freshening up her entire wardrobe. This, she said, was an important errand, which Djoubo could not do by himself; she must go along too, and for propriety's sake she must take a woman with her. Lucretia Borgia hurried away to the barn to give Djoubo his instructions and then back to the kitchen to change her clothing. She had only one decent black cambric dress and this she donned, leaving off the stiffly starched white apron she usually wore. If she, instead of the high and mighty Delilah, was going with Mrs Macklin, she wanted to make the best appearance possible. Soon they had started for the village. Mrs Macklin clutched at her reticule as though it held something very precious, but what that could be was a mystery to Lucretia Borgia, even when Mrs Macklin instructed Djoubo to go first to the post office.

Marysburg was a small town, scarcely more than a cross-roads, but it did boast a substantial brick bank and a general store which housed the minuscule post office. There were a few good houses where the banker, veterinarian, lawyer and storekeeper lived; but mostly it was a squalor of Negro hovels through which stray dogs wandered, their lean ribs showing that they had to scavenge for every morsel they ate.

When they drew up at the store, Lucretia Borgia hoped that she might be asked to go in with Mrs Macklin, especially when she saw her mistress take a letter from her reticule. Posting a letter was far from an everyday occurrence.

She waited impatiently in the surrey, making desultory

95

conversation with Djoubo while her mistress was in the store. Not only did she want to know what Mrs Macklin was doing with the letter, but she had never been inside the store and was anxious to see what it was like. Her agile mind soon manufactured a valid excuse to enter. They were getting to the bottom of the barrel of white flour back at the plantation; surely it would be a favour if she were to go in and remind her mistress of it. With pursed lips she alighted from the surrey and went into the semidarkness of the store. She could see Mrs Macklin talking with the storekeeper at a little wicket which marked the precincts of the post office.

Quietly, she edged nearer and heard her mistress ask the storekeeper how long it might take for the letter to go to Atlanta, and although she could not hear his reply, she knew that the letter was going to Mrs Macklin's sister – the one Mr Macklin had mentioned with his dying words. Cold fear possessed her. Was Mrs Macklin going to leave? Would Elm Grove and all the folk there be sold? Was all her hard work in trying to impress Mrs Macklin to be in vain?

Now Mrs Macklin turned and discovered Lucretia Borgia. 'What yo' a-doin' in here?' she demanded, a trace of temper in her voice.

'Kindly beggin' yore pardon, ma'am, but jes' came in to remind yo', Miz Macklin ma'am, that we a-gittin' mighty short o' white flour 'n thinkin' yo' might want to buy some whilst yo' here. Nigh to scrapin' the bottom of the barrel, we are.'

'I'll attend to it.' Mrs Macklin dismissed her. 'Now go back out with Djoubo. Store ain' no place for niggers nohow. When I git finished here, got another errand to do and don' want yo' a-leavin' the surrey again 'thout'n I say so.'

'Niggers a-gittin' mighty uppity these days.' The storekeeper frowned at Lucretia Borgia and waited for Mrs Macklin to nod assent, while Lucretia Borgia took her dismissal with as good grace as she could muster. But she had found out what she had come in for. Mrs Macklin was sending a letter to Atlanta. As for the other errand, perhaps she

96

would be able to find out about that also. In this, alas, she was disappointed. Mrs Macklin had Djoubo drive her from the store to the bank but instead of entering the bank itself, Mrs Macklin climbed up an outside staircase beside the brick building. Had Lucretia Borgia been able to read, she might have solved the problem of Mrs Macklin's errand, because the small sign beside the staircase said 'A. Owen, Attorney'.

Mrs Macklin was in there an interminable time. Lucretia Borgia was forced to sit and make idle talk with Djoubo while she tried to piece together the two events. Mrs Macklin had sent off a letter to her sister in Atlanta, of that Lucretia Borgia was sure; but what could she be doing in a bank for such a long time? Banks were a mystery to Lucretia Borgia. She did know that it had some connection with money, for she had overheard the Macklins talking about it, but of the services it performed she was completely ignorant. She knew the value of money, even though she had never handled any except the two silver dollars Mr Macklin had given her when her babies were born.

After what seemed hours, Mrs Macklin descended the steps and hoisted herself into the surrey. She threw back the heavy black crêpe veil from her face and wiped the sweat away with a handkerchief. Then she ordered Djoubo to drive home. Lucretia Borgia was dying to ask her about the bank, but didn't dare to broach the subject. There were certain lengths to which a servant could go, and Lucretia Borgia was well aware of those limitations. She would have to bide her time. Sooner or later she would know the answers.

After a week had passed, Mrs Macklin dispatched Djoubo every day to the post office to see if there might be a letter for her; if there were, he was to be most careful and not to lose it on the way home. Each day Lucretia Borgia was the first to see him come up the tree-bordered driveway. Invariably she was there before her mistress with the question, 'Git any letter today?' She was always relieved when he answered, 'No'. After nearly two weeks, however, Djoubo's response

97

to Lucretia Borgia's question was a jubilant 'Yes!' and he showed her the square of white paper which he had clutched in his hand all the way from town.

Lucretia Borgia felt that he should give it her to deliver to Mrs Macklin, but for once Djoubo did not fall in with Lucretia Borgia's wishes. He himself must see that it got to Mrs Macklin. Wasn't that what she had told him, not to let it out of his hands? Well, that was exactly what he would do. But Lucretia Borgia saw to it that she was standing by when Djoubo presented it. Impatiently she watched as Mrs Macklin carefully slit the paper with a silver knife, striving to read from her mistress's expression what the news might be; but Mrs Macklin's face was impassive and Lucretia Borgia had to go into the kitchen without an inkling of what the letter contained. Oh, how she wished she could read! Sooner or later she'd get a chance to look at the letter herself, but it would do her no good, for she did not know one word from another.

She was obsessed with the matter all afternoon. That the letter concerned her future she was very certain, and the mystery made her sharp and tyrannical with poor Emmy. Later that afternoon when the hands came in from the fields and a driver reported indolence and a tendency to sass back from one of the hands, Lucretia Borgia ordered the man to have ten lashes without first consulting Mrs Macklin, something she had always done before when punishment was due.

It was not until after Delilah had served Mrs Macklin her solitary dinner in the dining room and Lucretia Borgia had supervised the cleaning of the kitchen that her curiosity was finally satisfied. It was already dark and she was about to go to the barn to invite Djoubo to the house when Delilah entered the kitchen. As usual, she tried to lord it over Lucretia Borgia.

'Miz Macklin she a-settin' on the front gallery 'n she says to tell yo' to come out there. Wantin' to talk with yo', I reckon, but why I jes' cain' imagine. I her personal servant. Seems to me she'd want to talk to *me*. But yo' bin a-sashayin' 'roun' so important-like, guess she thinks the sun rise 'n set on yo', Lucretia Borgia.'

Lucretia Borgia gave the girl a disdainful look. 'If'n she a-wantin' me, she a-wantin' me, 'n tha's that. She a-knowin' she kin talk things over with me that even a lightskinned nigger like'n yo' cain' understand. Miz Macklin a-knowin' I kin handle anythin'.'

Delilah had no desire to bandy further words with Lucretia Borgia. She always seemed to come out on the short end of the stick in these verbal encounters. Nevertheless, she waited until Lucretia Borgia had slipped on her shoes and followed her out onto the gallery where Mrs Macklin was seated in a rocking chair.

'Yo' sent for Lucretia Borgia, Miz Macklin ma'am, 'n here she is.' Delilah waited, hoping that she might be included in the conversation, but Mrs Macklin dismissed her with a wave of her hand.

'Set yo'self down, Lucretia Borgia.' She indicated a straight-backed chair.

Lucretia Borgia perched her bulk on the edge of the chair, wishing that Delilah might see her. It was the second time in her life that she had been asked to sit down in the presence of white folks.

Mrs Macklin rocked back and forth for a moment. 'Got me a letter from my sister in Atlanta today,' she said. 'Mayhap yo' 'members, when Mista Macklin he a-dyin', he say for me to sell Elm Grove 'n go live with my sister. Well, I wrote her, and jes' got the answer today.'

'Yes ma'am, knowed that Djoubo he brought yo' a letter when he come from town. He right set up 'bout it.'

'I was shore glad to git it. Reckoned she would never answer, but she did. She a-wantin' me to come, sayin' I'll be right welcome there. Thinkin' that it best I take po' Mista Macklin's last word of advice 'n go to her. Like'n he said, plantation as big's Elm Grove ain' no place for a single woman.'

Lucretia Borgia hitched uneasily on the edge of her chair, Now the time she had been waiting for and dreading had come. It was up to her to convince her mistress that things could go along even better – under her management, of course – than they had while Mr Macklin was alive.

'Sorry to hear that yo' feels yo' must go, Miz Macklin ma'am. Ain' no use o' yore sellin' this fine place, though. Thinkin' we could make a go of it here, yo' 'n me together. Shore we could! This place stand to make a lot o' money for yo', Miz Macklin. I jes' a nigger wench 'n ain' very smart but I kin run this place. Look at all the time I bin runnin' it since Masta Macklin he bin ailin'. Everything under control 'n things workin' good. All the hands look up to me 'n willin' to take orders from me. Whyn't yo' try it for a while 'n see if'n we cain' make a go of it?'

The rockers on Mrs Macklin's chair squeaked and protested as she rocked several times before answering Lucretia Borgia.

'Have bin considerin' it. Don' jes' *want* to sell out. Mista Macklin 'n I we put a lot o' work into this place. He heired it from his father, he did, but we built it up. His pappy didn' have more'n twelve niggers when we took it over, 'n now look at it. Yo' did a good job, Lucretia Borgia. Bin tempted to go on with it knowin' I got yo'. Yo' shore took hold since Mista Macklin he begun ailin'. Everything under control 'n niggers workin' good.'

'Yas, Miz Macklin ma'am. Things shore hummin' here with me to watch 'em.'

'Bin puzzlin' on it since I got my sister's letter, 'n even before. But the worst thing is, it mighty lonely out here with Mista Macklin gone. Ain' no one but niggers to talk to. 'Sides, I'm a city girl. Come from Atlanta, I did, 'n always bin anxious to git back. Now that Mista Macklin gone, ain' got nothin' to keep me. So I'm thinkin' I'll take Delilah 'n go. Had thought some o' takin' yo' 'long too, Lucretia Borgia, but my sister's house it ain' big 'nuff for both yo' 'n Delilah 'n she bin with me so long she know how to wait on me better'n yo' do. She a fine seamstress 'n kin keep up my clothes for me. Yo' a good cook, but my sister's got a good cook, so don' look like there's any place for yo' in the city.

100

'Sides, yo' ain' a city nigger nohow; yo' a plantation nigger 'n ain' used to city ways. Lots o' difference, yo' know.'

'Shore admire to go along with yo', Miz Macklin ma'am.'

'Yo' a mighty capable gal, Lucretia Borgia. Shore hopin' yo' gits yo' a master 'n mistress what appreciates yo'. Ain' goin' to let yo' go to jes' any Tom, Dick 'n Harry what a biddin' for yo' neither. Wants that yo' should have a good home, seein' as how yo' such a good gal.'

Now finally Lucretia Borgia knew what was to become of her. It was just what she had been dreading all along: she was to be sold. But it didn't make much difference whether Mrs Macklin picked out a buyer for her or not. How was she going to know how a girl would be treated in another place? The tears came to her eyes and she got up from the chair, approaching Mrs Macklin. 'Yo' a-goin' to sell me, ma'am?'

Mrs Macklin sighed. It was evident that she had real feelings regarding the matter. 'Reckon as how I'll have to. Cain' take yo' with me. Goin' to sell everything, Lucretia Borgia. Sell the whole plantation and all the hands right down to the new suckers, 'ceptin' Delilah.'

'Oh, ma'am, take me too!' Lucretia Borgia was unused to begging, but this was the most important turning point of her life. She was to be *sold*. She couldn't bear the thought of it. 'Don' sell me, Miz Macklin ma'am. Wants to stay with yo', I do. We gits along fine, ain' never had no disputin' nor nothin'. Don' care if'n I have to sleep on the floor at yore sister's house. Don' min' nothing jes' so long as yo' takes me with yo'.'

Again Mrs Macklin sighed. She reached out a pale hand and took hold of Lucretia Borgia's black one. Then she did a very strange thing. She actually stroked Lucretia Borgia's hand.

'Cain' do it, Lucretia Borgia. Jes' cain' take yo'. But I want yo' to know I'm mighty appreciable over all yo' done for me. Want to thank yo', I do.'

Lucretia Borgia realized that there was no use in further begging. She knew when she was licked. She was black and Mrs Macklin was white, and Mrs Macklin could sell her if

101

she wished. All the hard work, all the effort she had put into impressing Mrs Macklin with her ability, now counted for naught. She could well have been the laziest hand on the place, just any no-account nigger wench that shirked all the work given to her. It made no difference. The worst had come. There was nothing worse than being sold, not knowing where you would go. There was just one more thing she wanted to know. She backed away, ashamed of her tears.

'When we a-goin' to git sold, ma'am? Tomorrow?'

'No,' Mrs Macklin shook her head. 'It'll be some time. Mr Owen, the lawyer in Emporia, he a-sayin' he knows of a buyer for Elm Grove but he don' want no niggers 'cause he got 'nuff o' his own. Mr Owen he a-goin' to git in touch with a vendue house down in Mobile 'n they a-goin' to take charge o' everythin'. Now don' yo' worry, Lucretia Borgia. Yo' goin' to git a good home. Mayhap yo' goin' to like it better'n this.'

'Cain' like any place better'n Elm Grove, 'n cain' like any mist'ess as well as yo', ma'am.'

'Thank you, Lucretia Borgia. Now I'm sayin' it again. Don' worry.'

Don't worry! How easy it was for this white woman rocking in her chair to say that. She had nothing to worry about, nor did that fool Delilah. She wasn't going to be sold, damn her yellow hide. But Lucretia Borgia was, and all the rest of the folks too. Now she didn't care if Djoubo did tell them. Let them all know. They'd have to know sooner or later and what difference did it make? Slowly she turned from Mrs Macklin and trudged into the house.

Lucretia Borgia was woefully ignorant about religion. True, she had heard the white folks talk about a God who was good and who directed things. She knew that they prayed to him, just like the minister did when he buried Mr Macklin. But as to what or who God was, Lucretia Borgia really didn't know. However, she was not one to overlook any angle and as she passed through the dark dining room on her way back to the kitchen, she stopped. There in the gloom she folded her hands together as she had

102

seen the minister do, and in a voice that was scarcely audible, she whispered.

'Oh, Gawd, look down on this pore nigger 'n git her a nice kind masta 'n mist'ess for her nex' one. Git her a good home. I'm askin' it o' yo', Gawd. Jes' a nice masta 'n mist'ess 'n a good home, tha's all I ask.' She unclasped her hands, staring into the darkness; then put them together again, ' 'N if it not askin' too much, dear Gawd, give me a good man too.'

CHAPTER TWELVE

The days of preparation for the sale of Elm Grove's slaves were endless. Mrs Macklin had decided to sell all the household effects too, as she did not wish to move them to Atlanta, as well as all the livestock on the plantation; of course that included the slaves, because they were livestock in the same sense as the horses and cows. There was so much to do, and most of the responsibility fell on Lucretia Borgia's shoulders. It was exactly like digging one's own grave. Mrs Macklin would say 'do so-and-so' and Lucretia Borgia would do it, knowing that whatever she did would be one step nearer to being sold.

She was somewhat mollified by the fact that Delilah was even busier than she was, although Delilah's not being sold stuck in Lucretia Borgia's crop. Now she was glad that she had never been handy with a needle; otherwise she would have had to help Delilah, who was sewing new clothes for all the slaves. They could not go up on the vendue table in the nondescript garments they had been wearing. The new clothes were nothing elaborate, to be sure, but each woman was to have a black calico dress and each man a pair of black pants and a white shirt. Delilah could not possibly do it all alone so Mrs Macklin brought in a couple of the handier wenches to help her; but making clothes for all the hands and all the wenches entailed much time.

Work in the fields could not stop, because Mrs Macklin had agreed with the new owner that things would be kept up until he took possession; but now Lucretia Borgia was not as interested in Elm Grove's productivity as she had been. Before, it had been home, she had had good reason to keep the hands at work; the greater the production, the more it would rebound to her credit. Now, nothing she could do would help. She was going to be sold. Even her praying had ceased. She could not truly imagine that God would be interested in her problem. God was for white folks. Look how he had blessed them and how he had condemned the blacks. Surely his beneficence did not extend to her.

One afternoon, just as the shadows were beginning to lengthen, Lucretia Borgia heard the sound of wheels in the driveway and ducked out of the kitchen to see a smart-looking chaise drawn by two horses. Two white men alighted and instructed Djoubo, who had come running from the barn door, to take their valises from the chaise and carry them to the house before leading the horses to the barn. The men were met at the door by Delilah, who hastily pinned her needle and thread to her dress and asked them to sit in the parlour while she summoned Mrs Macklin.

Lucretia Borgia, knowing that something important was about to happen, took up a vantage point in the dining room where she could overhear what went on. She heard the men introduce themselves to Mrs Macklin as Mr Perry and his clerk Mr Sinclair, from the vendue house of Perry and Atkinson in Mobile.

Risking detection, she peered around the corner of the dining room to get a good look at the men and to hear Mrs Macklin's effusive welcome. The older of the two, Mr Perry, was tall, stoop-shouldered and sandy-haired. She took an instinctive dislike to him. Somehow his booming voice, narrow lips and sharp grey eyes told her that he was the man who was going to sell her. Sinclair was shorter, with curly black hair and a fresh complexion, whose bright pink cheeks held a certain boyish appeal for Lucretia Borgia. He was not nearly so frightening as Mr Perry. She wondered if Mrs Macklin would provide bed wenches for the men. Probably not, but Lucretia Borgia felt she would not mind if *she* were assigned to young Mr Sinclair. Bedding down with him would be a pleasure, just because of his pink-and-white complexion.

'I think we'll be all set for next Monday, Mrs Macklin,' Mr Perry said loudly. He seemed almost to be shouting, as if to make himself heard a long distance away. 'We've done most of the preliminary work in Mobile. Advertisements have been put in all the newspapers in the surrounding towns, and we've written personal letters to many of the larger plantation owners who, we are sure, would like to attend. I can't guarantee any whopper of a sale from your lawyer's description of the servants. It appears that you haven't many good strong young bucks, which is what the buying public wants today. But he mentioned that you do have some good wenches and some of them have foals with them. They should sell well. A dam with foal always brings a good price.'

Mrs Macklin nodded her head in time to his words. 'The best nigger we had, Big Jem, runned a while back and was ate by a panther. But we got a few others that ain' so bad.'

'That boy who took our horses seemed a right likely young buck,' Mr Sinclair said to Mr Perry. 'Got any more like him?'

She shook her head. 'Mr Macklin bought that Djoubo boy when he jes' a saplin'. Brought him up to do the stablin'. He right good with horses. Drives me when I want to go out, but ain' had no 'sperience as a field hand.' She realized that she had been lacking in hospitality. 'Would either o' yo' two gentlemen like some refreshments? Still some of Mr Macklin's corn out in the barn if'n that what yo'd like.'

'Later, ma'am, later.' Mr Perry lowered his voice an octave. 'A glass would set right well after supper.'

'Ain' long to supper time, 'n I must tell my cook there'll be company for the next few days. One thing we do have, gentlemen, is a fine cook. She's one of the best wenches I ever had and I certainly hate to part with her. Like yo' to meet her. 'Specting she a-goin' to bring a good price at the vendue.' She rang a bell on the table beside her and when Delilah answered, she told her to summon Lucretia Borgia. The latter had just time to slip out of the dining room and into the kitchen and be standing by the stove when Delilah got there.

'Miz Macklin say as how yo' to come into the parlour, as she want to talk to yo'.'

'Them white men a-goin' to stay for supper?' It seemed diplomatic to pretend ignorance.

'Ain' a-sayin' nothin'. Miz Macklin she kin tell yo' what she wants. Better heist yo'self in there right away. She a-waitin' for yo'.'

Lucretia Borgia was glad that her apron was clean and she paused only a moment to arrange the folds of her red turban, then hurried to the parlour, stopping at the door to await Mrs Macklin's nod to enter. She stepped into the room, standing straight, tall and majestic, her bosom thrust out and her chin lifted, a welcoming smile on her face. She must make the best impression possible on these men. Her whole future was in their hands; she determined to give them the best meal they had ever eaten.

'This here Lucretia Borgia.' Mrs Macklin nodded towards her. 'She's our cook, and a right likely cook she is too.'

Lucretia Borgia felt the men inventorying her and she smiled even more broadly to show a row of dazzling white teeth, then bobbed a little curtsey.

'Mista Perry 'n Mista Sinclair they goin' to be a-stayin' with us for a few days, Lucretia Borgia. They a-goin' to sleep in the east room 'n I 'spects yo' to feed 'em good whilst they here. They from Mobile 'n they know what good cookin' is.'

'Yes'm, Miz Macklin ma'am. Goin' to see to it that these two gen'mun get good eatings whilst they here. Had bin thinkin' mayhap we have chicken tonight, that is,' she turned in the direction of the two men, 'if the gen'mun like chicken.'

106

They assured her that they did and she took her dismissal from Mrs Macklin and sped back to the kitchen. 'Emmy,' she called out. 'Go out 'n find me three good plump chickens. Don' want no scrawny ol' hens. Wring their necks 'n pluck 'em 'n bring 'em back in to me. We a-goin' to have a supper tonight like Elm Grove never seen afore. I got lots to do, so yo' *jump* when I tells yo'. Ain' a-goin' to take no sass from yo' tonight. Got to please these men mightily. Yo' know who they are?'

Emmy shook her head.

'They from the vendue house in Mobile 'n they a-goin' to sell us off soon. Miz Macklin a-goin' to have the servants sold afore she does the house things, 'n these men a-goin' to do it. The better yo' does, the better price yo' a-goin' to bring, 'n the better price yo' bring, the better home yo' a-goin' to git. So step to it, wench, 'n go fetch me those chickens o' I shore a-goin' to clobber yo'.'

The feast that Lucretia Borgia set before the visitors that night was indeed something special, and they ate as though they had not eaten for days. The chicken was crisply fried and tender inside so that it fell from the bones. The candied yams oozed beads of rich sweetness; the biscuits were so light they almost floated, and the watermelon pickles were spiced to perfection. The men groaned with satisfaction and when Lucretia Borgia brought on the pecan pie they told Mrs Macklin they shouldn't eat another mouthful but they just could not help it. Lucretia Borgia stood in the background watching Delilah serve and was right on hand when Mr Perry asked Delilah to call the cook in because he wanted to compliment her. She stood in the dining room doorway, proudly humble.

'That's one of the best meals I ever ate!' He turned to Mrs Macklin. 'What did you say this wench's name is?'

'Lucretia Borgia.'

'Well, Lucretia Borgia,' he boomed in her direction, 'I can promise you one thing. When you stand up on the vendue table next Monday I can personally attest and truthfully say that you are one of the best cooks in the country!'

107

She acknowledged his thanks with a courtly bow, then turned to Mrs Macklin. 'Kin I ask a question, Miz Macklin ma'am?'

'And she's got good manners too,' Mr Sinclair noted.

'She right nosey,' Mrs Macklin said, 'but she the most capable wench I ever had. Since Mr Macklin passed on, and before when he was ailin', she practically run this plantation, and run it better'n any white overseer. Ain' nothin' that Lucretia Borgia cain' do. She right capable.' She finally thought of Lucretia Borgia's question. 'Yes, what is it yo' want?'

'Kindly likin' to know if the two gen'mun have a hankerin' for ham 'n eggs for breakfast, 'n if so, how they likin' their eggs.'

'Sunny side up,' Mr Perry answered for both.

With another bow Lucretia Borgia left. She felt somewhat consoled because of the praise that had been given her and she immediately started planning a series of meals that would be even better than the dinner they had just eaten.

For the next few days, she had two jobs to do. First she had to superintend every morsel of food that went into the dining room, and second she had to act as overseer, presenting the hands to Perry and Sinclair.

They had set up a small table outside under a large pecan tree and Sinclair had a big ledger open before him, along with an inkpot and a supply of quills that he sharpened from time to time.

It was Lucretia Borgia's job to bring the hands and wenches up one at a time and introduce them to the white men. Only she knew their names and their histories. Of these things Mrs Macklin was woefully ignorant; had it not been for Lucretia Borgia, there would never have been a complete inventory of the coloured folk for the sale.

'This here's Benjy.' Lucretia Borgia would produce a reluctant field hand. 'He a bit puny but he a right good worker. Ain' so young's he used to be. But he kin take 'sponsibility 'n he one o' our best drivers. Knows how to git the work out o' the niggers. He always lived here at Elm Grove.'

All this would be noted down by Sinclair in his ledger; then Mr Perry would order the man to shuck off his clothes so that he could make a thorough examination of his body. This he did with experienced hands, noting any defects in the man's anatomy and remarking about them to Mr Sinclair. Then he would sit back and wait until Lucretia Borgia produced another.

'Here's Pansy.' Lucretia Borgia pushed the bashful girl forward. 'She a right pretty wench what Mista Macklin bought a spell ago 'n she bin covered by a white man 'n got a nice light-skinned sucker. A boy it is.' She went to Pansy and uncovered the bundle in her arms to show the light complexion of the baby. Mr Perry made an examination of both mother and child and Mr Sinclair again made notes.

' 'N here's May-Ann.' This time Lucretia Borgia's voice choked a little as she pushed the reluctant girl forward. 'Yo' see she got two suckers, both light-skins. One o' 'em's promised to Mista Ransom Lightfoot which sired 'em – the gal baby, which is this un, so it cain' be sold. Miz Macklin already sent word to Mista Lightfoot 'n he a-comin' to fetch it, 'n hopin' he gits here afore the vendue 'cause we cain' leave it here 'lone.' She gazed affectionately at the baby. 'It mine, if'n yo' wants to know, but cain' keep it. I a good breeder though. Cotches quick, I do. This is my second one, 'n if'n I git a good man kin give my new masta a sucker every year.'

Mr Perry examined the two babies in May-Ann's arms; then, as he had done with Pansy, he had her strip and went over her body with experienced hands. 'A right likely wench. Along with the sucker she's carrying, the male, she ought to bring a good price, especially as the sucker is extremely light-skinned.' He had Mr Sinclair write all this down in his book. 'Gal looks as though she had some human blood, so the baby must be a quadroon if what Lucretia Borgia says is true; and I have no reason to doubt her. Right truthful she seems to be.'

' 'N right truthful I am,' Lucretia Borgia declared. That was *almost* a fact, although when she felt distorting the truth a little would be more pleasant to a white person, she was never averse to doing so. She had learned that it always paid off to say the thing she believed would please them most.

And so she went through the whole troop of slaves at Elm Grove. Most of the men were middle-aged, even elderly, and Lucretia Borgia was not particularly interested in them; but when she finally produced Djoubo, she was more than a little enthusiastic about him.

'This Djoubo,' she said proudly, nudging him closer to Mr Perry. 'He 'bout twenty-two, I judge. Good man in the stables 'n right trustworthy too. All the time he bin here at Elm Grove he ain' never bin whopped, but he do the whoppin' for the plantation 'cause he right strong. He bin my man since Big Jem left us and they's just one more thing I got to say 'bout Djoubo. He kinda bozal-like in the face 'n pretty niggery 'cause he came from Africy when he nothing but a sucker, but he shore know how to pleasure a wench, don' yo', Djoubo?'

Djoubo, unused to talking to strangers, hung his head and made circles in the dust with his big toe. Mr Perry beckoned him to come a few steps closer. 'This is the best buck we've had so far, don't you think, Sinclair?' Mr Perry had already taken a proprietory air in regard to the slaves.

Mr Sinclair nodded as he made an entry for Djoubo in his ledger.

'Would say he's nearly a pure Krumantee, wouldn't you, Sinclair?'

Mr Sinclair closed one eye and scrutinized Djoubo, then nodded in agreement. 'Should fetch a good price. Pure African blood is something we rarely see these days, and Krumantees are always in demand.'

At Mr Perry's command, Djoubo shucked off his shirt and undid the button that held up his trousers, stepping out of them and standing before the two men and Lucretia Borgia. Conscious of his physical perfection, Djoubo danced a little

110

nervously on his toes, flexed his muscles and grinned at the men, knowing that he had nothing to be ashamed of.

After working so closely with both the white men, Lucretia Borgia had come to know them somewhat better, and had reached a point where she felt she could say things before them which a servant ordinarily could not have said.

'Like'n I bin a-sayin', gen'mun, Djoubo he mighty niggery in the face with them thick lips 'n that burr head, but he make up for it in other ways. He shore is well hung, ain' he?' She pointed to him with pride.

Mr Perry smiled back at her. Already he was accepting Lucretia Borgia as one who had a right to speak occasionally of her own volition. He put his left arm around Djoubo's naked waist and drew him close, hefting his huge genitals in his right hand. Then, drawing back the short black foreskin, he exposed the plum-coloured glans. Djoubo, aware that Lucretia Borgia was looking on, responded with an incipient erection which did not seem to embarrass him but was noticed by the others.

'Quick on the trigger, isn't he?' Sinclair laughed. 'That isn't anything I can put down in the ledger, but he is hung heavy, even for a nigger. Always heard that Krumantees were like that, although not as big as Mandingos. Looks like he ought to be a good breeder too. Mate him up with a good-looking wench and his get won't look so bozal-like.'

Mr Perry continued with his examination of Djoubo, but now there was a puzzled look on his face. He turned to Lucretia Borgia. 'You say that this Djoubo boy had been covering you, Lucretia Borgia?'

'Shore has.'

'For how long?'

She stopped a moment, trying to remember. 'A spell, I reckon. Since Big Jem got himself kilt. Ain' wanted me no other man once I got Djoubo. He not as good at pesterin' as Big Jem was,' she pointed to the skull on the pole before the barn, 'but once I got used to him, I rightly fond of him.'

Mr Sinclair regarded the two of them. 'Then there's one

111

thing I do not understand. You say that you are a good breeder, Lucretia Borgia?'

'Uh-huh,' she nodded her head proudly. 'That white boy, that Ransom Lightfoot, he just pestered me for two–three nights 'n I cotched right off, quicker'n lightnin'.'

'Then how come,' Mr Perry persisted in his questioning, 'that with Djoubo covering you all this time you haven't had a sucker from him? How do you explain that?'

Now it was Lucretia Borgia's turn to be puzzled. It was something she had never particularly thought of but after all the nights that she and Djoubo had shared her shakedown on the kitchen floor, she realized that she had nothing to show for it.

'Hasn't he got any sap?' Mr Perry persisted.

'Djoubo he got plenty o' sap,' she giggled. 'That boy he got so much sap he jes' a-boilin' over all the time. Cain' never seem to satisfy him, but I try, Mr Perry, I shore try.'

'Then it looks to me as though this boy's sap is no good. If you've had two suckers by others but he has never produced one, it can't be your fault. Must be his. Must be that he's sterile. Find a sterile buck every once in so often. Usually they're fine, upstanding bucks like this one, healthy and strong, but their sap just isn't any good. Djoubo must be one of those.' He turned and shook a warning finger at Sinclair. 'Don't put that down in the book. This's the best buck they've got here and it's a pity that he's sterile, but looks like he is to me. We won't mention it when we sell him, or it will take away from his price.'

Lucretia Borgia watched as Djoubo got back into his shirt and pants. Just seeing him standing there had aroused her and she was saddened to think there would be so few nights left that she could have him. But it must be true, what Mr Perry had said. Djoubo's sap was no good; no wonder she had not been knocked up. It saddened her to think that Djoubo was not a whole man. She had fallen in love with him despite his ugly face. He was good, Djoubo was, and he was kind and gentle and he loved her.

That night on her shakedown in the kitchen, Lucretia

112

Borgia put her arms around Djoubo. 'Know what night this is, Djoubo boy?'

'Thinkin' it Sattiday, Lucretia Borgia.' He tensed under the gentle administration of her fingers.

''N tomorrow Sunday 'n then it come Monday. We a-goin' to git sold Monday, Djoubo, 'n no telling if'n we ever see each other 'gain. Yo' go one way 'n I go another, 'n we never git to pleasure each other again.'

He started to sob, laying his head on her capacious bosom. 'Oh, Lucretia Borgia, jes' seems as tho' I cain' ever part from yo'. Cain' leave yo'!'

She felt the wetness of his tears. Her loving increased in tempo and finally his tears stopped.

'What that man say 'bout me?'

'He say yo' sterile. That mean yore sap no good.'

'Ain' my fault, Lucretia Borgia. Never tho't 'bout it afore but we bin a-beddin' a long time 'n I ain' never got yo' knocked up.'

She comforted him with her hands. 'Ain' yore fault, Djoubo. Ain' 'tall. Kinda sorry that yo' didn't get me knocked up. Sure would like to take a sucker along in my belly from yo' for my new masta. Not seein' yo' I could have yore sucker to 'member yo' by. Wishin' now I had one.'

'Yo' suppose if'n we try real hard tonight 'n tomorrow night, we could make a sucker?'

She shook her head in the darkness. 'Ain' thinkin' after all this time that we could, Djoubo, but we shore as hell kin try.'

'Les' do jes' that.' He had stopped sobbing and she could feel his head rise from her breasts and his tongue seeking hers.

'Yes, man, we try.' She kissed him, wondering where they would both be at the end of another week.

CHAPTER THIRTEEN

It was still dark when Lucretia Borgia roused herself at four in the morning on Monday. She lingered in semiconsciousness for several moments, wondering why today was going to be different from all others. Then it came to her that this was the day she had been dreading for so long. Where was she going to be tonight, and to whom might she belong? Regretfully and for what she knew would be the last time, she extricated herself from Djoubo's embrace. He yielded reluctantly, still asleep. Well, she would let him sleep a little longer because he too would be facing the unknown today, and a few moments more of unconsciousness would be that much less time for him to worry over it. She fumbled in the darkness and found her old dress, slipped into it, blew the embers in the fireplace into flames, put on fresh wood. She unhooked the big iron tea kettle from the crane, filled it with fresh water and put it back to heat. There was a chill in the air when she opened the back door and threw her old black shawl over her shoulders. Its warmth felt good as she went out in the darkness to ring the plantation bell.

Pulling on the rope as hard as she could, she let it resound for a full five minutes, confident that this prolonged ringing would rouse everyone on the plantation. This would be the last time they'd wake up in their own cabins and go through the familiar routine of munching their cold pone before they started out to the fields – although this morning there would be no work.

Shivering from the cold, she went back into the kitchen and rubbed her hands before the blazing fire. She could not help but think of the many days she had arisen in this kitchen, fixed breakfast for the Macklins, summoned the hands to work, and then gone about her own duties. Yes, she had grumbled then, but how happy those days seemed in retrospect! No more. Today was *the* day.

Djoubo crawled out of the shakedown and Lucretia

Borgia motioned him to a seat at the kitchen table. At least she could send him out with hot coffee in his stomach to warm him and give him courage. He grumbled when Lucretia Borgia made him fetch a pan of rain water from the barrel and splash it over his face, but he pulled her close to him when he returned and sat down at the table while she poured his coffee. His arms squeezed her to him, but he was unable to speak to her. She could see tears in his eyes but he brushed them away and drank the hot coffee, sweetened with molasses, while she ate the warm pone that she put before him. Then, at her prodding that he must attend to things in the barn, he got up and left, but not before kissing her a silent good-bye. This would probably be the last time they would ever kiss each other, so he prolonged it until she finally had to push him away.

Emmy came in rubbing the sleep from her eyes, and together they went through the mechanical task of getting breakfast for Mrs Macklin and the two white men. Afterwards, Lucretia Borgia shooed Emmy out of the kitchen and bade her stand guard over the kitchen door so that nobody could enter. She dragged the large wooden washtub from the laundry into the kitchen and filled it with warm water. No soft soap for her this time! She had stolen a bar of Mrs Macklin's perfumed soap. Its odour was so pleasant that Lucretia Borgia would have liked to linger over her bath, but each moment was precious. She dried herself by the fire so that all the dampness would evaporate, the warmth bringing a glow to her skin.

From the lower drawer of the chest in the kitchen, she took out a petticoat she had made of bleached sugar sacks; and although her stitches were crude, it even boasted a ruffle on the bottom. Over this she donned her best black dress. Around her neck she draped a well-darned lace fichu which Mrs Macklin had given her, knowing that this bit of discarded elegance would set her off from all the other wenches. She took particular pains with the turban of red cambric, which she twisted around her head to hide the short wool of her hair. One thing she had always admired and longed for was straight black hair, but this had been denied her, so she disguised the ugliness of her wiry hair with a turban. Nobody, except on rare occasions the men she slept with, had ever seen her without it. Telling Emmy to empty the tub of water, she stole into the dining room to look at herself in the big mirror. She would, she decided, look more prepossessing on the vendue table with one of her starched and ruffled white aprons, but she didn't want to wear it now and get it soiled before the sale. Going back to the kitchen, she took her few personal belongings from the drawer in the kitchen. She had another dress, not as good as the one she was wearing, several white aprons and a number of red headcloths. She also owned a pair of shapeless carpet slippers which she preferred to wear instead of the rough shoes she had donned. These few things she packed into a compact bundle which she did up in one of her headcloths and tied neatly. It was all she owned in the world except the two silver dollars Mr Macklin had given her. Even these things did not rightly belong to her. She had nothing, not even her own body.

During the previous day, Djoubo and several other men, directed by Mr Perry and Mr Sinclair, had erected a platform beside the barn under the shade of some live oak trees. It was perhaps six feet high and supported a rough platform the size of a small room. At one end of it stood the table and chair which Mr Sinclair had been using, along with his ledgers, ink and pens. In the centre there was a raised stand about three feet square. This was for the slaves to stand on in their turn, isolated, the focus of attention. Near the stand was a small table on which Mr Perry would later place a pitcher of water, a glass and a gavel. When Lucretia Borgia went out into the yard, this structure was the first thing she saw. It reminded her immediately of a woodcut she had once seen in Mr Macklin's newspaper. It represented a gallows with a man dangling from a rope in the middle. Lucretia Borgia knew that the man had been hung until he was dead. She realized that this platform might in a way witness her own execution. After all, death would be no worse than being sold to the wrong master.

Mr Perry came out from the barn and told her to go to the quarters and have all the bucks and wenches come up to the big barn – every man, woman and child. Here she was to have the men and boys stay in the open part of the barn, and the women and girls inside the stalls. Lucretia Borgia bobbed her little curtsey and was off to the quarters. She made sure that the men and wenches were dressed in their new clothes and that each one had made up a small packet of what personal belongings they had. Many had nothing but the old clothes they had worn every day of their lives. Others had pitifully small treasures: a cracked teacup from the big house, a discarded comb, a scrap of ribbon or coloured cloth which they had saved for its brightness, even a piece of shiny tinfoil that they treasured. Their lives were so drab that any little colourful thing attracted them and became a treasured possession.

By nine o'clock the first wagons had arrived, although the sale was not scheduled to start until eleven. Mr Perry had contacted the Ladies Auxiliary of the Marysburg Baptist Church and they had agreed, as a money-making scheme, to serve hot coffee and ham sandwiches to those buyers who got hungry during the sale. Although the good ladies were strictly temperance and would not provide liquor, Mr Perry had ordered a keg of corn to be placed in the springhouse, knowing well that men who had a few drinks of corn whisky under their belt would be more generous in their bidding. No provision had been made for the feeding of the slaves. Let them go hungry this one day. They were there to be sold and not to satisfy their appetites.

Mr Sinclair met the coloured folk at the door of the barn, directing the men to their section and the women to theirs. When they were all assembled, he went from one group to another, cautioning them that if some prospective buyer asked them to shuck off their clothes, they should do so with good grace. No man, he assured them, was going to buy a pig in a poke, and the only way a man could tell about slaves was to see them naked and to finger them. Although Lucretia Borgia was aghast to think that she might have to

117

strip before the eyes of some inquisitive white man and allow his hands to roam over her body, she reconciled herself to it by remembering that she had nothing to be ashamed of, that she could be proud of her fine body.

It was well that she had made up her mind not to let it bother her, because for an hour or more she was subjected to the scrutiny, the close inventory, the handling of men who had come to buy. There was not an inch of her body that they did not feel free to examine. She had difficulty in holding her temper when their examinations became too personal, yet she kept her lips shut and allowed them to feel her with as good grace as possible. Most of them, especially the elderly men and the red-neck farmers in their butternut and osnaburg clothing, were obviously doing it just to get a thrill, and were not seriously considering her purchase. Many of them looked too poor to own even one slave. She must, however, treat them all alike, because they were white men. She could not show the slightest sign of resentment, which was difficult with their calloused fingers poking into her.

When she saw two well-dressed men come into the stall, she perked up. She was naked – it was too much of a nuisance to keep putting her clothes on and taking them off – and she noted that both the men regarded her with more than idle curiosity.

'Now there, Tom, is a wench worth buying,' the shorter of the two men said. 'Not that I usually buy one as old as that, she must be in her early twenties; but she's the best o' the lot, though the boy yo' were lookin' at was pretty good.'

The other nodded gravely. 'Reckon I'll bid on him. Yo' a-goin' to bid on him too, Warren?'

The man addressed as Warren shook his head. 'Li'l too old for me. I like to get 'em younger and raise 'em myself. He's too damn expensive too. I kin git me a saplin' for half of what I'd pay for him. Matter o' fact, he's 'bout ready for my market. Usually sell 'em off when they get to be around twenty.'

118

'Then yo' won' be biddin' 'gainst me if'n I decide I want him?'

'Not at all,' Warren answered. 'We'll make a deal. I want this wench 'spite of her age, and mayhap yo' want her too. Cain' rightly tell *why* I want her, but she looks damned intelligent and I need someone like that. So, Tom, yo' don't do no biddin' on her, and I'll not bid on the Krumantee boy.'

Lucretia Borgia lifted her eyes to the two men who were talking. She decided then and there that she hoped either one or the other might buy her. Personally, she preferred the man called Warren. He was not a tall man, but stocky, with sturdy arms and legs. What appealed to her most was the kindliness and humour in his face. Brutality was entirely lacking and she could see no signs of violence or cruelty. Yet she judged that he was a man who would hold rigid discipline over any slave he owned. She could admire and respect him because she also demanded obedience from those under her. Not that the other man, Tom, would not make a good master too; but for some reason which she could not have explained, Lucretia Borgia favoured the man Warren. She was glad he had decided to bid on her and she wondered if the Krumantee boy they were talking about was Djoubo. Mr Sinclair had said that he was Krumantee. Another thing which raised her hopes was the fact that these men were together; they were probably friends and neighbours, and if one of them bought Djoubo and the other bought her, she and Djoubo might see each other occasionally.

Now the plantation bell was ringing and she realized with sinking heart that the sale was about to begin. Soon she could hear Mr Perry shouting and his gavel banging on the table. Young Mr Sinclair came running in with two white men he had hired from among the neighbours. These he left in charge of the slaves with instructions to bring them out one by one, the youngest saplings first, then the bucks, and finally the wenches. Lucretia was too far away from the vendue table to hear more than a few of Mr Perry's words but every so often she could hear him calling out 'Going,

119

going, gone. Sold to Mr so-and-so.' Then one of the white fellows would lead a boy back into the barn and stand him on the far side and take out another.

She saw Djoubo leave and waved to him as he passed. He waved back, forcing a brave smile. She did hope he would bring a good price and when he returned, after having stood on the vendue table, he got near enough to her to whisper. 'Man out there paid eight hundred dollars fo' me. That Mr Perry he say it the highest price paid yet. Lookin' pretty good for me.'

She was glad for him, but hoped that she would bring more than he had; she hoped that hers might be the highest price of all. It would satisfy her vanity to know that she was worth more than all the others – and inwardly she knew she was.

As the day wore on, it became extremely hot in the barn, and Lucretia Borgia grew weary of standing and waiting. She had been on her feet for hours and her clothes were soaked with perspiration. Fortunately she had folded her clean white apron and put it in her bundle; now she got it out, keeping it in readiness for the time when she would be taken out. Impatiently she watched the others go, May-Ann and Pansy with their suckers in their arms preceding her. She wished now that she had a sucker to carry in her arms. It would add to her value.

Finally it was her turn. The white fellow who was on duty in the barn came over to her and said, 'Hey yo' wench, 'bout time yo' climbed up there. Come on now.'

After the darkness of the barn, the bright sunlight blinded her, but she followed the man through the high grass which had by now been beaten down into a path. He led her to the foot of the platform steps and left her there. Picking up her long apron in one hand so that she would not step on it, she ascended the stairs. Mr Sinclair smiled at her and pointed to the stand and as she crossed the platform to ascend it, Mr Perry turned to look at her.

'Well, Lucretia Borgia,' he beamed. 'I certainly did miss that wonderful noon meal you would have prepared for me

120

if we hadn't been so busy.' He even came over to take her hand and guide her to the centre of the raised box. 'How are you, Lucretia Borgia?'

'Jes' fine suh, Mista Perry suh.' She essayed a wan smile.

He rubbed his hands together, as though he was anointing them with some perfumed ointment, and turned to the audience of upturned faces. Lucretia Borgia too peered down, but all she could distinguish at first was a blur of eyes staring up at her. One of those pairs of eyes was going to buy her. Which?

Mr Perry slapped her affectionately on the rump. 'Gentlemen, every once in a while a vendue merchant is called upon to sell a servant that he would really like to have for himself. By that I mean a perfect servant and here, gentlemen, I can assure you, *is* that perfect servant. She goes by the name of Lucretia Borgia and I want to tell you that she has been the mainstay of this plantation for the past few years, from the day Mr Macklin started ailing till he died, and after. Mrs Macklin herself will attest to this. But besides being one of the most able administrators I have ever known, she also has the distinction of being the finest cook whose victuals I have ever eaten. Yes, gentlemen, I will go even further than that and state my belief that she is the best cook in the South, if not the nation.

'How do I know? Well, I've been eating her meals for the past few days and I want to tell you that I have *never* tasted such fine food. Gentlemen, here is a paragon among servants; don't you agree with me, Mr Sinclair?'

'I agree, Mr Perry.' Sinclair bobbed his head in assent. 'The best cooking I've ever tasted and, remember this, she did it all while helping the two of us get this vendue started. We could never have done it without her, I believe, Mr Perry.'

Perry nodded solemnly. 'So you see, gentlemen, my assistant agrees with me. Now I want to offer this remarkable wench for sale. I don't want any niggling fifty-dollar bids on her, either. I'll take her myself rather than let you haggle over her in that puny fashion. Five hundred! Do I hear an opening bid of five hundred dollars?'

121

This was the highest price at which any of the slaves had been started and there was a momentary hush. Lucretia Borgia scanned the faces staring at her. Once again, as on the night when she had met Mr Perry, she straightened up to her full height, thrust out her bosom, lifted her head proudly and smiled into the sea of staring eyes. Now she was able to make out individual faces among the crowd and she hurriedly scanned each row, hoping to see the two men, Tom and Warren, who had examined her before the sale started. Finally she located them, standing in the third row. She willed that the man called Warren would bid on her and as though answering her thoughts, he raised his hand.

Mr Perry, attuned for such gestures, saw it at once and bowed in the direction of the uplifted hand. 'Five hundred dollars from Mr Warren Maxwell of Falconhurst Plantation. Thank you, Mr Maxwell. I know you are the best judge of nigger flesh in the country and I also know that you appreciate the quality of this wench that I am selling.'

Almost before he could finish, a drawling voice from the back yelled out, 'Six hundred dollars.'

Lucretia Borgia was distressed to see a sour-faced man in a butternut shirt raising his hand.

'Seven hundred.' This time it was a stout man with a bright red face, rather elegantly dressed in a white shirt with black stock and a plum-coloured coat, who stood somewhat to Lucretia Borgia's left.

'Eight hundred.' It was Warren Maxwell again and Mr Perry lifted his hands in a gesture of futility, as much as to say, 'Go ahead, gentlemen, I'll keep out of this.'

But the bid stood at eight hundred for several moments of silence until Mr Perry started haranguing them again. He commanded, he begged, he pleaded, he cajoled, until the stout man in the plum-coloured coat called out, 'You say she's a good cook?'

'The finest,' Mr Perry assured him.

'Nine hundred dollars,' the man answered after a moment's consideration.

Once again there was an hiatus in the bidding and once

122

again Mr Perry started to talk until he was interrupted by Mr Maxwell, who bid one thousand dollars.

'Eleven hundred,' the stout man said pugnaciously.

'And twelve hundred,' Warren Maxwell responded.

Now came a test of Mr Perry's oratory. His booming voice reached out over the crowd. 'Twelve hundred dollars, gentlemen! I'm ashamed of you. A wench like this if sold in New Orleans would bring fifteen hundred to two thousand dollars. I've a mind to bid her in and sell her for a handsome profit to someone who appreciates how valuable she is. Twelve hundred! Why, sirs, it's a mere bagatelle. Fire your white overseer and let Lucretia Borgia run your plantation. She'll get more work out of your hands in a day than a white overseer can in a week, and besides that she'll cook you three fine meals a day. I know. I've seen it happen right here at Elm Grove Plantation. Only twelve hundred dollars? Do I hear thirteen?'

He stopped, waiting expectantly for an answer.

The stout man shook his head. He had reached his limit and Mr Perry looked down at Warren Maxwell. 'Twelve hundred dollars – a mere one thousand and two hundred dollars. Are there any other bids? Any man here want to get one of the finest nigger wenches I've sold in a long time? Nothing fancy about Lucretia Borgia, gentlemen. She's not a pretty octoroon whom you can deck out in ribbons and bows and show off to your friends. She's just good honest nigger stock with a little human blood thrown in but she's quality, gentlemen, purentee quality.'

He paused and scanned his audience. By this time Lucretia Borgia had lost some of her fear and she also looked down on them. When her glance came to rest on Mr Maxwell, she smiled and he nodded his head a little as though to assure her that he was certainly going to buy her.

'Twelve hundred dollars!' Mr Perry was again exhorting. 'Is that your last word, gentlemen? Isn't any one of you anxious to own this fine specimen? Just another fifty dollars and she's yours.' He scanned the faces before him. 'Do I hear twelve-fifty?'

There was a silence from the audience that was throbbing with interest. This was the highest price offered that day. It was four hundred dollars more than had been paid for the splendid buck who was the best of the men.

Mr Perry rapped on the table with his gavel, making the water pitcher and the tumbler jump. 'Twelve hundred dollars. Going at twelve hundred dollars. Your last chance, gentlemen. Going, going, gone!' He hit the table with a final resounding thump. 'Sold to Mr Warren Maxwell of Falconhurst Plantation. Congratulations, Mr Maxwell, and may I say that I envy you the possession of Lucretia Borgia?'

He led Lucretia Borgia to the edge of the platform and she gathered up her clean white apron to make the steep descent, but not until she had again caught Mr Maxwell's eye. She nodded her head ever so little but it could easily be translated in a 'Thank yo', Masta Maxwell.'

Once again she was back in the barn. She was sold. No longer was she Mrs Macklin's Lucretia Borgia, instead she belonged to this unknown man who had just paid twelve hundred dollars for her. She knew nothing about him except that she instinctively liked him. Who could tell what kind of place she was going to or what she would get into? But somehow she felt it was going to be all right. She had a quick premonition that at this unknown Falconhurst Plantation she might be an even more important person than she had ever been at Elm Grove. And she could be thankful that the mean-looking cuss in the butternut shirt had not bought her. Neither had the pompous one in the plum-coloured coat. She was glad that it was – now what was his name? – Warren Maxwell.

'Masta Maxwell suh,' she repeated to herself as the other wenches in the stall welcomed her back. 'Masta Warren suh.' Somehow she felt she was going to call him by his first name. She was going to be a house servant. She wasn't going to be any ordinary burr-headed field hand. No sir-ee! White masters didn't pay twelve hundred dollars for a wench to work in the fields. 'Masta Warren suh!' It sounded good. She was anxious to get to know him better. 'Yes suh, Masta

124

Warren suh, would yo' like fried chicken or ham for supper tonight, 'n shall I make up some beaten biscuits or would yo' like waffles to go with it?' She clutched the small bundle with all her worldly possessions in it. It was all over and strangely enough she felt happy, really happy. 'Yes *suh*, Masta Warren suh,' she murmured.

CHAPTER FOURTEEN

Lucretia Borgia knew that the sale was over when she could no longer hear the banging of Mr Perry's gavel or his shouting. Now there was only a subdued mumble of voices as one by one the purchasers of the slaves began to appear in the barn to face Mr Sinclair, who had his table and ledgers moved there. As each purchaser approached him, he would call out the name of the slave or slaves purchased. These would then come forward and Mr Sinclair would make out a bill of sale and take the money that the buyer had bid. It was purely a business proposition: so many dollars for a slave and the slave became the property of the buyer. The slave himself had nothing to say about the matter; he was a chattel and must accept his new master with as good grace as a horse might. Even though he was more intelligent than a horse, he was still an animal that could be bought and sold. He was not, after all, a human being. He was livestock.

Lucretia Borgia waited impatiently at the entrance of the stall for her new owner to appear. She was momentarily cheered when she saw Mr Maxwell finally standing before Mr Sinclair's table on the barn floor, but she was immediately let down in spirits when she did not hear her name called and she could come forward to be claimed. It seemed, however, that she was not the only purchase he had made that day, although she was the last; so she had to wait for her name to be called while he paid for and claimed the others he had bought. Lucretia Borgia was surprised to see that these, when they answered their names and came up to him, were all youngsters. He had purchased four sapling bucks from about eight to fourteen, and Lucretia Borgia knew all of them well. They were the best of all the youngsters at Elm Grove. Rico, the eldest, was a fine, straight-backed young lad who was, Lucretia Borgia knew, one of Big Jem's git. Jem had also sired one of the other boys, Camp, who was younger by about two years than Rico. As to the two other boys, Zachariah and Sammy, Lucretia Borgia was not sure of their parentage, but she told herself that Mr Maxwell was certainly a good picker. In addition to the clutch of saplings, he had also purchased three adolescent wenches – again, the best on the plantation. Lou-Mary was the eldest, about thirteen, and Mrs Macklin had intended to make a house servant out of her, for she was good-looking and intelligent. Mamie was younger and lighter; her dam had been serviced by one of Mr Macklin's cousins, so Mamie had long dark curls which Lucretia Borgia envied. The youngest was called Cricket, a tiny child of about eight with the promise of good looks ahead of her. Lucretia Borgia certainly applauded Mr Maxwell's knowledge of nigger flesh. And why not? Hadn't he bought her, and wasn't she the best of all? That man sure had an eye for niggers.

But what puzzled her was that he had bought these children. They were too young to work or contribute anything to plantation life, except perhaps to use a twig broom for cleaning up, and they would mean just so many more mouths to feed. Of course, she reasoned, he had probably got them cheap, but somehow she couldn't believe that cost was all that influenced Mr Maxwell. Hadn't he paid twelve hundred dollars for her? Without batting an eyelash? Perhaps, she argued with herself, his stock might be running out and was too old to produce good suckers, so he was adding to it by purchasing these adolescents. She could think of no other reason, but certainly hoped that his bucks were not so elderly that there was not one upstanding young fellow on his plantation for her.

Again she was disappointed when he herded out the seven youngsters without picking her up. She saw his friend Tom come in, pay for Djoubo, and take him away; and still Mr Maxwell did not reappear. She began to grow nervous. Had something gone wrong? Had he changed his mind? She had felt so safe and secure in the knowledge that he had bought her, but with the long delay in claiming her she began to worry. All the other purchasers had come in to take the wenches that they had bought and she bade good-bye to each of them regretfully. They knew where they were going, and had a new master to claim them. One by one they departed until she was alone in the stall. She wrung her hands in desperation until finally her nervousness was assuaged by Mr Maxwell's reappearance. He came into the barn and headed straight for her. There was a coloured man with him who strode along with long-legged lusty steps. He was young, thank God!

Her eyes momentarily shifted from Mr Maxwell to the Negro who accompanied him. Surely he was handsome – about the handsomest young buck she had ever seen. He was tall and broad-shouldered and not too black, in his early twenties. His face had almost a Grecian cast and his lips, although slightly full, were not the African lips of Djoubo. She noticed that his hair curled on top of his head and that his eyes were dark brown and deep-set. He appeared to be possessed of immense physical force, yet somehow she knew instinctively that he would never use it to harm anyone. Moreover he was decently dressed – far better than any buck at Elm Grove. In these few seconds of watching him come across the floor, she had inventoried him to her own satisfaction, but what pleased her most was the obvious bulge that attracted her eyes to his crotch. She hoped she might be mated up with him – from what she had seen he promised far more than either Big Jem or Djoubo and they were neither trifling nor puny.

The two approached her. She reached down for her bundle,

preparatory to leaving with them. Mr Maxwell was smiling and she noted a surprised look of satisfaction on the coloured man's face.

'Bought yo' a fust-class wench, Memnon.' Mr Maxwell slapped him on his back. 'Needin' a good cook, we are, what with Mercy gittin' along in years, 'n that Perry he said that this strappin' wench was one of the best. She kin bed down with yo' in the kitchen.' Turning to Lucretia Borgia, he asked, 'Yo' thinkin' yo' like this boy? Say, what's yore name anyhow? Didn't rightly ketch it when Perry a-sellin' yo'. Too much int'rested in biddin' on yo'.'

Of the two questions her new master had asked her, Lucretia Borgia hardly knew which to answer first. She decided on telling him her name.

'Loo-cree-sha Bor-ja, suh,' she replied, proudly accenting each syllable. 'Old masta afore Mista Macklin, he done named me. He sayin' if'n I'm a good cook, mayhap I won' pizen him if'n I'm named that; don' rightly know what he meant.' She glanced boldly at the young man and then back at Maxwell. ' 'N as for this buck here, he a right likely lookin' boy but he don' 'pear like'n he last very long with Lucretia Borgia. Shore dreans 'em out, I do. Already gave Masta Macklin two good suckers 'n got lots more a-comin', that is if'n this boy know how to do a good job.'

Instead of rebuking her for her familiarity, Warren Maxwell laughed and slapped her on the rump.

'His name's Agamemnon but mostly we calls him Memnon or Mem. He our house servant 'n he a pretty good boy, though he gits mighty slothful at times. Needs someone 'round to jack him up every once in a while. Goin' to move old Mercy down to the cabins 'n let yo' bed with him in the kitchen. That is, if'n yo' as good a cook as Mr Perry say yo' are.'

'I kin cook,' she boasted, ' 'n cook *good*. Jes' have to try me out.'

'Will do jes' that.' He pulled a big silver watch from his pocket. 'High time we got ourselves started. Now remember one thing, Lucretia Borgia. I ain' a bad masta if'n a nigger do like'n I say. We don' whop much at Falconhurst, but we kin. I speak, yo' jumps to it, 'n we don' have no trouble 'tall. Don' question, don' argufy, don' sass back. Tha's all I ask.'

She fell into step beside him, her legs as long as Memnon's and longer even than Maxwell's. They had gone a few steps when she turned towards the white man. 'Beggin' yore pardon, Masta suh, but kin I ask yo' a couple questions?'

He nodded his head, noting that she had good manners.

'What am I to call yo', suh? I heared yore name as Mista Maxwell. Shall I call yo' Masta Maxwell suh?'

'Yo' a house servant. Calls me by my fust name, yo' do. Masta Warren, 'n don' never forget the *suh*. It necessary for proper respect. When we gits to Falconhurst yo' calls my wife Miz Sophie ma'am. We got us a boy; fine boy he is but jes' a youngster. He named Hammond 'n yo' kin call him Li'l Masta Ham.'

Well, she had at least established the family. It was not going to be too hard to cook for them – just husband, wife and small boy. It would make her duties light and she would have this Mem to help her in the house. Probably she'd have a kitchen wench too. Now there was just one other thing that was troubling her.

'Yo' say we a-goin' to Falconhurst Plantation. Kin I ask what yo' raises there? Cotton, like'n we do here at Elm Grove?'

He shook his head and laughed. 'If'n we raise jes' cotton, we a-goin' to be eatin' nothin' but fatback 'n greens. No, Lucretia Borgia, we ain' a cotton-raisin' plantation. Raises a little, but more to keep the hands busy than anything else. Soil's all leached out 'n cain' git a decent crop. We raise niggers instead. Yes sir-ee, we raises a crop o' niggers each year 'n takes 'em 'n sells 'em off. More money in niggers than in cotton, 'n lookin' like'n there's going to be more 'n more. Seems like everyone is wantin' niggers today. So, yo' see, niggers is our crop.'

'Yo' raises 'em 'n sells them off?'

'Ain' yo' forgettin' somethin'?' His tone was brusque.

'Masta Warren suh,' she added.

'That's better, 'n don' forget it never. Yes, we raises 'em 'n we sells 'em off. Gits us a couple good suckers out'n each wench 'n then sells her off. Let our bucks breed till we sells 'em off when they git to be 'round twenty or so.'

Her face dropped. So she was going to be sold again after she had brought in some progeny for her master. But, she argued with herself, if she was a good enough cook, she might not get sold and she was certain that she was the best.

'House servants too, Masta Warren suh? Yo' sells 'em off too?'

'Not if'n they any good. Ain' never sold Memnon, though I threaten to at times, he being so slothful. Ain' never sold Mercy neither, 'n now that she old, she a-goin' to live out her life on Falconhurst. Only sells the young uns – they the ones brings the good prices. Now come on, button up that lip o' yourn 'n don' be too nosey. Ain' got no use for a nosey nigger what want to know all my business. Step lively.'

They approached the wagon and she could see that the seven adolescents he had purchased were already in it, sitting on the floor. Maxwell told her to put her bundle under the seat and directed Memnon to sit on the tailboard so that none of the children would jump off and run for home. Lucretia Borgia was to share the seat with Maxwell. Already she felt that she was privileged. She was the only one on the seat with her master; all the rest sat on the floor of the big wagon, even Memnon had to sit there with his legs dangling over the end.

She took a long last look at Elm Grove Plantation; at the so-called skull of Big Jem; at the front gallery where Mrs Macklin was standing and waving good-bye to her; at the long line of trees which led down to the road. This had been her home for many years and she felt a pang as she left it. She had been appreciated here and had had authority delegated to her. She wondered about this new place – this Falconhurst. But a glance at her master did much to assure her that everything was going to be all right. She had purposely been a little too familiar with him, just to test him out. He had reacted well and had not censured her too severely. He was

130

going to be an easy man to get along with, and she knew how to butter up a white man so that everything would go pleasantly between them.

The wagon turned onto the main road and gradually Elm Grove became only a clump of trees in the distance. She wondered how far it was to Falconhurst and if they would reach it that night. She was tired. She had been up all of a long day and the nervous excitement of the auction block had proved too much for her. She wanted nothing more than to curl up and go to sleep.

From time to time she would turn in her seat to berate one of the crying youngsters in the back. Rico, the eldest, was taking the fate in store for him with taciturnity that bespoke his bravery; Camp and Zachariah also were riding along with a straight face, but Sammy and Cricket were crying for their mothers.

'Cain' rightly stand that squallin' no more, Lucretia Borgia. Goin' to give them brats a taste of the horsewhip if'n yo' cain' shut 'em up. Knows they wants their mammies but that don' make no neverminds. Do something! Shet 'em up.'

She turned in her seat and reached out a long arm, grabbing Sammy.

'If'n yo' wants to howl, goin' to have to give yo' somethin' to howl about,' she said as she smacked him hard across the cheek. 'Now yo' shet yore mouth 'n stop bawlin' or yo' goin' to git one harder on t'other side.' Cricket was beyond her reach, but she threatened the child with another such smacking and soon fear of Lucretia Borgia's strong right hand had replaced sorrow. Their cries died down into stifles and then they became quiet.

Mr Maxwell nodded his head approvingly. 'Guess yo' knows how to deal with niggers, Lucretia Borgia.'

'Yes suh, Masta Warren suh. Shore do. Bin a-clobberin' 'em all my life.' She regarded her right hand. ''N when I clobbers, they knows it. Ain' takin' no sass from no niggers, Masta Warren suh.'

He nodded in approbation and the wagon creaked along in comparative silence. Soon Rico began to hum a wordless

131

tune and the others joined in. When they turned in through the big wrought-iron gates of Courteney Hammond's plantation, all the children were apparently happy. Lucretia Borgia stared in amazement at the elaborate gates and the long avenue of trees that led up to the pillared plantation house.

'My goodness, Masta Warren suh! Is this Falconhurst Plantation?' She had not been prepared for such opulence.

He laughed at her and shook his head. 'Not by a damn sight. This here place belongs to a cousin o' my wife's. She's a Hammond 'n they quality folk. Falconhurst ain' near so fine 's this, but it's comfortable. Someday I'm a-goin' to build me a new house but the old one good enough for now. Goin' to take a lot o' niggers to git me a house as good as Cousin Courteney's.'

Courteney Hammond was standing on the front gallery when Maxwell drove up. He came down the steps and surveyed the group of adolescents in the back, then went to where Lucretia Borgia was sitting and scrutinized her carefully. 'Got yo'self a good wench, I see, Cousin Warren.'

' 'N they a-tellin' me she kin cook fust-rate too.'

'Beddin' her down in the barn with the rest?'

'Goin' to spancel her to Memnon. Goin' to spancel all the rest too 'cept the smallest. Ain' takin' no chances on they runnin'.'

Lucretia Borgia spoke up. 'Ain' a-goin' to run, Masta Warren suh. Ain' got no place to run to.'

He turned on her irately. 'Yo' speak when yo're spoken to. Spancel yo' if'n I wants. Always spancels a nigger on the fust night. Ain' takin' no chances on yo' neither, Lucretia Borgia. Trouble with yo' is that yo' got too much brains.'

Lucretia Borgia knew that she had gone too far. She had no mind to be punished for talking too much so she bit her tongue and remained silent while the team drove around to the big barn. Here she climbed out along with the children and Mem. A grey-haired Negro who apparently acted as hostler came out to unhitch the horses. Courteney Hammond had caught up with them.

He winked at Warren. 'Ain' sayin' that Miz Hammond

would approve, Cousin Warren, but if you want this wench for a bed wench tonight, I think it could be arranged. Mighty likely wench she is and lookin' as though she could keep you company. Wouldn't mind beddin' her down myself.'

Warren shook his head. 'She a-goin' to bed with Memnon 'n might as well get used to him. 'Sides, she pretty stenchy. Bin a-ridin' side o' her all the way 'n shore don' like a stenchy nigger.'

It was on the tip of Lucretia Borgia's tongue to tell him that she had not had a chance to wash all over since morning and that she was not usually stenchy, but she held her tongue. She'd have to keep her feelings to herself and not speak her mind as she had been in the habit of doing with Mrs Macklin.

The grey-haired barn-man filled one of the box stalls with clean straw and Maxwell ordered the coffle to go in. He sent the man out to the wagon to fetch in the iron shackles that were under the seat. When he returned, Maxwell carefully put one around Rico's wrist and fastened him to a stanchion, allowing plenty of room for him to lie down. Then he fastened Lou-Mary to him and spancelled her other arm to Camp. The younger children he did not secure. He motioned to Lucretia Borgia to come near him and slipped a shackle over her wrist, fastening the other end to Mem's wrist.

'Ain' takin' no chances, Lucretia Borgia, 'n ain' a-goin' to do yo' no harm to be spancelled to Mem. Mayhap yo' a-goin' to like it. Mem he ain' had a regular woman for some time 'n he jes' about bustin' out'n his britches.' His sternness relaxed and he smiled at her and designated a place on the opposite side of the stall from where he had secured the children. 'Make yo'self comfortable 'n supper'll be out soon.' Together with Courteney Hammond, he left; Lucretia Borgia was left alone with the children and Mem.

She was glad to sit down in the clean straw, although she wished for a chance to wash. Her face was damp with perspiration and she felt gritty and uncomfortable. With one hand spancelled to Mem she could not remove her apron

133

and she sat beside him, glancing up at him from time to time and admiring him. He sure was a handsome buck.

Before it became too dark, two servants from the big house came out with a bowl of stew which they ladled into tin plates and gave to the new slaves. The two men were dressed in what Lucretia Borgia considered the height of fashion with long black coats and black knee breeches. She admired the white lisle stockings which fitted snugly over their rounded calves and the shoes with silver buckles that they wore.

It was decent food, a far cry from what she could cook herself but she was so hungry, not having eaten since morning – and then only a cup of coffee and a piece of pone – that she used her fingers industriously and ate heartily, wiping up the last of the gravy with her forefinger and sucking it off. By the time they had all finished eating, it was dark.

She sidled up to Mem, feeling the warmth and strength of his body. He put his free hand in hers and she felt more secure with his arm encircling her.

'We a-goin' to git along right well together, Lucretia Borgia.' His voice was low and warm and he gave her an encouraging squeeze. 'Bin wantin' me a wench to bed with regularly. Lately bin havin' to skip out to the cabins to find a wench 'n if Masta Warren he find out, I'd shore git whopped. He mighty particular 'bout who covers his wenches. Ain' had me no real lovin' for a long time.'

She snuggled closer to him. An unknown male had always fascinated her and she had never before had one quite as prepossessing as Memnon. 'Shore a-goin' to try, Mem. I likes a man what is a real man. Cain' stan' no puny fellow what cain' make me happy.'

He spread his legs out before him. 'One thing, Lucretia Borgia, I ain' puny. Hung heavier'n a stallion, I am. Reckon yo' never had as much o' a man as I am.' He grabbed her unshackled hand and pulled it down to his crotch.

Lucretia Borgia had had Big Jem and she had had Djoubo and besides these two she had experimented with a few

134

others, but she had indeed never encountered so much of a man as Memnon. He exceeded all the others and she clutched at the hot hardness under the thin cloth of his pantaloons.

'My oh my!' She grasped him with a possessive hand. 'I kin see how I'm shore goin' to like Falconhurst Plantation.'

He drew her closer to him and kissed her on the mouth. The tip of his tongue sought out hers and for a long moment they kissed. Slowly his other hand reached down and pulled up the skirt of the white apron, then the black calico, and finally the sugar-sacking petticoat. His fingers started searching and probing.

Lucretia Borgia's hand abandoned him for a moment to pull her garments up around her neck. His lips left hers and sought the hard nipples of her breast.

'Yo' shore knows how to pleasure a wench,' she squirmed in ecstasy as his fingers entered her. 'Ain' never had such pleasurin' afore, 'n hopin' they's more to come.'

'We jes' a-startin',' he whispered, his hand helping her to undo the buttons of his pantaloons. 'Now see what yo' got comin' to yo'.'

Her fingers freed him from the restrictions of his clothes and she played with him as he was playing with her. When their preliminary lovemaking got too much for both of them, he gently rolled her onto her back, forcing her legs apart with his knees.

'Goin' to be better when we gits to Falconhurst 'n don't have clothes on. Cain' take the damned things off, spancelled like we are, so don' judge me by tonight.'

She cried out a little as he mounted her, more in pleasure than in pain, and he entered even deeper until it seemed she could stand it no longer. Her legs crossed over his back and pulled him into her. He raised up on his arms and started on her with long, slow, even strokes. Whenever he felt he was reaching a climax he would stop and then start again, leading her up to climax after climax. Suddenly with a guttural roar like that of a bull, he plunged and his body relaxed in her arms. For a moment they were quiet and she missed his

135

weight when he rolled off her, lying panting in the straw beside her, trying to catch his breath. She snuggled up to him, contented in every fibre of her body. Big Jem had been good at pleasuring. She thought there could never be anyone better. But with Big Jem it was on and then off again; he had had a mind only for himself. Djoubo had mixed his sex with love and she had returned his affection, but never before in her life had she enjoyed a man as much as she had enjoyed Memnon. She was so exhausted that she could scarcely lift her hand to pat him on the cheek.

After a moment of relaxation, she discovered that Mem's was not the only gasping in the stall. From the other side she could hear strained intakes of air.

She sat up, staring into the darkness. Both Rico and Camp were breathing hard.

'What yo' boys a-doin' over there?' she called out. 'If'n yo' bin a-pesterin' Lou-Mary, yo' shore as hell a-goin' to git whopped. She ain' never bin busted yet, 'n Mista Maxwell he a-knowin' it.'

'Ain' busted her, Lucretia Borgia. Ain' bin doin' nothin' 'tall.'

'Why-at yo' a-puffin' 'n a-pantin'?'

She heard Lou-Mary giggle. 'It Rico's fault, Lucretia Borgia. He made me do things to him, 'n Camp did too.'

If she had not been spancelled to Mem, she would have got up, tired as she was, and doled out punishment to all three, but Memnon's hand restrained her.

'Let 'em be, Lucretia Borgia. Cain' blame 'em, a-hearin' us together. Don' worry. Rico didn't bust her. He ain' big 'nuff for that yet. He 'n Camp they jes' lettin' her pleasure 'em a little. 'Sides, pleasurin' is 'bout all a nigger has to make him happy, 'n they might jes' as well learn. They'll all have a lot of pleasurin' to do at Falconhurst when they git a little older. That's Masta Warren's business; that's what he bought 'em for.'

'But they too young!'

'Nigger ain' never too young.' Memnon pulled her down into the crook of his arm. 'Le's go to sleep. Got a long

journey tomorrow. Falconhurst a whole day's ridin' from
here.'

CHAPTER FIFTEEN

Memnon was right. It was a long day's journey to Falconhurst from the Courteney Hammond Plantation. Mr Maxwell roused them before dawn for an early start; they had no
chance to wash or freshen up before a house servant (not
so gorgeously attired in the morning and rubbing sleep from
his eyes) brought out coffee, fried eggs and pone. Maxwell
advised them to eat hearty, as food would be rather skimpy
at noon and they would not arrive until late in the day. This
morning they had pewter spoons to eat with and Lucretia
Borgia did full justice to her breakfast. After she had
finished eating, she brushed the straw from her dress, looked
regretfully at the soiled apron, and wished she could retie
her headdress; but this was impossible, as she was still
shackled to Mem's wrist. It was not until they were about to
get into the wagon that Mr Maxwell unspancelled her.

At first it was a joy to be on the road. There was a fresh
breeze and all the world was waking up. Smoke came from
cabin fireplaces and there was a pleasant odour of burning
wood, mixed with the aroma of cooking ham and bacon.
But soon the sun beat down upon them unmercifully, and
Lucretia Borgia longed for water to wash in. Mr Maxwell
was equally hot and had he but known, his odour was as
offensive to Lucretia Borgia as hers was to him. The children
in the back were again fretful and it required more than one
threat of Lucretia Borgia's strong right hand to keep them
from bawling. Even the staunch Rico began to show signs of
weariness; Lucretia Borgia could not blame him, for she was
already tired herself.

137

Their route led through one of the most prosperous sections of Alabama. Occasionally big houses, set well back from the road, gave distant glimpses of pillared elegance and rosy colour of brick or immaculately white clapboards. Some of the big houses, however, were in stages of disrepair, although there were always plentiful gangs of slaves working in the fields. More often than the pillared plantations, they passed small farms belonging to poor whites which boasted of slab-sided cabins, a rooting pig or two and a flock of chickens scratching in the front yard. Often there would be a slatternly housewife on the canting front stoop hanging out washing, or a redneck farmer pulling stumps from the land he was clearing. Occasionally there would be a sole Negro helping, but more often than not the man would be working alone or with his sons.

They passed two fine coaches on the road and one open barouche in which a white woman shaded her face from the sun with a tiny black parasol. They saw a number of white men on horseback, all of whom, although strangers, greeted Mr Maxwell with a pleasant nod while they enviously surveyed the load of saplings in his wagon and let their gaze rest with admiration on Lucretia Borgia, sitting beside her master. The rest of the passersby were Negroes riding on flea-bitten mules with rope halters, doing errands between neighbouring plantations. They too ducked their heads to Mr Maxwell and looked admiringly at Lucretia Borgia.

There was no conversation. It would hardly be fitting for Mr Maxwell to carry on any extended talk with Lucretia Borgia, though there were a host of questions which she wanted to ask him. However, Mr Maxwell had warned her against being nosey. If she had had her own way, she would have enquired in detail about Falconhurst and its raising of niggers; she wanted to become acquainted with all the workings of its business, but, as Mr Maxwell himself was looking tired, hot and dusty, she knew he was in no mood to converse with her.

At noon they stopped and drew off the road under the shade of a grove of live oaks. The ground underneath was a carpet of dried leaves and tiny acorns and it was cool there. Lucretia Borgia unpacked the basket of food which the Hammonds had put up for them. One packet, wrapped in a fringed napkin, was for Mr Maxwell; it contained cold chicken, white bread and a bottle of wine which he did not particularly relish. The rest had to be satisfied with cold pone and hard-boiled eggs washed down with water from a nearby brook. Lucretia Borgia used the opportunity to wash some of the dirt from her face and hands. Mr Maxwell handed Mem the bottle of wine to finish, which he did, giving Lucretia Borgia a couple of swallows. It was a strong and heady Madeira and with her face clean and the warm glow of the wine in her stomach, she felt better. After a brief rest, they were on the road again, and soon it seemed to her that the creaking of the wagon wheels would never stop.

Late in the afternoon, Mr Maxwell broke the silence. 'Ain' far to Benson now,' he gestured down the road, and then for Lucretia Borgia's benefit added, 'that the nearest place to Falconhurst; it ain' much of a town. Got a general store, a tavern, a bank, 'n a few houses. It 'bout four miles from our place. Yo' may not even know it when yo' gits there – jes' a wide place in the road. But it convenient to live so near a village.'

'Uh-huh,' Lucretia Borgia murmured. She had seen few towns except for the visit she had made to Emporia and the time she went to Marysburg with Mrs Macklin, as well as the few hamlets they had passed through today, none of which was very prepossessing. Towns meant nothing to her; plantation life was what she was accustomed to and what she enjoyed. There was nothing better than to live in the midst of a hive of activity, with something for a body to do all day long.

Late in the afternoon, Mr Maxwell turned off the main road up a track with grass growing between the ruts. Forefinger pointing to a house, he sighed with contentment.

'We home, Lucretia Borgia.' He turned in his seat. 'Home again, Mem. Chance for yo' to stretch yore legs 'n fetch me a hot toddy soon's we git to the house 'n git things settled

139

around. My mouth's drier than this road. One o' yore toddies shore goin' to wet my whistle good.' He turned back to Lucretia Borgia. 'Likes my corn hot, I do. Bilin' water 'n a touch o' long sweetnin'. Tha's the best 'n the healthiest way to drink it. My pappy always drank it that way.'

Compared with the Hammond Plantation, Falconhurst, for all the bravery and elegance of its name was unimpressive; it even compared unfavourably with Elm Grove. Here there was no long avenue of trees leading from main road to house, but only a rutted lane. The house had once had a coat of white paint but only traces of that remained. It was a medium-large building of weather-beaten clapboards, two stories high with a sweeping roof of cedar shakes through which dormer windows peeked furtively. The roof continued down to make a covering for the gallery extending across the front of the house, which was supported by plain round posts with no pretentions to elegance. Two doors opened off this long verandah, which held a few splint-bottomed chairs and a number of rain barrels. The total effect was rather like an old man in a slouch hat with decayed stubs of teeth. Yet, despite its unimpressive appearance, Lucretia Borgia could see that it was a strongly built house and large enough for a good-sized family to live in comfortably. Around the verandah was a carefully tended flower garden which bespoke the mistress's love for flowers; and the gay blooms did much to take away the overall drabness.

Near the house stood a substantial barn, behind which were almost enough outbuildings to make up a small village. From the barn a number of young bucks came running, crying out, 'Masta's home! Masta's home!' All of them seemed anxious to take the horses and help with the unloading of the wagon, but Mr Maxwell shooed them all off save one. This was a well-set-up young buck addressed as Zeb who, Lucretia Borgia was afterwards to discover, was Mrs Maxwell's coachman and head man in the barn. He seemed overjoyed to see his master home and by the hearty welcome Maxwell received from everyone, Lucretia Borgia realized that she had been chosen by a good master. They all seemed to love him.

'Take these saplin's 'n wenches out to the barn,' Maxwell said to Zeb, ' 'n bed 'em down for the night out there. I'll see to where I want 'em in the morning.' He jumped down from his seat on the wagon and went around to the back. 'Memnon 'n Lucretia Borgia, git into the house.' His mind was immediately switched from taking care of his new purchases to the rather stout and pleasant-looking woman who had appeared in the doorway with a boy of about five clinging to her skirts.

'Warren, yo're home!' she exclaimed as he rushed up the steps and clasped her in his arms and kissed her, shouting, 'Sophie! 'N Ham! How's my boy? Wait till you see what papa brought yo'.'

'A present, papa?' The boy released his hold on his mother's skirts and ran to his father who picked him up in his arms.

'The best present of all, Ham. Done brought yo' four fine saplin's 'n three nice li'l wenches. They for yo', son. Time yo' grows up, they be ready to sell, 'n they all yours.'

'Warren.' There was a touch of anger in Mrs Maxwell's voice. 'What do yo' mean? It's absolutely ridiculous sayin' that yo' bought servants for Hammond. He's just a little boy. Far better if'n yo' had stopped somewhere 'n bought him a toy. That's what children like.'

'Got my toy horse, mama, 'n I like niggers better anyway.' Hammond was all excited. 'Did yo' git good ones for me, papa? Kin I see 'em? They got names o' we a-goin' to name 'em? What we a-goin' to call 'em? Where are they?'

'Zeb took 'em down to the barn. Yo' kin see 'em in the mornin'.' He put Hammond back down on the floor and squeezed his wife's arm. 'Got a present for yo' too, Sophie. They say she's the best cook in the world. Paid twelve hundred dollars for her. Hey yo', Lucretia Borgia,' he called as she was going into the kitchen with Mem, 'Come here! Wants yo' should meet yore new mistress 'n li'l masta.'

Lucretia Borgia put her bundle down and walked across the sloping verandah to the family group. She was sorry that

141

her apron was no longer white and clean; she was disturbed that her red headcloth was awry and that she had had no chance to wash the sweat and grime of the road from her face. This was no way to meet a future mistress. Slowly she came up to them and stood by Warren Maxwell.

'This yere's Lucretia Borgia, Sophie. Cain' wait to find out how good a cook she is, but everyone a-sayin' she prime. 'N Ham, here's a new servant for yore mama. Bought her a present too. This's Lucretia Borgia. She a-goin' to be with us from now on, I hope. That is if'n she don' git to runnin' Falconhurst like'n they say she did Elm Grove.'

Lucretia Borgia bobbed her little curtsey to Mrs Maxwell. She was surprised when Mrs Maxwell put out a hand and laid it gently on her arm. It was almost a gesture of affection – but Lucretia Borgia knew that it couldn't be that.

'For once I'm glad Warren he bought a new servant. Mercy been taken with one of her spells 'n she's down in Honor's cabin. I've been fixin' all the meals and was wondering what we'd do when Warren came home. Yo're jes' in the nick o' time, Lucretia Borgia. Ain' nothin' ready for supper 'cause I wan't 'spectin' my husband so soon. Ham and I jes' goin' to have a bite when he came. Come right out into the kitchen and I'll have someone show you where things are. Ham and eggs all right for yo', Warren?'

He grinned at her. 'Best meal in the world. Don' care if'n it for breakfast or dinner. Ain' never tired o' ham 'n eggs, but the way Mercy bin a-cookin' 'em lately, they ain' hardly fit to eat.'

Mrs Maxwell made a sweeping gesture with her hand, inviting Lucretia Borgia in through the front door. 'Seems as tho' Warren he jes' crazy 'bout buyin' niggers.' Lucretia Borgia was not sure whether Mrs Maxwell was talking to herself or to her, but there seemed no reply to make except a *sotto voce* 'Yes'm, Miz Maxwell ma'am.' Mrs Maxwell sighed deeply as though the burden were too hard to bear and continued to talk. 'He a-turnin' this place into a regular nigger farm. Tha's all he a-thinkin' 'bout. Come an auction anywhere 'n he goes 'n comes home with more niggers. Ain' respectable, I say. I'm gittin' ashamed o' Falconhurst. He's shorely a-turnin' it into a nigger farm. Now he don' raise cotton no more, 'cept jes' a piddlin' amount. A-sayin' there's no money in it 'n that the land's all growed out. Sometimes I git so sick o' niggers – lookin' at 'em 'n hearin' 'bout them – I could scream. 'N he's got Hammond so that's all the boy thinks about. At his age too!'

'Uh-huh,' Lucretia Borgia felt it best to agree with her.

'But one thing good,' and now a tiny note of pride crept into Mrs Maxwell's voice. 'Warren ain' never had to put no mortgage on this place nor the niggers. Everyone else a-blisterin' their land 'n their niggers up to the hilt 'cause cotton don' pay off no more, so maybe Mista Maxwell he's right. But I'm a Hammond, I am, 'n I jes' don' feel that it respectable a-raisin' niggers.'

While she was indulging in this monologue, they traversed the living room which was plainly but substantially furnished. A few fine mahogany pieces, heavy in their Empire stolidity, looked as though they might have been in the family for some time. These were at odds with the plain rag carpet and some home-made plantation furniture. There were neither curtains nor drapes at the small paned windows; the fireplace was tiny and boasted no elaborate mantel. A big clock ticked on the wall to add some measure of life to the room. It was a plain room but undeniably comfortable and homelike. It made no pretentions, yet seemed a room that was lived in and enjoyed.

From it they passed into the dining room and here Lucretia Borgia saw a table set with a red-and-white checked tablecloth which boasted a silver caster with a multiplicity of cruets in the centre. A long Empire sideboard displayed several pieces of silver, badly in need of cleaning. The chairs were ordinary splint-bottom and evidently home-made. Over the table hung a large fan made of wood, with a rope attached to it leading out of a hole in the farther wall.

Much to Lucretia Borgia's surprise, the door from the dining room led directly into the kitchen. It was the first time she had ever seen a kitchen that was an integral part of the house. Usually it was separated by a covered passage-way, which kept the heat from the house itself and also eliminated some danger of fire. Well, at least, it was going to make the work a lot easier for her; on the other hand, it would give her less privacy. Then she recognized another thing in its favour: by listening at the kitchen door, she could hear everything that went on in the dining room. That was going to be helpful, because experience had taught her that most of the plantation gossip was talked over when the family were together at meals.

There was a fire in the big fireplace, which was flanked by the iron doors of ovens built into the brickwork on each side. A large crane held a huge iron teakettle which was lift-ing its lid with a regular metronomic beat. Two candles had been lighted in the kitchen and an attractive coloured girl of about eighteen was sitting at the long, scrubbed table, evidently awaiting orders. She jumped to her feet as Mrs Maxwell and Lucretia Borgia entered the room.

'Alicia,' and Mrs Maxwell actually took Lucretia Borgia by the arm, 'this's our new cook, Lucretia Borgia. Mr Maxwell jes' brought her home. She a-goin' to git supper tonight, but she like a cat in a strange attic. Don't know where nothin' is. It up to yo' to tell her where things are at.'

'Yes'm, Miz Maxwell ma'am, if'n I knows. Mercy she never tol' me much 'bout things out here. Was a-waitin' to help yo', ma'am, but if'n this new wench a-goin' to cook supper, kin help her so much's I kin.'

'Alicia she the housemaid 'n don' do much in the kitchen,' Mrs Maxwell explained. 'But she kin show yo' some things.' She pointed to a mattress at one end of the kitchen. It was covered with a neat patchwork quilt. 'This is where-at yo' sleeps, Lucretia Borgia, 'n they's a cupboard where yo' kin keep yore clothes. Have Alicia tell us when supper is ready 'n hurry it up as much as yo' kin. Masta Maxwell he hungry after his trip.'

'Yes ma'am.' Lucretia Borgia put her bundle down on the bed and surveyed the kitchen. 'How many do I git supper for?'

144

'Jes' Mr Maxwell, Hammond 'n me. 'Course yo' 'n Mem eats here 'n Alicia too, but she don' sleep here.' She seemed suddenly embarrassed. 'Mem sleeps here in the kitchen with yo'.' She turned and walked towards the dining room door. Lucretia Borgia was left with Alicia in a strange kitchen to get a meal without knowing where anything was. First, however, she had to wash up and change her apron. There was no time to wash all over. She'd have to do with a face-and-hands scrubbing.

Alicia seemed to be an intelligent girl and so while Lucretia Borgia was washing, she bombarded her with questions as to the plantation, the master and mistress and coloured folk who lived there. Both Mr and Mrs Maxwell, so Alicia informed her, were easy people to get along with if one didn't rub them the wrong way. Mr Maxwell's temper was very near the surface, and he was always threatening to have a slave whipped or sold off to some itinerant slave-dealer, but his threats didn't amount to much. Of course they had occasional whippings at Falconhurst, and all the servants had to be on hand to witness them. The master was always threatening Mem, who could not seem to hurry if he tried, but nothing ever came of it. She had just finished mentioning Mem when he came into the kitchen, carrying a demijohn of corn whisky.

He poured a little into a glass, added some molasses from a large glass cruet, then poured the glass full of hot water, which he stirred with a spoon. He was about to carry it into the sitting room when Lucretia Borgia stopped him.

'That ain' no way to serve yore masta!' She took the glass from his hand. 'Where at the saucers in this house?' Alicia pointed to one of the cupboards and Lucretia Borgia found a china saucer which she inserted under the glass. 'That the proper way, Mem.' She dispatched him to the sitting room.

'Now, wench, we got to get along with it fast.' Lucretia Borgia suddenly became all business. 'Masta Maxwell he a-wantin' his supper 'n he a-wantin' ham 'n eggs. Think I'll beat up a batch o' biscuits too. Oven ought to be hot 'nuff to bake 'em if'n we start to hotten it up now. Come on, gal!

Tell me where-at everything is 'n jump, gal, jump! If'n yo' a-goin' to work with me, yo' got to move fast. Want flour 'n shortenin' 'n milk. Need to have a ham to slice, 'n eggs. Whilst I'm baking the biscuits I'se goin' to make a ginger-bread, so wants to know where Miz Maxwell a-keepin' her spices.'

Alicia hesitated a moment before following Lucretia Borgia's orders. 'Yo' a-goin' to be head wench here in the kitchen?' she asked, her chin at a stubborn angle.

Lucretia Borgia stepped over to her, extending her right hand with the pink palm up. 'I shore am, 'n when I speaks, yo' jump. 'N another thing. When we're here alone yo' 'dress me as Miz Lucretia Borgia ma'am! That's *proper*. Now I'm here, things are goin' to be done proper. Now step to it or I'm a-goin' to clobber yo'.' She made a threatening gesture from which Alicia retreated, knowing she had met her match.

The kitchen became a hive of activity. New wood was added to the fire after the hot coals had been taken up with a shovel and placed in one of the ovens. Lucretia Borgia, following Alicia's directions, found the ingredients for the biscuits and the gingerbread. She stirred them up, finding a rolling pin, bread board, and pans. Then she sent the girl scurrying to the springhouse for cream and milk. She herself located the ham, hanging from a cord in the buttery, and cut off several slices with such a practised hand that they were all uniform in thickness. Rummaging in the buttery, she found jars of sweet pickles and took one.

It was not long before the gingerbread and the biscuits were baking in the oven and the ham was sizzling in a big iron skillet on a tripod over the fire. Then the baked stuff was done and taken from the oven, and Lucretia Borgia removed the ham onto a hot platter, putting aside the three best slices for herself, Mem, and Alicia. She then broke the eggs into the sizzling fat. Mem returned to the kitchen saying that he had set the table. He mixed another toddy, put it on a saucer and took it in to his master only a few moments before Lucretia Borgia peeked into the dining room. The candles

146

were lighted and the table was set. The food was already prepared and she dispatched Alicia to the sitting room to announce that dinner was ready.

It seemed that both Alicia and Memnon were accustomed to waiting on table and Lucretia Borgia sent them with the piping hot viands into the dining room. While they were eating she took the bowl of heavy cream and, putting some aside for coffee, whipped the rest with a fork. When Alicia and Mem came out with the dirty dishes, she had the gingerbread all cut and on plates. Over it she heaped the rich cream. Then for the first time, she sat down and waited expectantly.

Soon the summons came. Mem entered and asked her to follow him back into the dining room. He opened the door but instead of following him, she pushed him behind her and went in first. This time she did not feel ashamed. Her apron was white and stiffly starched, albeit a little wrinkled, and her red headcloth was folded neatly around her head. She stood a few paces inside the dining room.

'Yo-all asked for me?' she enquired ingenuously, as though it were the last thing in the world she was expecting.

'I shore did, Lucretia Borgia.' Warren Maxwell beamed from the head of the table. 'Want to tell yo' that that's one o' the best suppers I ever et. Sits good on the stomach, it do.'

'And the gingerbread, Lucretia Borgia,' Mrs Maxwell said. 'Land's sakes, I don' know how yo' did it all. Mercy never cooked us any sweets! It shore tasted good.'

'With cream on it,' Master Hammond added, scraping up the crumbs from his plate and feeding them to the little Negro boy who crouched beside him.

'Pshaw!' Lucretia Borgia belittled her efforts. 'Ain' much of a supper, jes' ham 'n eggs, but I new here 'n don' know much 'bout yore kitchen. Once I gits acquainted, kin promise yo' some real cookin'.'

'Be lookin' forward to it. Be lookin' forward to it.' Maxwell pushed back his chair and wiped his mouth with the red-and-white checkered napkin. 'Time now that yo' 'n Mem got a bite too. Reckon yo' both as hungry as I was.

After yo' gits the kitchen cleaned up, yo' go to bed. We gits up early here, 'round five, 'n likin' to have breakfast ready.'

'Yes sir-ee, Masta 'n Mist'ess. Will do jes' that.' She headed for the kitchen door but before she could leave, Mrs Maxwell spoke.

'Thank yo' also, Lucretia Borgia, for having Mem serve Mr Maxwell's drink with a saucer under it. I know that it's proper, but we bin gittin' a little slack lately, what with Mercy ailin' 'n everythin'.'

'Ain' a-goin' to be no more slackness, Miz Maxwell ma'am, not whilst I'm here.' She left for the kitchen but she had only just closed the door when it opened again and young Hammond came into the kitchen.

'Kin I have 'nother piece o' gingerbread with cream on it?' he asked. ' 'N kin Aleck have some too?' He gestured to the little slave who accompanied him. 'He my play-boy 'n he eats white folks' food too. Kin we eat out here with yo' 'n Mem 'n Alicia?'

'Why, bless yore heart, 'course yo' kin.' She cut two slices of gingerbread and topped them liberally with cream, placing them on the long table. Hammond accepted his but pushed the other portion back. 'Aleck he don' eat off'n nothin' but a tin plate. He kin have white folks' vittles but he cain' eat off'n white folks' plates. Please to change it. Cain' have niggers eatin' off china plates.'

She realized her mistake and jumped to correct it.

Between bites, Hammond looked up at her. 'Yo' a-goin' to bed down in the kitchen with Mem?' he asked.

'Now, Masta Hammond . . .'

'Masta Hammond suh,' he corrected her.

'Yes suh, Masta Hammond suh, but yo' too young to be botherin' yore head 'bout such things. Yo're jes' a li'l boy.'

'But I knows 'bout niggers, I do.' He lapped his spoon, getting all the cream from it, then reached over and helped himself liberally to Aleck's cream. 'I shore knows 'bout niggers. My pappy he teaches me. We got a nigger farm here 'n I got to learn 'bout 'em. We goin' to be the biggest nigger farm . . .' he hesitated, wondering with what to compare it 'in all the world, 'n we goin' to raise the best niggers o' all.'

'Shore yo' are,' she agreed with him, ' 'n I'm a-goin' to help yo' do it.'

Yes, she'd do just that, she promised herself, and she'd start right in. As soon as Mem came into the kitchen and had his meal and they washed the dishes and got into bed. Somehow she thought very little about Elm Grove and Mrs Macklin. That was another life. This was a *new* life, and promised to be an interesting one. Sure, niggers *were* a better crop than cotton. Why not? She was one and she knew. She just hoped that Mem would hurry and come out to the kitchen.

PART TWO

CHAPTER SIXTEEN

In the ten years that had passed since Lucretia Borgia had cooked her first supper of ham and eggs at Falconhurst, many things had happened; but as she looked back on those years, one day seemed to have followed another with a pattern of monotonous, albeit mostly happy, regularity. There were, to be sure, several periods that stood out in her mind, but on the whole the days had been more or less alike and usually pleasant.

The one thing that displeased her and had contributed to the monotony of her days, or rather nights, was the fact that she had tired of Mem, or perhaps he had tired of her. They had nothing in common any more. She had become the dominant one and Mem obeyed her. He was meek and mindful of her authority and she was *tired* of him! She had never been a one-man woman and she was mightily fed up with being one now. Not that she hadn't tasted other men during those years, but never in her bed in the kitchen, and that was where she wanted them – not merely chance encounters in the barn or in the high weeds.

Of course the biggest and most sorrowful event of those ten years had been Mrs Maxwell's death, and neither time nor work had been able to eradicate Lucretia Borgia's sadness at the loss of her mistress. Neither had Mr Maxwell ever become reconciled to the death of his wife. He had never married again – in fact he had never looked at another white woman – and for this Lucretia Borgia was extremely grateful. It had given her an opportunity for greater power and, although unacknowledged by Mr Maxwell, she was now the actual mistress of the house. Little by little she had taken over all of the many responsibilities of running it, and had had almost no opposition from her master. Although he never failed in his constant carpings about her nosiness she knew all along that he was glad she was doing a good job but was loath to let her think that he had given up one tittle of his own authority.

Hammond, now fifteen, seemed like a grown man. He had been an apt pupil of his father and was always eager to learn more about their stock in trade, the Negroes they had been buying and selling. When he was thirteen he had been sent away to school but at the conclusion of the first term, had come back to Falconhurst. He had stolen away from the school, borrowed a horse from the nearest plantation, and arrived home in the middle of the night. He had no interest in learning more than the rudiments of reading, writing, and ciphering. Further learning seemed of little use to him. He felt that it was far more important to be able to tell an Ibo from a Krumantee, or a Fan from a Hausa. To be able to trace those bloodlines in a Negro was important to him and certainly these things were never taught at school. So he had returned home and although his father had scolded him for not staying, he was secretly glad and even proud. They were together constantly, although during the past year, Warren Maxwell had developed a form of rheumatism which had severely curtailed his activities. Many days he would be confined to the house because his joints ached so badly and he had to delegate the plantation work to Hammond. Now, at fifteen, Hammond was practically running the plantation under his father's tutelage. On the days the older man was unable to leave the house, he had to be content to stay by the fire in the living room and be coddled by Lucretia Borgia, something he outwardly resented but inwardly accepted with gratitude. However, although he might be confined to the house, his mind was always with his son on whatever errand he had dispatched him, and he could hardly wait until the boy returned and reported to him. Hammond was, in some ways, more of a son to Lucretia Borgia than her own twin boys. Despite the difference in their colour, she mothered him with an all-consuming love to which he in turn responded.

Mrs Maxwell's debility had also given Lucretia Borgia a wider authority outside the house. True, Hammond was the one who carried out Mr Maxwell's orders, but more often than not it was Lucretia Borgia who initiated those commands. She had a way of implanting things in her master's mind so that he felt he had thought of these things himself, and although at times he railed at her, nevertheless he was wont to take her advice. Thus her scope of activity had increased considerably. She kept a finger on the pulse of the plantation and there was almost nothing that happened which she did not know about. She, of course, had access to the plantation grapevine which served only the slaves, and so often knew about things long before her two masters. Not only had she adapted herself to a plantation whose principal crop was Negroes rather than cotton, but she herself had added to its prosperity.

During these ten years she had been pregnant three times by Mem. No wonder, she often thought, that she was tired of him. Her first two children were girls and she had not demurred when Mr Maxwell ordered them to be taken away from her. Her last pregnancy, however, had resulted in the twin boys; for the first time in her life, she had pleaded with her master not to take these two from her. He was so pleased with them – they were such a rarity, so absolutely identical that nobody could tell them apart – that he promised her she could raise them. He would not sell them, but train them later to become house servants. Lucretia Borgia's cup truly ran over. Now she would have something of her own. She was entirely in agreement with Mr Maxwell when he named them Alpha and Omega, although she did not know the meaning of the names. Soon they were shortened to Alph and Meg. They were now five years old and although supposed to be confined to the kitchen, Mr Maxwell admired them so much that he often asked Lucretia Borgia to bring them into the living room so that he could play with them. Naked as jay birds, they crawled all over him and he regarded them with the same pleasure as he would have taken over two small, playful puppies.

There was not a blemish on either of them and they gave promise of great good looks. Lucretia Borgia would tie a red string around Alph's head and a blue one around Meg's, although this was not a sure identification as the boys would often exchange strings and answer to each other's names. When he got to tell the difference between them, Maxwell felt he leaned a little bit towards Alph; and it was just as well, because Hammond favoured Meg, who always sought him out and whose loyalty to him was unquestioned. Young as he was, his 'Masta Hammond suh' always claimed Ham's attention and was good for a piece of bread dipped in molasses or a lemon drop on those occasions when Hammond had one.

Lucretia Borgia managed the twins with the same high hand she used for all the rest of the plantation. Every morning she smacked them well so that they would remember that if anything went wrong there would be more vigorous slaps coming. These morning punishments were always followed by howls of anguish from the kitchen and both Mr Maxwell and Hammond would look up at the clock in the living room and nod to each other. It meant that breakfast would be on the table in about five minutes. As a result they never had to be called for breakfast. Lucretia Borgia's walloping of her progeny was sufficient.

Mem, although he had been peacock-proud of the fact that his seed had produced twins, took very little interest in them, despite the fact that he was around them all day. He merely followed the pattern of most plantation fathers. They were quite willing to plant the seed but had no hand in its cultivation. Were it not for the Maxwells' big ledger in which was recorded the birth and ancestry of every slave born at Falconhurst, it is doubtful that any of the youngsters, running naked and loose on the plantation, could have named either mother or father. In other plantations, where children lived with the mother, they were often unaware of who had sired them.

Lucretia Borgia's babies were born in the kitchen, but all the other females on Falconhurst gave birth to their children

154

in what was known as the 'birthing house', attended by one of the few elderly female slaves on the plantation. Maxwell had never sold her because of her knowledge of midwifery and now that she was getting old he had chosen a young wench to learn as much as possible of the old slave's methods. When the babies were born they were allowed to be with their mother for a matter of several days or a week, during which she could nurse them; but at the end of that time they were taken away. Her milk was not wasted. It was given to any infant in the birthing house, where they were all kept until they were weaned; but she was never sure whether it would be her own child or some other that she was nursing. The Maxwells avoided family ties, which were always disturbing when slaves were sold.

The girl would then be sent back to one of the cabins on the street behind the stables. These cabins were presided over by women who had been at Falconhurst for a longer-than-usual time. They were mostly in their late twenties and early thirties – young enough to sell but old enough to have a certain authority. They each had charge of the three or four couples who lived in their cabins. It was their duty to get the morning and evening meals, see that the cabin was kept clean, and make sure that the men did not neglect their duties at night. No woman ever mated according to her own desires. Her partner was always chosen by Mr Maxwell. It was he who would check the books, seeking the lineage that he felt would produce the best offspring. When he had decided on a couple he would put them together in one of the cabins until the woman became pregnant. After that the man would go back to sleeping in the barn until it was time to mate him up with another woman, chosen for him, of course, by Mr Maxwell.

This procedure had caused many arguments between Mr and Mrs Maxwell. Mrs Maxwell was a religious woman and she felt that slaves should be married and that each marriage should produce a family unit. She even had a small chapel built at the end of the street of cabins, complete with belfry and bell. Here she would conduct Sunday services whenever

155

there was no itinerant preacher around, despite Maxwell's belief that religion was not for slaves. Her services were well attended, although attendance was not obligatory. But if Maxwell did permit her to have the chapel, he stood out against any form of marriage between his slaves. Even 'jumping the stick', a primitive marriage ceremony brought over from Africa, was forbidden. He wanted no families or attachments; his slaves were raised to be sold, which put them in a different category from slaves who were born, lived, and died all on the same plantation.

From infants to adolescents and up to grown men and women, there were some three hundred slaves at Falconhurst. It was Warren Maxwell's practice to sell off a good-sized coffle each year. For this he would choose wenches who had brought in one, two, even three children. As they were mated up at around fifteen, eighteen was the ideal age for putting them up for sale and he always liked to sell them with a baby in their arms. Not only did they bring a higher price but it was proof of their fertility. As often as not the baby might not belong to the girl sold; but he never cheated and sold a barren girl with a child in her arms. Maxwell was honest in all his dealings. The men he would keep a little longer, selling them off anywhere between twenty and twenty-two. During their years at Falconhurst, they would have covered several wenches and would have sired a number of offspring.

So there was an annual sale of Falconhurst slaves and it had been Mr Maxwell's procedure to take them either to New Orleans or to the famous Forks-of-the-Road at Natchez. He rarely, if ever, sold to any of the itinerant slave dealers whose miserable coffles followed their buckboards from plantation to plantation picking up their suffering merchandise here and there. These despised slave merchants were only able to pick up those unfortunates who were not able to meet the high standard of quality set for Falconhurst slaves. That meant that only the maimed, the injured, the ugly and the imperfect were sold off in this manner. Thus he disposed of the undesirables and every Negro that was sold at a Falconhurst vendue had to be good-looking, of strong physique, capable of procreating or bearing children, and intelligent.

Occasionally some planter in need of replenishing his stock would come to Falconhurst to buy privately; on these occasions, Mr Maxwell offered only his best, giving the prospective buyer a chance to pick out his needs from the entire Falconhurst herd.

It was on just such an occasion as this that Lucretia Borgia smacked the tobacco-coloured rumps of Meg and Alph and made them set up such a howl that it was heard in the sitting room, where Maxwell and Hammond were entertaining a Mr Bagley, whose High Pines Plantation was considered one of the most opulent in the state. He had arrived the night before with his own coachman and valet and the avowed intention of buying at least two or three Falconhurst slaves. He had purchased from Falconhurst vendues before, so was not unknown to Maxwell and his reputation for being one of the wealthiest men in the Territory of Alabama made him doubly welcome.

Maxwell listened to the caterwauling of the twins. 'Them twins a-bawlin' in the kitchen jes's good's ringing an alarm bell.' He rose from his chair and waited for Mr Bagley to precede him into the dining room. 'It meanin' that Lucretia Borgia just smacked her twins, which is the las' thing she always do before breakfast is served. Kin count on it every day.'

Mr Bagley, who had met Lucretia Borgia briefly the night before (he had not arrived in time for supper), and had not seen the twins since they were asleep, went into the dining room followed by Maxwell and Hammond.

'Twins, you say, Mr Maxwell?' he asked lifting his eyebrows in surprise. 'You know it's rather a remarkable thing for niggers to have twins. Never had it happen at High Pines and have heard of only a few instances of it ever happening. Are they identical?'

'As 'like as two peas in a pod. Cain' tell the difference 'tween 'em. Named 'em Alpha and Omega, we did.'

157

Mem pulled out a chair for Mr Bagley. For the special occasion he wore a black coat and a starched white shirt with a red neckerchief. After they had all seated themselves, and Mem had poured coffee, passing the sugar bowl, the syrup jar, and the pitcher of thick, clotted cream, Mr Maxwell leaned back in his chair, waiting for the breakfast which he knew Lucretia Borgia would have prepared with special care. Company was not usual at Falconhurst and when she had a chance to display the excellence of her cooking, she always took particular pains.

And this morning they were not disappointed. Mem brought in a high stack of golden waffles, just waiting for a liberal application of butter and molasses. There was also a bowl of grits, snowy white except for a sprinkling of black pepper and the oozing goodness of lumps of golden butter. Following this he brought in a platter piled high with tiny sausages.

Mem served the white men with courtly bows. He could be the ideal servant when he wished. They all fell to, even Mr Bagley smacking his lips with relish over the delicious food. When he had finished, refusing Mem's offer of just another waffle, he pushed back his plate and relaxed in his chair over a second cup of coffee.

'Must compliment your cook, Mr Maxwell. One of the best breakfasts I've ever eaten. We think we serve good food at High Pines, but I must say our cook cannot compare with yours.'

Maxwell nodded in satisfaction. 'Tha's Lucretia Borgia for yo', suh. She the best cook we ever had 'n she shore spoils us. Wouldn't sell her for her weight in gold. She the mama o' those twins I bin tellin' yo' 'bout.'

Mr Bagley sipped at his coffee. One could almost follow his mental processes. 'Twins are rare and unusual, Mr Maxwell. How old are they?'

' 'Bout four o' five, I reckon. Jes' brats now, but someday they a-goin' to be prime stock. Yes sir-ee, high fancies if'n I know niggers – 'n I believe I do.'

Mr Bagley took two or three more sips of coffee in a

pregnant silence while Maxwell and Ham waited for him to speak. 'I certainly would admire to have them. They'd be a sight to show off at High Pines. You thinking of selling them?'

Maxwell smiled to himself. He certainly had no idea of selling them, but he always did enjoy a chance to show off his stock. He called Mem over to his side and whispered to him in a voice loud enough for Bagley to hear, 'Tell Lucretia Borgia to come in 'n to bring the twins with her.'

Ham jumped up from his seat and went around to Maxwell's side, laying a cautionary hand on his father's arm. 'Yo' ain' a-goin' to sell 'em, papa? Yo' know yo' promised. . . .'

'Pshaw, boy! Every nigger's for sale if'n the price is right, but don't kindly think Mr Bagley a-goin' to buy 'em. All he a-wantin' 'em for is to show 'em off like'n a couple o' peacocks.' He waited for the kitchen door to open and Lucretia Borgia to come in. She was holding each twin by the hand. The trio advanced a few steps beyond the door and she shoved the naked little boys ahead of her. 'Yes suh, Masta Warren suh. Yo' called for me?'

'Mista Bagley he a-wantin' to tell yo', Lucretia Borgia, that that was a right fine breakfast, 'n he a-wantin' to see yore twins. He say he thinkin' they be right fine to show off at High Pines. Ain' many plantations got a set o' twins.'

'But yo' ain' a-sellin' 'em, Masta Warren suh.' Lucretia Borgia smiled in the confidence that she had her master's word.

'Anythin' I don' like, Mista Bagley,' Warren Maxwell ignored her and her remarks, 'is a nosey wench what don' know when to keep her big lip buttoned up. Push them brats over so's Mr Bagley kin see them. Finger 'em if'n yo' wants, Mista Bagley.'

Lucretia Borgia was suddenly frightened. There had never been any question in her mind that her master would sell the twins. He had given her his word and she had never known him to break it. Now she felt a trembling in her stomach. Of

159

all the children she had had, these two were the most precious to her and she knew she would die if they were sold. Yes, she would pine away and die. Still, she let no semblance of her fear show. Instead she pushed the two little boys over to Mr Bagley.

He compared them with his eyes. Both of them seemed to favour Mem but surely nobody could tell which one was which. They were absolutely identical, lighter by a few shades than either their father or mother – a pale, rich, tobacco brown. Their small heads were well-shaped, and covered with a crop of soft hair like a cap of black velour. Their eyes were a dark, melting brown and their lips curved and full but not negroid. They had not outgrown their small pot-bellies but their arms and legs were sturdy and the wormlike appendages which betokened their manhood were already well developed. Both had Lucretia Borgia's proud stance and lofty tilt to their heads.

Bagley beckoned to them and they approached him without fear. 'Fine boys,' he said, letting his fingers roam over the smooth velvet of their skins. 'Can see they're perfect in every detail. Yes, Mr Maxwell, I'd like to have them. Purely as a show piece for High Pines; something to bring out and make my guests sit up and take notice. I'd dress them up in red suits with brass buttons and have one of my men show them a few jig steps so they could perform for my guests. How much are you asking for them?'

Hammond had returned to his seat and gripped the edge of the table while he studied his father's face. Maxwell leaned back in his chair, a slow smile playing over his features. 'Am asking a hundred dollars more'n any amount yo'd be willin' to pay, Mr Bagley. I'll tell yo'. Them twins is really not for sale. Jes' a-wantin' to show 'em off like'n yo'd show 'em off if'n yo' had them, 'though they ain't got no brass buttons 'n cain' dance no jig. They show pieces for Falconhurst, Mr Bagley, jes' like'n yo' want 'em for show pieces at High Pines. No, I promised their dam I wouldn't sell 'em. She'd have a conniption fit if'n I did, 'n we'd git nothin' decent to eat for a month. Lucretia Borgia she rather special 'round here, 'n I have to cater to her once in a while. Promised her 'n Ham I wouldn't sell 'em – so I cain'.'

Lucretia Borgia heaved an inward sigh of relief. Now that the danger was past, she didn't care how much this strange man admired her sons and fingered them.

'She being such a good cook and all, I might just buy her too.' Bagley looked at Lucretia Borgia admiringly.

Maxwell shook his head, and Hammond began to laugh. 'She ain' for sale, Mr Bagley.' He stood up and put one arm around her waist. 'Lucretia Borgia she's Falconhurst 'n Falconhurst it's Lucretia Borgia.' He remembered the nights he had clung to her after his mother died, the tears he had shed on her bosom. 'Lucretia Borgia ain' *never* goin' to be for sale.'

'Reckon we cain' make no deals on her, Mr Bagley; but now,' Maxwell gestured for Lucretia Borgia to go back to the kitchen with the twins, 'mayhap yo'll tell me jes' what yo' had in mind in the way of stock. Ain' a-goin' to show yo' nothin' but the best, 'n don' want to waste yore time lookin' at so-so stock. Tell me, what yo' considerin'?'

'It's been in my mind to buy two or three fine boys for stud. We have a lot of good wenches at High Pines. Seems that every sucker born there is a wench, so there's a shortage of upstanding young bucks. I'm always looking for a chance to improve my breed, and there isn't anything like your Falconhurst stock to do it. I got some good whelps out of those boys I bought from you in New Orleans a couple of years ago, but I sold them to my brother-in-law over in Louisiana.'

'Hope he ain' goin' to put 'em in the cane fields.' Maxwell frowned slightly. He didn't raise his niggers to kill themselves cutting cane.

'Hell, no! They're the pride of his plantation. Shows them off to everyone. But it's left me short of good studs and that's what I'm here for.'

'Then come into the settin' room.' Maxwell pushed back his chair from the table and wiped his lips with the fringed napkin, beckoning for Ham to follow. ' 'N yo', Ham, go git

161

down my ledgers. I want Mr Bagley to see some prime stock 'n I've got to pick 'em out first.'

'Yes, papa.' Ham dashed ahead of him into the sitting room. 'Purentee Falconhurst, yo' mean. Like'n Dabney or Crown or 'Thusalah.'

'That boy shore knows his niggers, Mr Bagley.' Maxwell beamed with pride. 'Sometimes I think he knows more 'bout niggers than I do.'

Lucretia Borgia had been listening at the kitchen door. In her relief, she smacked the twins' bare bottoms lightly, affectionately.

'Waffles 'n 'lasses for yo' boys this mornin',' she announced. 'Ain' no danger o' yo' bein' sold or me neither. Masta Ham he right set on yo', 'n like'n Masta Warren done say, Masta Ham he knows more 'bout niggers, even at his age, than *anyone* else!'

CHAPTER SEVENTEEN

Monday was observed religiously as washday at Falconhurst, and early in the morning Nancy the laundress would arrive at the kitchen door to be invited in by Lucretia Borgia for breakfast. It was the only meal of white folks' victuals that poor Nancy was ever able to eat at the big house, and Lucretia Borgia knew that the better she fed her, the more work she would get out of her. Although she did not deign to do any of the actual washing, she superintended every move that Nancy made, so that there were no cleaner clothes in the world than those at Falconhurst. Sheets and pillowcases were glistening, snowy white; the Maxwells' shirts were faultlessly ironed, as were Lucretia Borgia's stiffly starched white aprons, to which Nancy had to pay particular attention.

On this Monday morning, Nancy was regaling herself with grits and warmed-over bacon at the long table in the kitchen when Hammond entered, followed by a fine-featured *café-au-lait* quadroon boy. Lucretia Borgia, just pouring herself another cup of coffee, had been ready to join Nancy in some plantation gossip. It was thus she kept her finger on the pulse of Falconhurst, and she was annoyed at Ham's interference. 'What yo' 'n Audrey a-wantin', Masta Ham suh?' As a vent to her feelings she shoved one of the twins away from the table.

'Me 'n Audrey a-goin' down to the river to swim in the deep hole. Thinkin' yo'd put us up some sandwiches so's we wouldn't have to come back at noon. Papa he a-sayin' we kin go 'cause he 'n Mem's a-ridin' over to the woodlot 'n ain' nothin' for me to do over there.'

Even though she did not want him to go, she did not dare veto Mr Maxwell's permission; but she had to voice her own forebodings. 'Pretty deep down there. Deep 'nuff for a body to git drowned. Yo' shore yo' kin swim good, Masta Ham?' Although she loved her twins, it was Hammond whom she adored. For Audrey, who had been his playboy for several years – he was a little older than Ham – she had nothing but contempt. This was partly because he was with Ham more than she was, and partly because of his light colour which she envied. Also something about the boy's too-good looks offended her. He was far too pretty to be a boy: his hair was too long and curly; his cheeks too smooth; his eyes too deeply fringed with sooty lashes; his lips too full and red.

'I taught Masta Ham to swim, Lucretia Borgia, 'n now he swim real good.' Audrey smiled an ingratiating smile at Lucretia Borgia, showing a row of perfect white teeth.

She returned his smile with a glare of utter contempt. 'Better save yo' smile till yo' gets put up on the vendue table in N'Orleans. Don' know who a-goin' ever to buy yo'. Yo' ain' sired a single sucker 'n yo' shore old 'nuff to. Reckon all Masta kin sell yo' for is some namby-pamby house boy what ain' got 'nuff sap for a good sucker.'

163

'Got plenty o' sap, Lucretia Borgia ma'am, 'n plenty else too.' His hand clutched at the crotch of his pants to prove his statement, while Lucretia Borgia looked with some degree of interest. 'Ain' sired no suckers tho',' she remarked.

'Jes' give me time, tha's all. Bein' play-boy for Masta Ham, ain' had no chance to cover no wench, but when Masta Maxwell give me one, goin' to knock her up higher'n a kite.'

'Pshaw,' she derided him, 'yo' jes' one o' them pretty boys 'n that's all. Goin' to see 'bout yo', I am. Yo' bin teachin' Masta Ham more'n swimmin'.' She pointed an accusing finger at him and walked over to a splint basket; she dumped the dirty laundry onto the floor and sorted through the sheets. Disregarding the two small sheets from the trundle bed that Audrey occupied in Ham's room, she concentrated on the four large sheets which had come from Maxwell's and Ham's beds. At length she found what she had been looking for, then jerked her thumb at the door.

'Yo', Nancy, git out 'n git some rain water into the big cauldron 'n git a fire lighted under it. We ain' got all day to git the washin' done, so clean up yore plate 'n stir yore stumps 'n git started.'

Although Nancy had not finished her breakfast, she knew enough to obey Lucretia Borgia when she was in one of these moods, with her lips set in a grim line and her eyes blazing. Nancy rose and headed for the kitchen door. The twins, who had been clinging to Hammond's legs, relinquished their hold on him and scuttled across the floor to jump on the pile of dirty clothes but Lucretia Borgia yanked them up, slapped them both soundly, and sent them squalling to the other side of the kitchen, where they stood, rubbing their eyes and whimpering.

Holding a sheet which she had picked out from the rest, Lucretia Borgia advanced on the two boys. 'Why ain' yo' bin a' sleepin' in yore own bed, Audrey?' Her eyes snapped fire.

'*Bin* a-sleepin' there, Lucretia Borgia ma'am,' he stuttered,

164

but although his words were a bold refutation of hers, he was really frightened.

With pursed lips she looked from him to Hammond. Although he was her master's son and white and due the respect she usually gave him, she was very stern. 'That true, Masta Ham suh?'

'Shore 'nuff, Lucretia Borgia. Audrey he sleep in his trun'le bed 'n I sleep in the big bed.'

'Cain' stand lyin' even from yo', Masta Ham suh. Cain' stand it from no white boy nor from no light-rindled yaller boy neither. Not when I knows better. Yo' thinkin' yo' kin fool me? Jes' by turnin' down Audrey's bed, yo' think yo' kin fool me! Goes up each mornin' to make the beds 'n I find Audrey's all smooth 'n his piller not even dented, but the big bed all tousled up 'n both pillers slept on.' She glared at them both for a long moment of ominous stillness. ' 'N then I find *this*,' she pointed to a stain on the sheet, ' 'n this too,' she pointed to another. 'What I want to know is what yo' two boys bin a-doin' nights a-sleepin' together?'

She waited but no answer came. With a quick step she came up to Audrey and slapped him across the face. The force of her blow sent him reeling and he started to cry.

' 'N if'n yo' ain' white 'n Masta Warren's son, I'd clobber yo' too!' She turned on Hammond. 'Yo' don' have to tell me what's bin a-goin' on. I know. It ain' right nor natural. Yo' know what a-goin' to happen to yo' if'n yo' go on a-doin' them things?'

Hammond retreated a step. Not that he thought that Lucretia Borgia would strike him the way she had Audrey, but he was fearful of her anger.

'We ain' bin doin' nothin', Lucretia Borgia. Audrey 'n me, we like to sleep together sometimes. Likin' to talk, we do.'

'Yo'-all bin doin' more'n talkin'. Cain' fool me. What yo' bin doin' is *bad*. It a-goin' to make yo' foolish, tha's what it a-goin' to do. Ain' natural. Ain' good. I bin a-meanin' to speak to yore papa 'bout it but know he a-goin' to hit the ceilin' if'n I do. He goin' to be so mad he string this Audrey

165

boy up 'n whop the yaller meat right off'n his bones. Thinkin' he might whop yo' too, Masta Ham.'

'Not if'n yo' don' tell him.' Hammond hung his head and then raised it sheepishly so he could look at Lucretia Borgia. ' 'N papa ain' a-goin' to whop Audrey neither. He a mighty valuable nigger, a fancy, 'n papa a-sayin' how he goin' to send him off in the next coffle 'cause he bring a good price in N'Orleans. Papa ain' goin' to scar him up none. Take five hundred dollars off'n his price if'n he go up on the vendue table with his back all waled up.'

'Niggers, niggers, niggers! Tha's all yo' think 'bout, Masta Ham boy. How much this nigger goin' to bring 'n how much that one. Time yo' got to thinkin' 'bout somethin' else.' She dropped the sheet with its telltale stains and sat down at the table, motioning for Ham to sit down opposite her. The anger left her face and her next words, though stern, were not ill-tempered. She reached across the table and took one of his hands in hers.

'Boy yore age, Masta Ham suh, don' need no play-boy no more. Yo' grown up, nigh onto sixteen yo' are, 'n don' need no nigger play-boy a-sleepin' in yore room 'n taggin' along everywhere yo' go. Time we changed all that. Time we sent Audrey out to the barn. Time I talked to yore papa. He mighty ignorant about some things.'

'Yo' ain' a-goin' to tell papa 'bout Audrey 'n me, Lucretia Borgia? Yo' don' want to git him all riled up.'

She shook her head. 'Ain' got it in me to shame yo', Masta Ham suh, not in front o' yore papa, but a-goin' to talk to him jes' the same.'

'Mighty glad yo' ain' a-goin' to tell him,' Ham squeezed Lucretia Borgia's hand. 'Yo' know somethin', Lucretia Borgia? I love yo' a lot.'

'Now don' go a-butterin' me up.' She reached across and patted his cheek.

' 'N don' tell him 'bout Audrey neither. Don' want him all waled up. He too good a nigger.'

'All right,' she answered. 'Am a-goin' to take yore word for it that nothin' like this happen again. It for yore own

good, Masta Ham suh. Jes' for yore own good. Now'll pack
yo' up a lunch 'n if'n yo' wants to go swimmin' yo' kin, but
when yore papa comes in I shore goin' to have a talk with
him.'

' 'Bout what?' Hammond was anxious again.

' 'Bout some changes what goin' to be made 'round here.'

'What yo' a-goin' to say to him?'

'Leave that to me, Masta Ham suh. Ain' aimin' to git yo'
in no trouble, nor get Audrey all waled up neither, though it
don' make me no neverminds if'n he git waled or not. He
a right pretty nigger boy 'n knows he a-goin' to bring a good
price, but my business is to protect yo', Masta Ham suh.
Yo're my boy 'n ain' wantin' nothin' bad to happen to
yo'.'

He got up from the table and came around to put his
hands on Lucretia Borgia's shoulders. 'Yo' mighty good to
me, Lucretia Borgia.'

She patted his hand. 'Gotta be, Masta Ham suh. Yo' ain'
got no mama to watch over yo'. Jes' got ol' Lucretia Borgia,
tha's all, but I shore a-goin' to look out for my boy.' She
hoisted her weight from the chair and went to the breadbox,
taking out a loaf of bread which she proceeded to slice.

'If'n yo' wants to go swimmin' in the deep hole, yo' better
take Audrey with yo'. Ain' havin' yo' go there alone. But
remember! No more funny business. I kin still tell yore
papa.' She went into the buttery to get the ham for the sandwiches and Hammond looked across at the frightened
Audrey.

'She knows,' he whispered.

'She shore as hell does. Ain' no more funnin' for us. That
damn Lucretia Borgia she got eyes in the back 'n on top o'
her head. She know everything what's goin' on all over
Falconhurst.' He ceased his whispering as she came back
and started to make the sandwiches, buttering the bread
liberally. She wrapped them in a white napkin, placed them
in a small basket, and handed this to Audrey to carry, wag-
ging an admonishing finger before his nose. He scuttled from
the kitchen, his face ashen with fear. Hammond swaggered

just a little bit, knowing that he was safe. Lucretia Borgia would not tell on him.

She followed them onto the porch, toting the basket with the soiled laundry. 'Got that water bilin', Nancy?' The coloured woman started to hurry. ' 'N git some soap. Some hard soap on the top shelf in the buttery. Don' spare no elbow grease when yo' a-scrubbin' them clothes. Got to have 'em good 'n white 'n if'n they ain', some good-for-nothin' nigger wench goin' to git clobbered.'

Knowing that with Hammond away there would be only Maxwell himself for dinner, she took particular pains with his meal. She had never heard the old adage that the way to a man's heart is through his stomach, but she knew that a well-fed man is far more approachable than one who has dined poorly. Although fried chicken was the rule at Falconhurst, this day she took a succulent young hen, stuffed it with a dressing of bread, sage, thyme and savoury, and roasted it, along with small white potatoes. Knowing how he liked them, she fixed a mess of black-eyed peas and ham hock; cracked pecans and made a pie. This with fluffy baking-powder biscuits and honey was for him alone.

When she heard the front door close and knew that he was there, she waited for Mem, who had been with Maxwell on his rounds that morning. As Mem came out into the kitchen, she handed him a freshly made toddy to take to his master in the sitting room. Then when Mem returned, she fixed up another, knowing that the toddies would somewhat mellow him.

When she heard him go into the dining room, she peeked through the kitchen door. She saw him smile as Mem laid the victuals before him, but noted that his rheumatism was bothering him by the way he had to rub his hands before he could manipulate his knife and fork. When she sent in the overlarge piece of pecan pie by Mem, she again took up her position at the kitchen door, listening. When she knew that he was through eating, she opened the door and came into the dining room.

'Thinkin' yo better rest yo'self a little, Masta Warren suh.

168

Bit of a nip in the air today, 'tho Masta Ham he went a-swimmin' down in the river. Tol' me yo' said he could go, 'n that Audrey boy went with him. I laid a fire in the fireplace in the settin' room 'n thinkin' yo' git comfortable if'n yo' set awhile 'fore yo' go out 'gain.'

He made his way slowly into the sitting room, grumbling as he went. 'Yo' always tryin' to run me 'n my business, Lucretia Borgia. Ain' got no time for no fiddle-faddlin' in front o' the fire. Got things to do 'n Ham he out funnin' himself. Don' care though. That boy he a-workin' mos' o' the time 'n don' git much chance to fun himself.'

'No suh, Masta Warren suh,' she was quick to agree. 'Masta Ham he a right fine boy. Keeps his nose to the grindstone mos' o' the time.' She followed him into the sitting room, struck a bit of tinder and applied it to the shaved pine kindling in the fireplace. In a moment it burst into flame and she fanned it with her apron. 'Yo' jes' sit there a minute, Masta Warren suh. Thinkin' yo' might like another toddy 'n havin' Mem fix yo' one.' She saw that he was going to take her advice; he was heading for the big old Empire rocker in front of the fireplace. With a practised motion she shoved the footstool in front of him and when Mem came in, she took the toddy from the saucer and handed it to him.

He accepted it but looked up at her quizzically, the shadow of a smile on his face. He started to sip the toddy, adjusting himself to the chair and stretching his feet out towards the fire. 'Now what in hell yo' a-wantin', Lucretia Borgia? Somethin', I know. Damned shore of it, I am. Stuffed chicken 'n pecan pie, 'n me eatin' all alone. Other days yo'd give me cold meat 'n pone, me eatin' alone. Then there's the fire in the settin' room 'n the toddy. What yo' a-butterin' me up for? Something yo' a-wantin'. Know by that look on yore face.'

Her expression was blandly innocent. 'Why, Masta Warren suh, whatever for yo' think I bin wantin' somethin'? Got everything I want. That is, almost everything. Ain' nothin' 'tall that I a-needin' ceptin' perhaps another man. Gittin' mighty tired o' Mem with his tom-cattin' all over the

169

place 'n too tired at night to do nothin' but go to sleep. Mem he a-gittin' old. Cain' git it up no more.'

He shook his head in vigorous denial. 'Ain' that, Lucretia Borgia. If'n yo' wants 'nother man, reckon yo' kin have one. Mayhap yo'd better pick one out, 'cause when I git through strippin' Mem down, he won' be able to pester yo' for a week. He a-gittin' worser 'n worser; time I stripped some o' the hide off'n his back. He more slothful-like every day.'

'Yes suh, Masta Warren suh, Mem shore is slothful.' She continued to stand beside his chair, the saucer in her hand. He finished his drink and set the glass on the saucer, but still she did not move.

'Well, what is it, Lucretia Borgia? Yo' a-makin' me nervous standin' there like'n a bump on a log.'

'Jes' one little thing, Masta Warren suh. Nearly forgot to mention it. But it not for me; it for Masta Ham, suh.'

'What 'bout him? He's a right good boy 'n ain' got no complaints 'bout him. Nary a one. He takin' right hold o' runnin' this place, me with the rheumatiz 'n all.'

'Yes suh, Masta Warren suh. Masta Ham's a fine boy but they's just one thing we got to remember. Masta Ham he ain' 'zactly a boy no more. He growin' on sixteen 'n mos' a man. Got a birthday a-comin' up soon. Goin' to make him a big cake, I am, when he gits to be sixteen.'

'Sixteen!' Maxwell rocked back and forth a few times. 'Don' seem possible, Lucretia Borgia. Jes' yesterday he nothin' but a li'l tad a-playin' with his wooden horse. He shore grow up fast.'

'Uh-huh.' She nodded her head wisely in accord with her master's words. 'He mos' a man. Masta Warren suh, kin I say somethin'?'

'Hell of a time to ask me; yo' bin standin' there a-shootin' off that big mouth o' yourn for ten minutes. Yo' askin' me kin yo' say somethin' 'n yo' ain' closed yore mouth since yo' came in here – 'thout being asked, neither.'

Her silence irked him until finally he blurted out, 'Well, what in hell yo' a-wantin' to ask me?'

'Like'n I was sayin' it 'bout Masta Ham, suh. He still

a-beddin' down in his room with that Audrey what bin his play-boy for a long time. I bin a-thinkin' he too much o' a man now to have a play-boy.'

'So?' Maxwell stared up at her.

'So, bin a-thinkin' it 'bout time yo' changed things for him. He a-needin' somethin', gittin' to be the age he is. Time yo' were thinkin' o' gittin' him a bed wench. Ain' right for no young fellow to be sleepin' all 'lone up there in that room o' his 'cept for a play-boy. Boy sixteen years old, he a-needin' a wench, he is.'

'A bed wench, huh?' Maxwell considered. 'Yo' know somethin' yo' ain' a-tellin' me, Lucretia Borgia? He bin a'sneakin' out to the cabins 'n pesterin' some wench?'

She shook her head in vigorous denial. 'Masta Ham he ain' that kind, Masta Warren suh. He ain' don' nothin' like'n that less'n he gits yore say-so, but skeered he soon a-goin' to, less'n yo' give him a bed wench.'

He pointed a swollen, distorted finger at her. 'Sort o' takin' the words right out o' my mouth, ain' yo'? Bin a-thinkin' 'bout it. High time he started pesterin' a wench. Now let me see; we got any nice clean pretty li'l wench for him?'

'We got Dite, Masta Warren suh. She the one yo' calls Aphrodite but everyone else call her Dite. She right pretty she is, 'n ain' never bin busted. Right fittin' that she have her young white masta bust her wide open. She bin a-livin' down in Lavinia's cabin 'n yo' know how strict Lavinia is. Don' let none o' her wenches out o' sight, she don'. Ain' no bucks a-hangin' round her cabin or she a-takin' a broomstick to 'em.'

'God damn it!' He pounded on the arm of his chair, forgetful of his aching hand. 'Got it all figured out, ain' yo'? Always a-workin' behind my back. Some day I'm a-goin' to get mighty sick o' the way yo' a runnin' Falconhurst 'n me 'n Ham too. Jes' 'cause yo' a wench ain' no reason why I cain' string yo' up 'n strip the meat off'n yore bones. But this time, yo're right. Ham a-needin' a wench. Best thing in the world for a boy his age. Where-at that Dite?'

'Done tol' Lavinia to keep her in the cabin today. Tol' her

to have Dite wash all over 'n put on a clean dress. Yo'
a-wantin' me to fetch her?'

He laughed out loud. 'Shore got everythin' worked out,
ain' yo', Lucretia Borgia? Damn you! Man cain' say his life's
his own with yo' round runnin' everything for him. Yes, go
'n fetch her. Thinkin' I know her but want to look her over
good. 'N when Ham come in, better mayhap that yo' talk to
him. Kind-a shames me to talk to him 'bout these things.'

'Jes' have Dite a-waitin' in his room when he goes to
bed, tha's all. He 'n Dite'll know what to do.'

Maxwell nodded his head reminiscently. ' 'Members my
first wench, Lucretia Borgia. Had to take her down in the
cotton field 'cause I didn't want my pappy to know 'bout it.
Younger'n Ham is now, I was. Better that he do it here in the
house 'n not go hidin' off somewhere. Yo' 'tend to it all,
will yo'?'

She nodded, glad that her point had been won. ' 'N that
Audrey boy, I'm a-thinkin' it better he stay out in the barn
now, or if'n yo' wants, he kin sleep on a pallet front o' Masta
Ham's door.'

'Tha's right. Let him be Ham's body servant 'stead o' his
play-boy. He 'bout ready to sell off, 'cause he ain' never
goin' to make no field hand. Too fine-boned for that, so
right fittin' he be a body servant. Git a higher price for him
if'n he got experience.' He grinned up at Lucretia Borgia.
'Yo' know somethin'? If'n it wan't for this rheumatiz I
might jes' take me a bed wench myself.'

She grinned back at him. 'Wan' me to pick one out for
yo', Masta Warren suh?'

'Yo' jes' mind yore own damn business. I ain' so ol' but
what I kin pick one out myself if'n I wants one. Now
skedaddle! Next time I gits stuffed chicken 'n pecan pie, I'll
know yo' got somethin' on yore mind.'

'Yes suh, Masta Warren suh. Yes suh. Goin' now to fetch
that Dite. Young Masta Ham be a lot better off with her
a-beddin' with him. Yas suh, yas indeedy suh.'

CHAPTER EIGHTEEN

As usual, after the evening meal, Hammond sat down with
his father in the sitting room. This was their habitual time to
discuss various matters about the plantation and its workings, but they never sat for very long. The whale-oil lamp on
the centre table gave only a feeble light and, as they always
rose early, they also went to bed early. There was no particular reason for spending time in the semi-obscurity of the
sitting room once their business had been finished. The
matters that they had to talk over were never very lengthy or
very involved. It was barely half-past eight when Maxwell
yawned and suggested bed. Hammond was quite willing to
follow him. From long habit which had existed from early
childhood, Hammond kissed his father before they went
upstairs.

There was no grand hall with curving staircase at Falconhurst's big house. Instead the stairs, hidden by a closed door
in the daytime, went directly up from the living room. Hammond opened the door then, bethinking himself of his
father's lameness, returned to his chair to help the old man
up and put a hand under his elbow as they walked across the
room and ascended the stairs slowly step by step. Ham
stopped at his father's room at the head of the stairs, entered
it and put down the candle he had carried up. Mem was
waiting in the dark room; the candle showed him sitting in
a straight chair beside the bed.

'Mem, he'll git yo' undressed 'n into bed, papa.' Ham
motioned for Mem to come over and assist his father. Together the two of them walked with Maxwell to the bed so
that he could sit down on the edge while Mem backed up to
him to take his boots off and then his clothes. There was
a candle in a brass candlestick on the chest of drawers, which
Ham lit from the one he had brought upstairs. He did not
wait for Mem to undress his father. Ham was strangely

modest in many ways and did not want to look on his father's nakedness. With another good night, he left the room, closing the door behind him and walked down the hall to his own room. Much to his surprise, a pallet lay in the hall with Audrey stretched out on it, covered with a ragged quilt.

Anger surged up in him. Who had given Audrey the authority to bed himself down in the hall, when his rightful place was in the trundle bed which was under Ham's big bed during the day and rolled out on casters to accommodate Audrey at night? He was about to wake Audrey and give him his come-uppance; then, on second thoughts, he decided against it. There had been enough to-do this morning with Lucretia Borgia about his and Audrey's carryings-on and he did not want to add fuel to Lucretia Borgia's anger by disturbing anything he was sure she had arranged. However, he resented the usurpation of his own authority. What right had she to give orders? Yet he realized that he *had* been in the wrong. Lucretia Borgia had something on him and he didn't want her to go to his father about Audrey and himself. Better to swallow his pride for the time being.

He stepped over Audrey's sleeping form and, still resentful, entered his room. His bed was turned down. He could see the whiteness of the sheets. He set the candle on the small night stand but did not see the girl who was sitting in the far corner until she stood up and came into the circle of light. Surprised, he stared at her for a moment, then took up the candle and held it close to her face.

'Yo' Dite, ain' yo'?' He found himself trembling as he asked the simple question.

'Yes suh, Masta Ham suh. I'se Dite. Lucretia Borgia she say . . .'

'Lucretia Borgia she always a-sayin' too goddamn much.' Ham was not addicted to profanity, but some inner sense of assertive masculinity prompted him to indulge in it now. 'What that old wench say, anyway?'

The girl was trembling. She stood before him in the circle of light, attractive, even beautiful. The bloom of adolescence was still on her face and passion had not as yet coarsened it.

Her hair hung to her shoulders in tight, damp curls and her eyes, pinpointed with the flame from the candle, were large and luminous. Her lips were moist and inviting – not so thick as to be repellent, but large enough to be sensual. A slender neck in which he could see one pulsing artery seemed hardly strong enough to uphold her head. Under the clean osnaburg dress he could see her protruding breasts, still unformed but large enough to make two inviting projections. He put the candle down on the night stand beside the bed and noticed that his own hand was trembling too. He had never been with a woman before. To all Audrey's connivings for them both to take a wench in one of the cabins or behind the barn or even in the fields, he had turned a deaf ear. Not that he had not wanted one. God! But strict obedience to his father was so deeply ingrained in him that he had never dared consider disobeying him. One of the strictest rules at Falconhurst had always been that no wench should be covered by anyone unauthorized to do so.

'Well, what did old Lucretia Borgia say?' He repeated the question, this time with a note of tenderness in his voice. He placed one finger tentatively against the soft skin of her cheek and let it trace a line down to her mouth, touching her lips gently. His voice sank to a whisper. 'What did Lucretia Borgia say?'

Dite reached out and clasped his finger following it down to her chin and into the soft hollow of her throat. She smiled at him with growing confidence and whispered back. 'She a-sayin' that I come to yore room tonight. Tellin' me to wash myself all over 'n put on clean clothes 'n come here 'n wait for yo'.'

He realized that any such order given by Lucretia Borgia must necessarily have the approval of his father. His conscience was relieved. 'Why?' His hand, accompanied now by hers, vanished inside the loose neck of her dress and discovered the roundness of one breast. Slowly and searchingly his fingers touched the tip of it, then pinched gently, marvelling at how it hardened under his touch.

'She a-sayin' that I'm to be with yo' tonight. That is, if'n

175

yo' a-wantin' me. She a-sayin' that if'n yo' don', yo' kin tell me to go back to Lavinia's cabin; but she a-thinkin' mayhap yo' want me. Please, Masta Ham suh, don' send me back. All the wenches they a-tellin' me how it a great thing for a gal like'n me to be busted by her white masta. Hope yo' ain' a-sendin' me back, Masta Ham suh.' She turned her head so that her lips could touch his arm and her tongue flicked lightly against his flesh.

His other arm drew her closer to him, so close that he could feel the entire outline of her body under the thin dress. The warmth of her and the faint clinging smell of musk stirred him. Gently he disengaged her hand from his and took it away from her breast, undoing the buttons that held her dress together. He manoeuvred the thin material until it slipped from her shoulders and fell down around her feet. Then, still holding her, he took her hand and guided it to the buttons of his shirt which she undid. He had to undo the big brass buckle of his belt himself, but when it was loosened, he pushed her hand down to the buttons of his trousers which she slowly unfastened until her hands contacted the pulsing rigidity of his maleness. He took a step, drawing her alongside of him, forgetting that he had not removed his boots. He tripped over his trousers, fell and brought them both together down onto the bed.

'Them damn boots!' He was angry that he had forgotten them. 'Audrey he always help me off with my boots, but to-night I plumb forgot. Yo' goin' to help me, Dite? Cain' do nothin' the way I hog-tied by my boots and britches.'

'Kin I help yo' off with 'em?' She extricated herself and got up to kneel beside the bed with one of his boots in her hand.

He laughed at her awkwardness. 'Cain' do it that a-way. Kin see yo' never took off a man's boots afore. Have to stand up with yore back to me and my boot between yore legs. Then I puts my other foot on yore ass 'n pushes. That the only way. Mayhap I better wake Audrey up. He knows how.'

'Kin do it, Masta Ham suh.' She was so proud of her

176

position that she did not want to share him with anyone else. 'Kin do it if'n yo' shows me.'

'But yore little ass so sweet 'n tender, hates to push on it.'

'I strong,' she asserted, turning around with his booted foot between her legs. 'Kin pull 'em off.'

Softly he pressed against her with his shod foot as she eased off one boot, then, his bare foot against her naked flesh, she took off the other. Kneeling before him, she stripped off his trousers and when they were on the floor she encircled his legs with her arms, kissing his knees and the inside of his thighs. He reached down and pulled her up to him, edging over on the bed to make room for her. Awkwardly they both managed to pull the bedspread and the pieced quilt from under them until they were between the clean sheets which Lucretia Borgia had thoughtfully provided.

Now there were no longer any barriers of cloth between them. Flesh met flesh. He stretched his body alongside hers, feeling the animal warmth and sleek smoothness of her body as it touched him from head to foot. He did not kiss her on the mouth, although his lips were close to hers. He had heard – and it was true – that kissing on the mouth was not for white men and black wenches, although he encouraged her to kiss him everywhere on his body except on his mouth. That alone was taboo.

The mere feel of female flesh was indeed no novelty to him. He had let his fingers slide professionally over countless wenches of all ages, exploring the most secret parts of their bodies, yet it had never excited him. That was business, no more and no less than the examination of a mare or a heifer for purchase. His fingers had probed and examined. They had parted secret crevices and poked themselves into mouths to see if teeth were perfect. He had accepted or rejected on the basis of his findings. Yes, he *was* a good judge of nigger flesh, of this he was certain, and his father confirmed his opinion.

But this was different! Although he already owned this wench called Aphrodite, he felt now a different sense of

177

possession. This was not business; it transcended it. The body that he held in his arms belonged to him and was now joined to him by more than mere ownership. He felt himself rising to meet her encouragements and for the first time, as he would do many times afterwards in his life, he envied the physical endowments of his own black bucks. Compared with them he was puny. The thought flashed through his mind that he would never buy a buck so small and insignificant in endowment as he was himself. But, he consoled himself, Dite did not seem to mind. Other and more experienced wenches might compare him unfavourably with their black bedmates: Dite would not. After all – and now he was congratulating himself – he was white and his very whiteness conferred an honour on her. Nevertheless, in some secret corner of his mind he was still envious. He dismissed the thoughts that had momentarily troubled him. Goddamn it! He was white and she should be glad to have an opportunity to bed herself with a white boy.

Now he changed and instead of being merely the passive acceptor of her attentions, he began to be the aggressor. His hands crept over the satin smoothness of her skin and his fingers titillated his emotions, raising them to unprecedented heights; as he had never before felt the way he did now. He realized that he was near to exploding before he had even begun, and for a moment he had to separate from her, forbidding her to touch him. When he had partially regained control, he let his fingers toy with the rigid and swollen buds of her breasts, pinching them until she emitted little yelps of pain. While he encouraged her hands and mouth to resume their dalliance with his body, he buried his face in the hollow of her throat, wishing now that he might kiss her and taste the wet smoothness of her mouth. He was tempted, but great as the temptation was, he overcame it. Better not let her get any ideas this first night. He must remember she was only a nigger wench. She was merely something for his convenience – but what a wonderful convenience it was!

Slowly he hitched his body onto her until she was under him. He was awkward in his movements and somehow sensed his own ineptitude but he lay, with his weight on her, feeling her body twitch in spasmodic tics while he clutched her tightly to him with sweaty hands. She began to moan and then move under him, pulsing slowly up and down and as she moved, she gradually spread her legs so that his knees, instead of being on her, rested on the bed. Although she was no more experienced in such things than he was, some primitive instinct guided her. Using his arms for leverage, he pushed himself up until he was kneeling between her outstretched legs. His fingers sought, found, widened her, then guided himself into her. He entered but only barely, then rested for a second.

'How's that?' he mumbled.

'Fine, Masta Ham suh.' She moved her body up as if to accommodate more of him and he plunged into her with all his force, unmindful of the cry of pain which curdled in her throat. Having gained this advantage, something warned him to cease for another moment, not only to catch his own breath and to prevent an immediate dénouement, but to give her a chance to recover from the pain he had inflicted on her.

'Yo' all right, Dite honey?' He knew he did not have to ask her. It should make no difference to him how she felt. But with his present feeling of tenderness towards her he had momentarily forgotten that she was black and he was white.

'Hurt somethin' terrible, Masta Ham suh, but I don' min'.' She was beyond pain, even that which she had felt had seemed both desirable and good. She knew now that she was 'busted' and it had not been as bad as the terrible pictures the other wenches had painted for her. Never again would she have to endure it. From now on it would be only pleasure. Her hips started to move and she engulfed him tightly, pressing him into her.

He lowered himself onto her, cushioning his body against her breasts and half-supporting himself on his elbows. He rose, withdrawing by accident, and had to guide himself in again. This time his hand encountered a wetness which had not been there before.

'Yo' ready?' he whispered.

'Uh-huh.' Words were impossible to her.

Now his thrusts became bestial, with all the force of his strong adolescent body behind them. He rode her without mercy and she moved to meet him, timing her own body to each stroke as if she would embed him deeper and deeper. All too soon he gasped, sucking the air into his lungs as though it might be his last breath, plunged once more and then fell upon her, drained of all strength and energy, his nerves a-tingle from head to foot. He could not move but remained there, his whole weight upon her, until she reached up a tentative hand and brushed the shock of hair from his eyes.

'That good, Masta Ham suh?'

'Mighty good. Ain' yo' a-goin' to thank me for it?'

'Thank yo', Masta Ham suh. Glad it my masta what busted me.'

He heaved his body off her, rolling to the other side of the bed so that he would not touch her. For a moment he felt almost nauseated by the musk of her body, and could not bear to have the slightest contact with her. When she reached over a timid hand to rest on his belly, he pushed it away. She realized that he had satisfied himself and wondered why she, herself, had not been. She would have willingly submitted to more – much more.

'Don' yo' want me no more?' She wondered if in some way she had failed him and not done her part. She had tried to do everything right, not only as she had sensed it but as she had been instructed by Lavinia and the older wenches.

Ham's sudden sense of repulsion was diminishing and he reached out to clutch the hand he had pushed away, bringing it back to rest on his body. It remained there for a time; neither of them spoke nor moved. She was puzzled as to what she should do and he was waiting until he could breathe regularly. The heat of her hand on his body brought back desire and he pushed her hand down, letting it cover the crumpled flesh which had completely lost its rigidity.

Her fingers toyed with its limp and slippery moistness. Now desire began to mount in him again but more slowly this time. He lay rigid, letting her fingers tantalize him back to life, arching his body as they resuscitated and revived him.

'Yo' a-goin' to kiss me?' he asked.

'On the mouth?' She had been hoping that he would allow her this unprecedented privilege.

'Hell no!' He was angry at her for even suggesting such a thing. 'Yo' a-knowin' what I mean. Like'n yo' did before.'

'Yes suh, Masta Ham suh, if'n that what yo' wants.' She obeyed his instructions with such a force that he had to restrain her.

Now he could stand it no longer. For the second time he took her and although his explosion was not as spontaneous as the first time, it seemed to him that he enjoyed it more because it lasted longer. But once he was spent, the measure of his enjoyment became the measure of his rejection of her afterwards. Now he did not want her. The thought of more dalliance with her was repulsive and he pushed away from her as far as he could get.

'That's 'nuff,' he groaned. 'Don' wan' no more tonight. Got me all dreaned out, yo' have. Heist yo'self up. There's a trundle bed under this one. Pull it out 'n bed yo'self in it.'

She edged closer to him. 'Did I do somethin' wrong, Masta Ham suh? Did I?'

'Hell no, yo' did jes' fine, Dite, but I'm tired now. Woman kin take pesterin' all night but a man cain'. Want to go to sleep now 'n know I cain' with yo' here alongside o' me. Two times is enough. Better I sleep alone.'

She climbed down from his bed and pulled out the trundle bed, its casters squeaking. She snuggled down onto it, pulling up the pieced coverlet.

'Good night, Masta Ham suh.' Her voice gave evidence that she was awaiting some consolatory word of approbation, even of affection.

He was silent for several breaths, then essayed a good night which had an edge of affection to it. He raised himself up on one elbow and smiled at her in the dark.

'Reckon that the first time for both of us, ain' it?'

'First time for me, Masta Ham suh.'

'Knows it was 'cause I busted yo'. Yo' a good wench, Dite. Likes yo' I do, 'n yo' kin be my bed wench from now on. Every night. How yo' like that?'

'Like it fine, I do.' She pictured how she would strut before the other wenches. She would occupy a unique position of honour at Falconhurst, comparable in a way to that of Lucretia Borgia. She'd be known as Masta Ham's bed wench.

Ham settled himself in his bed and the room was silent. There was, however, a rustling in the next room, then the stealthy closing of a door. Lucretia Borgia tested her weight on the floor boards so they would not creak and made her way slowly down the hall to the stairs. She had been listening in the next room to Ham's, through the latch hole of a connecting door. She smiled to herself. That Masta Ham was a lusty young fellow. Twice on his first night. Well, it was about time. At least she'd eliminated Audrey, who was sleeping soundly outside Ham's door when she passed.

Once back in the kitchen she sighed, listening to Mem's snores. She wished she could go back through time to the night when she had been busted. She wished even more that there was a puissant young buck on her pallet who would welcome her now with open arms. Mem! Huh! She was *mighty* tired of him. She'd have to see about getting him changed for another.

CHAPTER NINETEEN

Lucretia Borgia waited patiently behind the kitchen door while Mem served breakfast to Hammond and his father. When she finally heard their chairs scrape back she went to take her place beside the sink. Her present slavey in the kitchen, a young wench called Dexie whom she was just breaking in, was finishing her own breakfast at the long table. Lucretia Borgia berated her for not getting through earlier. There were dishes to be washed, she informed her, and she'd better step to it. Lucretia Borgia had more important things on her mind than washing up. She wanted to talk with Maxwell senior but had to be sure that Hammond had left for the fields before she broached the subject.

'They through eatin'?' she asked as Memnon came out into the kitchen with a large japanned waiter piled high with dirty dishes.

He nodded his head. His taciturnity, especially with her, always made Lucretia Borgia angry. It was difficult to get any information out of Mem.

' 'N Masta Ham, he done left?' she enquired in the condescending voice which she used towards Mem.

Again Mem nodded. Although Lucretia Borgia was long tired of Mem as her bed partner, she was aware that he was also equally bored with her. Because he had been there far longer than she had, he resented her superiority and her constant telling him every move that he might make.

But his nod was sufficient for her. All traces of annoyance disappeared from her face as she passed into the dining room. It was empty; Mr Maxwell was sitting in the big Empire rocker, his feet stretched out towards a fireplace in which there were only a few dying embers.

'That Mem!' she exclaimed, glad to find something which he had left undone. 'He a-gittin' more slothful every day. Don' have sense 'nuff to come in when it rains. Jes' cain' see nothin' that ought to be done, less'n yo' sticks his nose in it. Could of put a few more sticks o' wood on the fire to make it warmer for yo', what with yore rheumatiz 'n all.'

She moved with bustling efficiency, placing the pine sticks on the fire and blowing on it with the bellows until they ignited and burst into flame. 'Jes' triflin'.'

'What yo' a-sputterin' 'bout now, Lucretia Borgia?' Although it was too soon for the freshly ignited wood to have warmed him any, the mere sight of the flames seemed to do Maxwell good and he stretched out his gnarled hands

183

towards the fire and rubbed them together with satisfaction.

'Mem so slothful.'

'Yes, he a-gittin' downright shiftless. Tol' him to bring me a hot toddy 'n he bin philanderin' 'round 'n ain' brought it yet.'

'Needin' a little touchin' up, I reckon, Masta Warren suh. When yo' a-goin' to do it?'

'When I gits damn good 'n ready, tha's when. Why ain' yo' out in the kitchen a-tendin' to yore work?'

' 'N let yo' freeze to death in here? 'Thout'n a fire to warm yore legs 'n a toddy to warm yore insides? No suh, Masta Warren suh, jes' wantin' yo' to be happy. Tha's why I a-checkin' up on things. 'Sides, ain' got no kitchen work to do today. Got dinner all prepared, 'cept Dexie she a-goin' to fix us a mess o' collard greens. She kin do that 'thout'n my bein' there. Thought mayhap I'd leach out some wood ashes 'n git me some lye. Got a lot o' grease saved up 'n needin' to make some soap but jes' a-waitin' till it git a bit warmer out. Yo' a-wantin' me to git that hot toddy for yo', suh?'

'Seems as tho' with a house full o' servants some one might git it for me,' the old man grumbled, pulling the worn coverlet from the back of the chair over his shoulders. 'Do declare, the cold jes' seem to git in my bones this mornin'. Where Ham gone?'

She shook her head, not knowing how to answer him, as she had not overheard Hammond's plans for the day; but with a reassuring pat on his shoulder, and an adjustment to one of the pillows in his chair, she left the room. Her shapeless carpet slippers made no noise and, as she opened the kitchen door, she surprised Mem and Dexie who were standing by the sink.

Mem had his arm around the girl and she had unbuttoned the fly of his pants and was fondling him while he kissed her. They were too engrossed in their love play to have heard the door open; and Lucretia Borgia stood there for a small moment, watching them. She dashed across the kitchen like a demon, her hand upraised, and brought it down on Dexie's face; then lifting it again, she smacked Mem.

'Yo' slut!' She raised her hand again, but Dexie ducked. ' 'N yo', Mem! 'Pears like'n yo' kin git it up for Dexie, cain' yo'? Got a good mind to go right in 'n tell Masta Warren what goin' on out here the minute my back's turned. Yo' know what he'd do. He'd have yo' both hung up 'n strip the meat right off'n yore bones. 'Nuff to make a body puke, it is. Mem a-standin' there a-kissin' whilst yo' a-playin' with him. If'n yo' old 'nuff to fool 'round with Mem, yo' shore old 'nuff to git busted. High time yo' were too. Why ain' yo' got Masta's toddy ready, Mem?'

'Teakettle empty 'n havin' to wait for water to git hot.' He buttoned his pants. ' 'N yo' mind yore own business, Lucretia Borgia. Yo' too goddamn nosey. If'n yo' tells on me, I a-goin' to tell on yo' too. Knows yo' 'n that Erastus boy bin a-foolin' round. Saw yo' t'other mornin' out by the smokehouse. 'N yo' know that Erastus he a-coverin' Maybelle. What Masta Warren a-goin' to say if'n he knows Erastus a-wastin' his seed on yo'? What he a-goin' to say, huh?' For once Mem had the upper hand, and Lucretia Borgia had to accept it with as good a grace as possible.

She turned from them to the twins, who were sitting naked by the fire playing with their toes. 'Yo' two git yore shifts on! Yo' jes' so bad as yore papa. Shiftless like'n him. Ain' decent for house folks to go 'round nekkid as a jaybird.' She lowered her voice when she turned to face Mem. 'Go out 'n git some pine knots. Pore masta he a-freezin' to death 'cause yo' forgot to hotten up the fire in the settin' room. I'll make masta's toddy myself. Water's hot now, 'n sure ought to be with all the things a-goin' on out here. Ain' yo' 'shamed o' yo'self, Mem, lettin' Dexie pleasure yo' 'n yo' a grown man 'n she homely 'nuff to stop a clock?'

She went to a cupboard and took down a flint glass then went over to the broad shelf where there was a jug of corn whisky. She measured out a more-than-generous amount of the whisky, added a finger of molasses, filled the glass with hot water. She stirred it with her finger to mix the contents and to test the heat of the water. With a withering look at Dexie, she placed the hot toddy on a saucer, reminding her to pick the collard greens, wash them thoroughly, and put them to cook with a ham bone she had been saving.

' 'N wash yore hands good with soft soap 'n water afore yo' pick them greens. Yo' bin a-handlin' Mem 'n he always right stenchy.' With a swish of her starched white apron, she left them.

Once again her demeanour changed and she became all solicitude when she entered the sitting room and handed the toddy to Maxwell, who sipped it with gusto.

'Do declare, Lucretia Borgia, your toddies always taste better'n Mem's.'

'Yes suh, Masta Warren suh, 'n somethin' I bin a-wantin' to talk to yo' 'bout, if'n I kin,' she added.

'Knew yo' had somethin' on yore mind again already, Lucretia Borgia, or yo' wouldn' a-bin sashayin' 'round here, tendin' to the fire, gittin' me a toddy, fussin' over me. Yo' so damned nice that sweet butter wouldn't melt in yore mouth. Well, what is it? Thinkin' mayhap yo' wantin' me to have Mem whopped, but cain' spare him even for a day. What other deviltry yo' got on yore mind?'

With a bland look of injured innocence, she faced him, hands on hips. 'Why, Masta Warren suh, how yo' do carry on. Ain' a-thinkin' o' no deviltry. Jes' bin a-thinkin' that day after tomorrow, Masta Ham he a-goin' to have a birthday. He'll be sixteen 'n nigh onto a man. Plannin' on makin' him one o' my pound cakes; or do yo' think he'd rather have a fruit cake? Got plenty of raisins 'n currants 'n citron. Kin make him a fine one.'

'Kin make both, cain' yo'? Ham he mighty fond o' fruit cake 'n I like yore pound cake.' With the fire burning, the hot toddy in his hand, and Lucretia Borgia's mention of Ham's birthday together with her impending plans, he became jovial. 'When yo' a-goin' to git me another pair o' twins, Lucretia Borgia? Like to have two pairs. Thinkin' what it mean to Falconhurst to have two pair o' twins. Don' know if'n it yo' or Mem what brung 'em, but wishin' yo' git busy 'n make me another pair.'

'Ain' a-goin' to ever git yo' another sucker if'n I have to

186

depend on that Mem. All he kin do is turn over 'n go to sleep every night. He a-wastin' his sap on the wenches, ain' got none for me no more. Needin' me a new man, Masta Warren suh, if'n I'm ever a-goin' to bring yo' a new set o' twins.'

In his present mood Maxwell could deny her nothing. He promised with a sincere nod of his head that he would consider the matter.

She decided not to press her luck by asking for an immediate decision. Later she would be able to remind him of his promise. Just now she had something important on her mind, a favour she wanted for somebody else – rare for Lucretia Borgia – but it was for Ham, whom she worshipped.

' 'Bout Masta Ham's birthday, Masta Warren suh.'

'Well, what about it?'

'Kin I ask what yo' plannin' to give him for a present?'

'Yo' too goddamn nosey, Lucretia Borgia.' His feeling of amiability changed immediately. 'Whaffor yo' askin' me what I'm a-goin' to give my son for his birthday? Thinkin' mayhap I buy a nigger for him. Tha's what Ham likes best o' all.'

'A nigger?' She was disdainful. 'He got more niggers than he know what to do with. Got Audrey for a body servant; got Dite for a bed wench. He got me here, 'n he right fond o' the twins. 'Sides, the whole place cluttered up with niggers. Take a step 'n they underfoot. Whaffor he a-wantin' more?'

Maxwell rocked silently in his chair, staring up at her. He realized the truth of what she said; actually, he had not yet made any plans for his son's birthday present. Although niggers were Ham's life, the gift of another would not mean much to him. After all, the niggers at Falconhurst all belonged to him anyway. A gold eagle which he might give him for a present would be just another piece of money that he would not spend. Perhaps – just perhaps – Lucretia Borgia might know of something that Ham would like. Maxwell hated to ask her because he did not want to be faced once more with a display of her omniscience, but there were ways of getting it out of her without his asking her.

'Could send him into Benson 'n git him a new suit o' clothes. Tailor there right good, kin make him up a nice suit. How about blue broadcloth? That ought to look good on him.'

She regarded him as she would a man whose brains were more than a little addled. 'Now what Masta Ham a-wantin' a suit o' blue broadcloth for? Git it for him 'n before he gits a chance to wear it, he outgrow it. He a-growin' up mighty fast. He sixteen now. 'Sides, ain' never goin' no place to wear it anyway.' She pursed her lips together. 'They's somethin' he is a-wantin', though.'

Maxwell kept silent; damned if he was going to ask her what it was.

'Yes suh, Masta Warren suh,' she continued. 'They's somethin' he a-wantin' mighty bad but he ain' tol' yo' 'bout it. Yo' know Masta Ham. He ain' never hintin' 'bout things he a-wantin' less'n yo' say so first. Like yore thinkin' o' givin' him that Dite for a bed wench. He ain' never asked yo' but he mighty pleased that yo' thought 'bout it. Yes suh, Masta Warren suh, he mighty happy with that Dite.'

'Them twins a-comin' in here?' Maxwell knew if he waited long enough, he'd get out of her what Hammond wanted without having to ask a direct question.

'Jes' soon's they eat their breakfast 'n git dressed. Ain' havin' 'em run around nekkid no more. Ain' fittin' in the big house. All right in the quarters if'n they don' wear a stitch, but in here ain' respectable.'

'Likes 'em better 'thout'n them shifts yo' a-makin' them wear. Cute little devils they are, 'n cuter nekkid than with them god-awful shifts yo' put on 'em.'

'Did yo' see Masta Ham when he lef' the house this mornin'?' She had no desire to discuss the twins further and let Maxwell get her away from the subject on her mind.

He nodded. He always looked out of the front window, following his son with his eyes until he was out of sight.

'He a-ridin'?'

Again he nodded.

'Then yo' know he a-ridin' Ol' Bess. She 'n Tom Patch the

only horses we got here at Falconhurst, 'n Tom Patch he even older'n Bess. Got us hundreds o' niggers, but ain' got us one decent horse for Masta Ham to ride. Jes' t'other day, his friend Masta Lewis Gasaway o' Burnt Hill Plantation came by on a fine dapple grey stallion; Ham admirin' it, wantin' to ride it. Burnt Hill ain' no bigger'n Falconhurst, 'n ain' got no decent niggers nohow, but young Masta Lewis he kin have a fine horse, 'n he a year younger'n Masta Ham!'

'Took the words right out'n my mouth, Lucretia Borgia.' Maxwell rang the bell on the table beside him for Mem and another toddy. 'Was jes' a-goin' to suggest that I git Ham a new horse for his birthday. Mista Luke up at Twin Creeks he got some fine horses. Thinking I rides over in the surrey 'n see him. Be a nice surprise for Ham, it will.'

She smiled to herself. She had put her point over, and in such a way that Maxwell as usual felt he had thought of it himself. Ham would get the one thing he wanted most for his birthday – a horse of his own.

Mem shuffled into the room. 'Yo' rang for me, Masta Warren suh?'

' 'Course I did. How come it takin' yo' five minutes to answer?'

Mem turned to go without replying.

'Masta Warren he askin' yo' a question.' Lucretia Borgia was determined to put Mem in the wrong.

'Jes' a-waitin' for the water to git hot, Masta Warren suh, was a-goin' to bring yo' in another toddy 'thout'n yo' askin' for it.'

'Water's hot.' Lucretia Borgia faced him. 'Git out 'n wait on yore master, Mem.' When she heard the kitchen door close, she came even closer to Maxwell's chair. 'If'n yo' a-goin' to Masta Luke's, Masta Warren suh, kin I go with you? Be right proud to be there when yo' pick out Masta Ham's horse.'

He snorted in disgust. 'Ain' traipsin' 'round the country with no nigger wench! What yo' tryin' to do, Lucretia Borgia, make a baby out o' me? Why don' yo' make me up a sugar tit 'n rock me to sleep? How it look, a grown man

189

actin' as if he needed a wench to go with him? Got 'nuff bucks here to go with me. Mem, *he* kin drive me.'

This was the last thing that Lucretia Borgia wanted. It would be a feather in Mem's cap and if there was to be plumage in anyone's headgear it would be in Lucretia Borgia's alone. She realized too late that she had played into Mem's hand. Now he would have the pleasure of the outing and not she.

'Masta Willoughby, he always a-drivin' out with that wench o' his.'

'Mista Willoughby nigh onto eighty,' Maxwell asserted, ' 'n 'sides, if'n yo' a pretty young light-skin like'n her all dressed up in taffeta 'n bangles, wouldn't mind yo' goin'. But yo' ain' young, Lucretia Borgia, 'n yo're blacker'n a stove-lid. Ain' a-traipsin' round the country a-showin' *yo*' off.'

Luck was with her, however. She did not have to connive any further. Mem approached, the hot toddy in his hand. As he came into the sitting room, he caught his toe in the edge of the rag carpet, stumbled, and fell, spilling the toddy. He scrambled to pick up the glass, looked at the big wet stain on the carpet for a long moment, then without a word started back to the kitchen.

Warren Maxwell's eyes met those of Lucretia Borgia and she nodded in affirmation of what she knew he was about to say.

'That Mem!' Maxwell was so angry that he pounded on the arm of the chair, and this hurt so much that he howled. 'That goddam Mem! Clumsy, lazy, wuthless! Goin' to have Ham give him ten whacks with the paddle tonight. He shore a-goin' to be too sore to sit his ass in the surrey tomorrow. Better that yo' go with me, Lucretia Borgia. Right proud o' yo' I am, even if'n yo' not young 'n pretty 'n light-skinned. It bin a long time since yo' bin anywhere, 'n yo' kin swop recipes with Miz Luke's cook. Mayhap yo' learn somethin' new.'

'Kin help yo' pick out a horse for Masta Ham too.' She pulled the coverlet more snugly over Maxwell's shoulders. 'Mighty good judge o' horses, I am.'

' 'N niggers too?'

'Yes suh, Masta Warren suh. Niggers too. I'll tell Masta Ham that yo' wants Mem whopped tonight. Yo' a-thinkin' ten strokes 'nuff?'

'I'll tell him myself. Yo' jes' keep yore nose out'n my business, Lucretia Borgia. Let me handle this. Yo' go out in the kitchen 'n stir me up another toddy. Then yo' let those twins come in here, 'n go leach yore lye or whatever yo' have a mind to, but leave me 'lone. Do yo' hear? Leave me *'lone!*'

CHAPTER TWENTY

It was right after breakfast next morning that Lucretia Borgia appeared at the door of the sitting room dressed in her best black dress. It had belonged to Mrs Maxwell but she had begged it from Mrs Maxwell and Empie, the plantation seamstress, had let it out by inserting gussets and then patched and darned the worn places. Lucretia Borgia had prettied it up with a white lawn fichu, fastened with a brass breastpin which Mrs Maxwell had once given her. Today she was shod and freshly turbanned and her skin glowed from scrubbing. Ham had gone to the fields and Mr Maxwell himself was dressed in fawn-coloured trousers, a blue coat, and a brocaded waistcoat from which hung a massive gold watch chain with a large dangling seal.

'My goodness, Masta Maxwell suh, yo' shore do look scrumptious.' It was so seldom that Maxwell dressed up or went anywhere that Lucretia Borgia had forgotten how prepossessing he looked in anything but the butternut trousers and shirts he wore every day.

'Sent Mem out to the barn to have the surrey hitched up.' He smiled at her. 'Poor Mem, he a-limpin' pretty bad. Shore got a sore ass. Reckon Ham laid it on heavy last night. But it good for Mem. He ain' really a bad nigger, but he gits slothful. Needs touchin' up every once in a while, then he pretty good. Brought me in a hot toddy 'thout'n me askin' for it afore he left for the barn, so thinkin' that the whoppin' did him some good. Git me my hat, Lucretia Borgia.'

She handed him a white beaver hat, which she had brushed until it was smooth and glossy. Maxwell put it on and then tried to get out of his chair. He had considerable difficulty and when Lucretia Borgia offered him her arm he did not decline. Together they walked out onto the gallery. Mem was standing by the surrey, holding the horse's head. He looked sad and woebegone.

'How yo' a-feelin', Mem?' grinned Maxwell. 'Feelin' like fallin' over yore big toe again soon?'

'No suh, Masta Warren suh. It an accident. Didn't do it on purpose. Got somethin' for yo', Master Warren suh.' He limped up to the gallery, took a steaming glass and handed it to his master. 'Thought yo' like'n a toddy to start yo' on the way, Masta suh. My ass still sore but kin drive for yo' today if'n yo' a-wishin'.' He eyed Lucretia Borgia in the splendour of black dress and red headcloth. He also noticed that she wore shoes instead of her shapeless every-day carpet slippers. 'Feelin' mighty sore but kin drive for yo' jes' the same. Don' make me no neverminds, if'n yo' wants.'

Maxwell shook his head as Lucretia Borgia helped him into the back seat of the surrey. 'Lucretia Borgia she's a-goin' with me. Ain' said nothin' to Masta Ham that we a-goin'. It a surprise for him, seein' as his birthday a-comin' up. If'n he asks where we are, jes' tell him Lucretia Borgia 'n I drove in to Benson to get some things.'

Mem was dumbfounded at his master's starting off with Lucretia Borgia but he knew enough not to ask questions. The ten strokes with the paddle that he had had the night before were a sufficient reminder to keep his mouth closed and not butt into his master's business.

Lucretia Borgia unfolded the plush laprobe and tucked it around her master's legs. Then she cramped the wheels and

192

climbed into the front seat, removing the whip from its socket and proudly taking up the reins, slapping them against Old Tom's back to get him started. He ambled slowly down the drive to the main road, but once there, Lucretia Borgia managed to urge him into a trot. This was a most eventful day for her; the first time she had been away from Falconhurst in many months. More important than anything else was the fact that she alone had been chosen to accompany her master on this mission. It served to enhance her standing among the other folk at Falconhurst. Gradually she was achieving the position she had long struggled for – that of being the third most important person on the plantation.

There were no other big houses between Falconhurst and the little hamlet of Benson. A few slab-sided cabins crouched on small farms where poor white farmers were trying to wrest a living from the land. The only crop they seemed able to raise was tow-headed children, who clustered round the steps of the cabins or worked with their fathers to rid the land of stumps so that it could be planted to cotton. With the privileged eye of a slave who was owned by one of the leading families, Lucretia Borgia looked down on these poor whites and considered that black slave though she was, hers was the better lot.

'Mighty triflin', some o' these white folks,' Lucretia Borgia turned her head to speak to Maxwell. 'Do declare they live worser'n our niggers. Look at that.' She pointed her whip at a particularly disreputable cabin where a bedraggled white woman sat on the rickety porch, pawing over a mess of greens. Tall weeds grew around the cabin except for a patch of muddy water where slops were thrown out. Two children were playing in the mud and all looked up as the Maxwell carriage passed. The children waved but the woman looked at them with bitterness and envy.

Warren Maxwell waved back at the children. 'But they white, Lucretia Borgia, don' forgit that. White man may be poorer'n Job's turkey. May be so poor he don' have a pot to piss in or a window to throw it out of, but he still white 'n so

193

he better'n any nigger in the world. He's free, he is. Cain' nobody buy him nor sell him.'

'Yes suh, Masta Warren suh. Reckon yo're right.' And he was. It made no difference how much a coloured person had, they did not have that one thing – that one precious and in- alienable thing – that a white man had: freedom. She herself, regardless of how she had schemed and played her petty politics to be at the top of the ladder at Falconhurst, was nothing more than a chattel. She had already been sold twice. If Maxwell wished, he could sell her tomorrow; up- root her from all her familiar life and sell her to anyone. Instead of feeling contempt and scorn for the bedraggled figure on the porch, she began to envy her. Why was it that the colour of one's skin could make such a difference? Why was she, Lucretia Borgia, a servant for life? Why? Just be- cause she was black. She knew that she was intelligent, that her mind worked faster and better than most, but what did it avail her? She could never have that one glorious possession – freedom.

Bah! She banished the thoughts from her head. What did she want to be free for, anyway? She didn't want to exist in abject poverty with snotty-nosed children grubbing in the dirt outside a sway-backed cabin. She had everything she wanted. She was happy as things were, happy at Falconhurst with Masta Warren and her beloved Masta Ham. Who could ask for more than she already possessed? She wouldn't trade places with that poor woman for anything in the world. She fingered the breastpin at her fichu and smoothed down the skirt of her black dress. She was Lucretia Borgia of Falcon- hurst Plantation and that was good enough for anyone.

When they arrived at the town of Benson, Maxwell had her drive up to the tavern, which was kept by a man strangely named Pearl Remick. She pulled Tom Patch up to a stop and cramped the wheels to help her master down; instead, he told her to go inside and ask the owner to come out. She found him standing behind his zinc-covered bar, more than a little surprised to see a decently dressed coloured woman coming through the door. When she told him she was from Falconhurst and that Mr Maxwell was outside and wanted to speak with him, he wiped his hands on a dirty towel and came out from behind the counter, almost running to the door. The Maxwells were important people and he was more than ready to serve them.

'Mornin', Mista Remick,' Maxwell reached down a gnarled hand to shake the other's. 'Sort of choked up with the dust 'n wonderin' if'n yo' could fix me up with a drink o' corn. Bin afflicted with rheumatiz, else I'd git down 'n come in, but it right hard for me to git around. 'Preciate it, suh, if'n yo'd bring it out to me.'

Remick swiftly disappeared inside while Lucretia Borgia climbed back into her seat. In a moment he was back with a glass of whisky, which Maxwell sipped slowly. 'Mighty fine corn, Mista Remick.' He rolled a mouthful appraisingly on his tongue. 'Mighty fine. Don' know when I've tasted any as good. Yo' got any to spare?'

'Kin let yo' have a keg, 'n honoured, Mista Maxwell.'

'Thank yo'. We'll pick it up later.' Maxwell, strengthened by the whisky, bade Remick a hearty farewell and urged Lucretia Borgia to slap up Tom Patch. They had a distance of about eight miles still to travel and Maxwell was anxious to get there, get his business over with, and return home. He made so few trips away from Falconhurst that he did not care to be travelling about. Home was the best place to be.

Tom Patch at his best was not a speedy horse and it took them over two hours to arrive at Twin Creeks. Lucretia Borgia was agog with interest and excitement. She could see from the long avenue of live oaks that led up to the big house and framed the white wooden pillars that Twin Creeks was a much bigger and handsomer house than Falconhurst; but when a shuffling old Negro who could scarcely walk came down the steps to take their horse, she was abruptly contemptuous. Twin Creeks must be a pretty poor place if *he* was all they could afford.

A white man in a rocking chair on the gallery got up and came down to the surrey. He did not recognize Maxwell immediately but once he did was all hospitality. His statement that he was honoured by Maxwell's presence was altogether sincere, as was Maxwell's acceptance of it.

After the formalities of greeting and the mutual inquiries as to the health of the various members of each family, Maxwell hitched himself forward in his seat. 'Rheumatiz a-botherin' me somethin' awful, Mista Luke, so if'n yo' don' mind, I won't git out here but we'll drive down to the barn. My business with yo' is down there, 'n ain' up to walkin' so far.'

A woman appeared on the gallery and hurried down to the surrey to shake Maxwell's hand. 'Why, Mista Maxwell! What a pleasure! Yo'll stay for dinner with us, won't yo', after yo' gits through with yore business with Mista Luke? Heard yo' say yo' had rheumatiz 'n know how a body kin suffer with that. I'm having one o' the servants take a chair down to the barn so's yo'll be able to set comfortable-like whilst yo' do yore business with Mista Luke.'

'Thank yo', ma'am. Right thoughtful o' yo'. It'll be a pleasure to stay for yore midday meal. I don' git out much these days 'n will enjoy eatin' someone else's cookin', though I must say we have a good cook at Falconhurst.' He gestured towards Lucretia Borgia. 'This the wench right here; yo'll have to come over sometime 'n try her meals.'

'She kin eat in the kitchen with our cook Ophelia.' With another pleasant bow to Maxwell she went back up onto the gallery, turning to watch as Lucretia Borgia slapped at Tom Patch for his short journey to the barn, followed by Mr Luke and a small coloured boy toting a rocking chair bigger than he was.

Once out in the barn and ensconced in the rocking chair, Maxwell stated his business. He had come to buy a horse as a present for his son's birthday, and he complimented Luke by saying that he had the best horses for miles around. Naturally he was not looking for anything cheap.

Mr Luke nodded in agreement as Maxwell stated his business.

'Yo' come at the right time, Mista Maxwell. Jes' three days ago, Miz Luke 'n I returned from New Orleans, where

I took a drove o' horses down for sale 'n bought a few more to bring back. Got some fine ones for yo' to look over. I'll have my boy bring 'em out. All stabled they are, so's I won't have to send out to the pasture for 'em. 'A wave of his hand indicated the long row of box stalls in the barn. At his call, a white-polled Negro came out of a stall to stand at attention before his master. Luke ordered him to bring out the horses, one by one.

There were ten horses for Maxwell to choose from. These included three powerful stallions, five mares, and two geldings. Of one of these, a chestnut stallion, Luke seemed inordinately proud. He had all the horses paraded before Maxwell, stopping each one and going over it with his hands, explaining its fine points. Maxwell agreed they were a fine lot of horses but protested that he did not want a stallion.

'Ham he only sixteen, 'n I fear one o' them big brutes be too much for him. Like the mares fairly well, I do, but somehow don' quite like to give my boy a mare. 'Sides we ain' in the horse-raisin' business. Niggers is our crop. Now if'n I a-buyin' niggers, would want them stallions 'n the fillies too. Got good blood lines, all o' 'em. Jes' now I'm leanin' towards that geldin'. He 'bout the best-lookin' horse yo' got. Ain' too big, 'n yet big 'nuff. 'Pears he gentle too, 'n I like the white star on his forehead. Right smart-lookin' horse he is.'

To Lucretia Borgia, who had alighted from the surrey and was now standing at a respectful distance behind Maxwell's chair, it appeared that buying a horse was just about the same as buying a nigger. True, Mr Maxwell did not examine the horse himself, as he would a nigger buck or wench. He let Mr Luke do that for him. Perhaps buying a horse was not quite so important as buying a man or woman.

'That a fine horse,' Luke nodded in agreement. 'He the most expensive o' the lot.'

Maxwell disregarded the reference to price. 'Don' hold much with geldin' either a horse or a nigger. Gelded niggers, particularly light-skins, are in demand in New Orleans. Usin' 'em for house servants, they are, so's the ladies o' the house don' have to be fearful 'bout gittin' raped by some randy nigger. All foolishness if'n yo' ask me. Give a nigger a wench to cover 'n he not interested in pesterin' any white woman. No, don' hold with geldin' niggers. Poor bastards ain' got much in life 'cept eatin', sleepin', 'n fornicatin'. We ain' never gelded no nigger at Falconhurst 'n don' intend to. The randier they gits the better we like it, 'cause we always got plenty o' wenches for 'em to cover. Tha's our business, Mista Luke.'

'Know it is. Know yo' got some o' the best niggers 'round; that somethin' I want to talk to yo' 'bout, once we get this horse deal over. Don' know as I hold for geldin' niggers either, but as for horses, that's different. A gelded horse, he mighty gentle. Takes all that randiness out'n him when he 'round mares. Yo' know what a stallion's like when he needin' a mare. But now this Starfire, tha's his name 'cause o' the star-shaped blaze on his forehead, yo' git all the strength 'n beauty on a stallion with none o' their orneriness.'

Maxwell asked that the horse Starfire be brought out again and the hostler paraded him up and down several times on the barn floor, then mounted him bareback and trotted and galloped him out in the yard. Maxwell continued to nod his head in approbation. He knew he was going to buy this Starfire, regardless of how much he cost and he was ready to start bargaining when the plantation bell began to toll.

'Time for dinner.' Luke motioned for the man to put Starfire back in his stall. 'Cain' be late, Miz Luke she always upset if'n we don' git there on time. But want to offer yo' a drink o' corn afore yo' go in. Miz Luke she temperance, 'n don' allow corn in the house. But I ain', so keep it out here in the barn; she a-knowin' it, but never a-sayin' anything.' He walked to a cupboard in the wall and taking out a demi-john, poured two glasses. This time Maxwell did not sip but followed his host's lead and gulped it down as quickly as possible.

Lucretia Borgia, who had remained in the background, yet near enough to hear everything, went towards Maxwell,

but he waved her away. 'Kin walk, I kin.' He did not want
Luke to see that he was in any way dependent on others,
especially a woman. He got up from his chair with some
difficulty and started hobbling towards the house. They were
halfway there when Luke stopped, turned around and called
back to Lucretia Borgia.

'Go 'round to the kitchen,' he indicated a path, ' 'n tell
Ophelia that yo' a-goin' to eat with her.' He resumed his
slow pace with Maxwell. 'Reckon as to how yo'll have to
take pot luck today. If'n we'd a-known yo' was comin',
would have had somethin' special.'

'Anythin' yo' got's fine.' Maxwell was puffing from his
efforts. 'Jes' fine. Still thinkin' 'bout that geldin'.'

'Kin see him 'gain after we eat.' Luke slowed his footsteps
to accommodate those of Maxwell. ' 'N by the way, remind
me to show yo' something else I brought back from New
Orleans. Know yo' interested in niggers, 'n I got something
special.'

'Always like to see something special in the way of a
nigger.' They ascended the two steps to the gallery and
passed through the open front door into the cool semidarkness of the house.

CHAPTER TWENTY-ONE

Lucretia Borgia betook herself up the path from the barn to
the kitchen door. As at Elm Grove, the kitchen was a separate building, connected by a covered passageway to the
house. She congratulated herself that the Falconhurst kitchen was an integral part of the house, so that she was better
able to keep things under her thumb. She could always overhear the dining-room conversation and was an avid listener.
Mem had even greater opportunities, because he was present

while the Maxwells were being served, but he paid little attention to their talk. As long as the matter did not concern him personally, he was not interested; but for Lucretia Borgia, everything was of interest, to the slightest detail.

The kitchen door was open and a horde of flies buzzed in the doorway. Aware of the proprieties, Lucretia Borgia knocked on the door jamb before entering. She wouldn't like a strange nigger wench barging into *her* kitchen without warning. An elderly woman with a fleece of white kinky wool on her head – were all the Negroes at Twin Creeks old and white-haired, Lucretia Borgia wondered – looked up from the hearth where she was kneeling to transfer pork chops from a tripod iron skillet to a blue-and-white Stafford-shire platter.

'Who yo'?' She paused to take in Lucretia Borgia's decent black dress, her white fichu, and the red headcloth. 'Who yo' come a-knockin' at my door jes' as I'se gittin' dinner on the table?'

'I'se Lucretia Borgia, ma'am.' She could be polite when the occasion demanded it, though it was rarely that she condescended to politeness with one of her own colour. 'Servant to Mr Warren Maxwell, I am, 'n he a-eatin' in the dinin' room. Masta Luke he done say I take my repast with yo' out here in the kitchen. He a-sayin' yore named Ophelia. Tha's a right pretty name.'

'Huh!' Ophelia grunted, getting up to her feet with some difficulty and placing the platter on the kitchen table. 'Zeb,' she called, all the time appraising her caller. 'Come 'n git it. White folks a-waitin' for their dinner 'n yo' ain' nowhere around.' The ancient man who had answered the front door came down the passageway into the kitchen.

'Miz Luke askin' yo' to git down a jar o' them damson plum preserves her sister in Kentucky brought down when she comed.'

Ophelia wiped the sweat from her face with the corner of a dirty apron. 'Jes' one thing after 'nother. First off we have company for dinner 'n have to set the table all over with the weddin'-ring china. Then this nigger wench she a-comin' to the door a-sayin' she a-goin' to eat here. Now yo' a-wantin' plum preserves 'n yo' a-knowin' they down in the spring-house. How'm I ever goin' to git dinner on the table?'

'Kin I git 'em for yo', Miz Ophelia ma'am?' Lucretia Borgia was not only polite but unctuous. 'If'n yo' tell me whereat is the springhouse, kin jes' run down there 'n git 'em for yo' 'n yo' don' have to trouble yo'self none.'

Ophelia shoved the platter of pork chops towards Zeb and with her hands on her hips surveyed Lucretia Borgia. At first she had thought that this was going to be an uppity wench, but now she changed her mind. 'Miz Ophelia ma'am' and the offer to help mollified her. Her manner changed.

'Yo' mighty gracious, Miz Lucretia Borgia ma'am.' She could in her turn be equally polite. 'Shore would 'preciate that. Cain' miss it. Jes' follow the path to the barn 'n turn left by the cabins. Springhouse right there. Them preserves Miz Luke a-wantin' in a crock on the top shelf. Ain' so big's the other crocks where I keep my watermelon pickle, 'n kinda brown coloured.'

A brief glance at the kitchen had convinced Lucretia Borgia that things here were not as prosperous or pro-gressive as at Falconhurst. The floor was merely a puncheon floor, uneven and dirty. The furniture was sparse, and cer-tainly the battered table top did not have the snow-white scrubbed appearance of her own. The Falconhurst kitchen was far bigger, lighter and more pleasant, and she was glad she could return to it. As slothful as Mem was, he was several cuts above the doddering old Zeb who served here. But she would be gracious to this Ophelia and she'd even offer to help with the washing-up, hoping, however, that it would not take her too long; she was determined to get back to the barn by the time Maxwell and Luke were ready to discuss business.

She followed Ophelia's directions and came to the string of cabins, ramshackle affairs. On the steps of one, a dodder-ing old crone was sitting, gumming her food from a tin plate while she talked with a man who was even older than she. The springhouse on her left was only a slab-sided shack, and

201

water had made the ground around it muddy. In the dim light she had difficulty in locating the right jar of preserves, then nearly slipped on the slimy rocks as she went out the door.

She pursed her lips and harrumphed in disgust. Regardless of how impressive the big house of Twin Creeks looked from the front, with its white pillars and avenue of trees, it was certainly a different story round at the back. Paint was scaling from the clapboards, one window had been boarded up, and the stink from the open-doored privy was enough to make a person ill. Weeds and wild roses were growing in the backyard, and had certainly not been scythed in years.

And as for the niggers! Those she had seen were a poor lot. They all looked ready to die and she wondered how Luke got any work out of them.

However, she was surprised to find in the kitchen a fairly attractive coloured wench of about twenty-five whom Old Ophelia introduced as Vivian and explained that she helped out in the kitchen when it was necessary. Lucretia Borgia acknowledged the introduction with just the right amount of condescension. This Vivian, with her torn and dirty osnaburg dress, was not a peer of Ophelia. She was only a helper; therefore she must not be treated as an equal, but as an inferior, and Lucretia Borgia's curt nod put her in her place.

Doddering old Zeb had taken the tray into the dining room and Ophelia, with a bow worthy of a *grande dame*, indicated a place at the kitchen table for Lucretia Borgia to sit. She was somewhat surprised to see that while she had been gone, two places had been set at the table, each with a gold-banded china plate, cup and saucer. Of course the second place was for Ophelia, who sat down and indicated Lucretia Borgia's with a wave of her fringed napkin. Here in the kitchen, Ophelia was queen and she demanded that Vivian wait on both of them, although, looking at Vivian's dirty hands, Lucretia Borgia would have preferred to wait on herself.

To her trained palate, the dinner was far from successful. Evidently they had recently butchered a hog, and although

202

the pork chops were fresh they were fried so carelessly that the fat around the edges was either undercooked or burned black. The corn bread was soggy and the white-flour biscuits were hard and crusty. For dessert they had a rice pudding which had wheyed and had neither sugar nor cinnamon enough to suit Lucretia Borgia's taste. She hoped that Maxwell would appreciate her cooking all the more after this meal away from home. She wondered how people of Mr and Mrs Luke's supposed wealth and importance could put up with such miserable cooking. Perhaps they didn't know anything better. Well, she would show them if they ever came to visit Falconhurst. As for Maxwell's suggestion that she trade recipes with Ophelia . . . bah! What could she learn from her?

As she ate, Lucretia Borgia observed all the niceties of manners she had ever seen her various mistresses use. She held her teacup with her little finger elegantly crooked; she cut her meat into small pieces with her knife and used her fork to transfer it to her mouth; she even wiped her plate clean with a crust of biscuit. Ophelia, sitting across from her, hogged down her food, using her fingers more than her knife and fork, taking up the greasy pork-chop bone and gnawing on it with her stubs of teeth. Conversation was at a standstill during the meal, except when Zeb came to ask Vivian to replenish a dish, get more butter, cream for the coffee, or fill the sugar bowl.

After the meal was finished, however, Ophelia pushed her chair back, leaned her elbows on the table and started the gossip that was always so joyfully indulged in between servants. First she was anxious to know how it was that Lucretia Borgia accompanied her master instead of a man. 'Ain' yo' got no bucks on yore place?' she asked disdainfully, as though the Maxwells were poor white trash, too poverty-stricken to afford a single male Negro.

'Bucks?' Lucretia Borgia cackled in a shrill falsetto. 'Bucks, Miz Ophelia ma'am? Tha's all we got at Falconhurst. 'Bout a couple hundred o' 'em, I'd say, 'n all young 'n healthy, bustin' out with sap. Got us a lot o' wenches too.

Ain' no old bucks nor wenches at our place. No sir-ee.'

'Then why . . . ?' Ophelia stared across the table at her guest.

'Then why Masta Maxwell he have me drive him over here? 'Cause he depends on me, tha's why. Masta Maxwell he don' even do nothin' less'n he talk it over with me. Don' even draw a long breath, he don'. It my idea to buy a horse for young Masta Ham for his birthday, 'n Masta Maxwell he a-sayin' I better go 'long with him so's he be sure 'n git the right horse for Masta Ham. Like'n I told yo', he don' do nothin' less'n he askin' me.'

'Uh-huh!' Ophelia was outwardly impressed, although she felt sure that Lucretia Borgia was stretching the truth. To change the subject, she shouted, 'Yo' there, Vivian, git a-stackin' these dishes 'n if'n yo' breaks one o' Miz Luke's best weddin'-ring chiny, yo' a-goin' to git waled.'

'Yes ma'am.'

' 'N if'n yo' ever tells Miz Luke that we et off the good chiny plates, I'll wale yo' myself.'

Lucretia Borgia appraised Vivian as she bustled about the kitchen. 'She a good strong wench. How come she ain' knocked up? How many suckers she had?'

Ophelia shook her head dismally. 'Nary a one. She plumb man crazy too, 'cause she ain' never bin busted.'

'At her age?' It was unbelievable to Lucretia Borgia.

'Ain' never had us a buck on this plantation what kin do it. We all old folks here 'ceptin' four-five wenches like'n Vivian. Masta he always a-sayin' that he git some buck from yore place to stud 'em if'n Mista Maxwell allowin' him, but never got 'round to it. Horses is all he think about. Jes' horses! He right willin' to git stallions for the mares, but no studs for the wenches. But all that a-goin' to be changed now.'

'How?' Lucretia Borgia demanded. 'If'n yo' ain' got no bucks, how yo' gits the wenches knocked up?'

Ophelia smirked, a triumphant little grin. 'Ain' a-sayin' we ain' got no buck *now*. Ain' never had one, but Masta 'n Missus they jes' got back from N'Orleans 'n brought a buck home with them. Finest-lookin' boy I ever did see, must be mighty good 'cause Masta Luke he swopped three o' his best horses for him.'

'Do tell.' Lucretia Borgia was all ears; the conversation had taken an intriguing turn. Anything to do with men was of interest to her. 'He good-lookin' yo' say?'

Ophelia closed her eyes and waggled her head in a pantomime of ecstasy. 'Jes' wishin' I forty years younger. Even gives an old wench like'n me the itch to look at him, with his britches a-bulgin' out at the crotch.'

'He well hung, uh?' Lucretia Borgia was even more interested, so much so that little points of light danced in her eyes.

'Mus' be. Masta put him first to Amy Lou 'n she bin a-walkin' spraddle-legged ever since.'

Not to be outdone, Lucretia Borgia countered with, 'We got plenty bucks like'n that at Falconhurst. 'Course I beds down with Mem, our house servant, but I gits a chance every once in a while to try 'nother one out. Mem he a-gittin' dreaned out 'cause he a-pesterin' most any wench he kin git to. If'n Masta Warren cotch him, Mem a-goin' to git the biggest whoppin' he ever had.'

'Yo' whop much at Falconhurst?' Ophelia changed the subject abruptly. 'We never do no whoppin' here. Masta he talk a lot 'bout it but never do nothin'. Cain' remember when we had a proper whoppin'. Nothin' 'ceptin' a little whoppin' with a horse whop that don' 'mount to a hill o' beans.'

'Whops nearly every day at Falconhurst.' Lucretia Borgia lied boldly to impress the other woman. 'Masta Maxwell, he right strict he is. One thing makes him madder'n anything else. He mate up a buck 'n a wench 'n he ain' havin' no other buck touch that wench till she knocked up. Cotches any pesterin' in the grass or in the fields, he whops plenty. Whops wenches too if'n they triflin' with any buck.'

Ophelia stared at her with mouth agape and eyes wide. 'Whops wenches? *Yo'* ever git whopped?'

Lucretia Borgia gazed back, with disbelief that any sane

person should ask such a question. 'Do *I* ever git whopped? What foolishment! Why, sometimes Masta he lets me do the whoppin', specially if'n it a wench, but he ain' a-whoppin' me. No sir-ee! How kin he do that? Didn' I tell yo' I'm Masta Maxwell's right hand? He dependin' on me. He ain' never doin' nothin' at Falconhurst, nor Masta Ham neither, less'n they talk it over with me.'

Zeb shuffled into the kitchen with a tray of dirty dishes. With difficulty he set them down on the broad shelf and caught his breath. 'Masta Luke 'n t'other white man, they a-goin' out to the barn now. Man a-goin' to buy that geldin' what Masta Luke set such a store by.'

Lucretia Borgia pushed her chair back from the table. 'Gotta git started. Mighty 'bliged for the dinner, Miz Ophelia ma'am, 'n sorry I cain' stay to help yo' straighten things up, but my masta he a-needin' me.'

'If'n we'd a-known yo' folks comin', would of had a company meal,' Ophelia apologized. 'Sorry I didn' have a chance to bake a cake for yo'. Or a pie. Masta says my pecan pies the bes' he ever et.'

Lucretia Borgia shuddered inwardly at the thought of any pie that Ophelia might make. She started for the open door, bowing to Ophelia with just the right amount of respect mingled with condescension, then turned and spoke to the old woman. 'What the name o' that boy Masta Luke jes' bought?'

'He got a funny name,' Ophelia answered. 'Ain' rightly like'n any name I ever heard afore. Name Omar. Talks funny too.'

'Right peculiar name,' Lucretia Borgia agreed, and hastened down the path. Whatever was going to happen in the barn, she wanted to be there and know about it.

CHAPTER TWENTY-TWO

Maxwell and Luke were so engrossed in the chestnut gelding that neither of them noticed Lucretia Borgia when she tiptoed into the barn. She was afraid that her shoes might give her away; her old carpet slippers made no noise in the rooms at Falconhurst, so she could go almost anywhere without detection. But fortunately, the shoes did not squeak, nor did the boards of the barn floor protest as she walked over them, and she was able to take up a position in the cobwebbed shadows where she could hear but might not be noticed.

Maxwell himself was going over the horse and, although she knew he couldn't judge a horse as well as he could a nigger, she was glad he was doing it. This Starfire seemed by far the best horse that Luke had but good as it was, it couldn't be too good for her dear Masta Ham.

Now that Luke and Maxwell had arrived at the matter of price, she knew that the sale was a *fait accompli*, because Maxwell never started haggling until he was determined to buy. She had seen it happen dozens of times, when itinerant slave traders came to Falconhurst and happened to have a sapling or two that seemed promising.

Luke started by asking four hundred dollars for the horse. Starfire was, he informed Maxwell, part pure Arabian. Although Maxwell was an authority on the blood lines of the Negroes he purchased, he knew little about horses, and the fact that the gelding had Arabian blood meant nothing to him. He countered with an offer of three hundred dollars, but Luke was adamant. Even 'splitting the difference' did not cause him to change his mind.

'Tell yo' what I'm a-goin' to do,' Luke said. 'Yo' ain' really seen this horse perform rightly yet. I'm a-goin' to show yo'. First let me tell yo' somethin'. Jes' got back from N'Orleans like'n I bin a-tellin' yo'. Took a big drove down for sale and brought back a few, but this time I bought somethin' more'n horses.'

'Like'n what?'

'Like'n a nigger.'

'A nigger?'

'Yes suh, Mista Maxwell. The finest nigger I ever did see. Going to use him for stud, 'n raise me some fine niggers. Got four good wenches all needin' a stud, so bought me this one. Cain' rightfully call him a nigger though I reckon.'

'What do yo' mean, cain' call him a nigger? Yo' bought him, didn' yo'? He a mustee, yo' mean? Ain' got no damned use for mustees myself. They got too much human blood in 'em. Tricky, they are.'

Luke shook his head. 'This un ain' a mustee, but ain' rightly a nigger neither. He got black blood in him, tha's shore, but he ain' all black 'n he ain' part white neither. Man what sold him to me tol' me he half Mandingo 'n they ain' full-blooded niggers. They more Arab than nigger, accordin' to this man.'

Maxwell sprang up from his chair. Momentarily he forgot his pain. Luke had just spoken a magic word to him. '*Mandingo.*' All his life he had wanted a Mandingo. They were, as he himself had often said, as scarce as hen's teeth, but they were without a doubt the finest breed that had ever come out of Africa. Not only were they superb in physique and handsome in looks, but they were gentle and docile as lap dogs. A Mandingo! He had never expected to see one and even if this one was only part Mandingo, that was better than nothing.

'A Mandingo, yo' say?' He was so excited he could hardly utter the words. 'Whereat is he? Want to set my eyes on him. Always bin a-wantin' to see a Mandingo, but never had the chance.'

'He ain' a purentee Mandingo, Mista Maxwell,' Luke cautioned. 'Maybe half, maybe a quarter. Bought him from the man I bought my horses from. Seems these Arabs they mighty good with horses, 'n this man got him right off'n a ship from Africy. Wantin' him to work as a hostler. This boy only bin in N'Orleans 'bout a year 'n he cain' talk too good, but he understands mos' everything yo' say to him.'

Maxwell sank back into the chair, conscious now of the pain in his joints. 'Got to see him, Mista Luke, jes' *got* to see him. Bin a-lookin' for a Mandingo for years 'n ain' never seen nary a one. Would certainly admire to lay eyes on him. Kin I?'

'He in the upper pasture, herdin' some colts what I have. Was goin' to send up for him 'n have him put this Starfire through his paces.' He called to the old groom and told him to ride up to fetch Omar. 'Tell him it all right to leave them colts for a while 'n ride back down here soon's he kin.' The old man ducked his head, saddled a horse, and was gone.

Lucretia Borgia shared Maxwell's interest in Mandingos. They had been a topic of conversation between Maxwell and Ham ever since he could remember and she was as curious as Maxwell to see one of these super-beings. A Mandingo – or at least half a Mandingo! Well, half was better than nothing.

Maxwell harrumphed and cleared his throat. 'Shore do want that geldin', Mista Luke, 'n tell yo' what I'm a-goin' to do. I'm a-goin' to offer yo' two hundred dollars cash for that horse. Now jes' a minute,' he raised his hand as Luke started to protest, 'that ain' all.'

Luke leaned forward while Maxwell sank back in his chair. 'That ain' all?' he asked anxiously.

'No it ain'. I bin a-lookin' at yore servants 'n I don' see no young saplin's a-runnin' round like'n it usual on a place this size.' He peered out the barn door to where, on most places, there would have been two or three adolescents, sweeping the driveway with twig brooms or pulling up weeds.

'Tha's true, Mista Maxwell, tha's why I got me this Omar boy. Got some wenches what are fillies 'n jes' a-waitin' to be broke to the saddle, 'n thought with this Omar a-ridin' 'em, I'd have a crop o' suckers a-comin' along.'

'Good thinkin', Mista Luke. Don' do to let a herd run out whether it horses or niggers. Saplin' 'round ten or twelve years old be a good thing for yo' cause he be ready to start

209

ridin' the wenches come a few years. So, I give yo' the pick o' my young saplin's along with the two hundred dollars for the horse. Saplin's run 'round three hundred dollars – specially good ones like'n mine – if'n yo' buy them at a vendue, so that makes 'bout five hundred dollars for the geldin'.'

Lucretia Borgia knew just the boy that Luke should have. He was about thirteen, a well-set-up youngster with a budding interest in wenches; she made a mental note to recommend him to Maxwell when they started home. His name was Watts and he'd be a good boy for Luke. She watched Luke settle back in his chair. He was nodding his head in thought, considering the proposition. It was a good one, he knew, but he didn't want to give in to Maxwell too soon. It was a matter of pride that the dickering should not end at once. 'A saplin', uh?'

Maxwell nodded.

' 'N I kin pick him out?'

Again Maxwell nodded.

It took Luke only a few moments more to make up his mind. He rose from his chair and went over to Maxwell and proferred his hand. 'Sold, Mista Maxwell, 'n it lookin' like'n I'm gitting the better o' the bargain.'

Maxwell grinned up at him. 'Thinkin' so myself, but I want that horse for my boy. See yo' got a nice saddle over there 'n bridle too. Reckon yo' could throw those in to boot. Ain' never doin' no tradin' less'n I gits somethin' to boot.'

'Reckon I could. Saddle jes' 'bout right for a growin' boy. We'll make it a deal. Yo' wantin' a bill o' sale?'

Maxwell shook his head.

'Gentlemen's agreement, Mista Luke. We friends 'n neighbours. Reckon yo' ain' a-comin' after me sayin' I stole the horse.'

'We'll seal it with a drink.' Luke got up and went to the cupboard to fill two glasses with corn. This time they sipped it slowly, although Maxwell was on pins and needles, shifting his weight in the chair and looking up from time to time towards the doorway to see if the groom had come back

210

with the Mandingo whom Luke had been talking about. If he was any good at all, Maxwell had already made up his mind to have him regardless of cost. True, he had heard that a mixture of Mandingo with any other blood produced a mean and uncertain-tempered progeny, but he put that down to superstition. There were so few Mandingos on the market, and so little was known about them, that he didn't believe all he heard. He did know that they came from northern Africa and that they were, as Luke had said, more Arab than Negro, though considered in the same category as the true Negroes. Everyone seemed to know about them but nobody had ever seen one. Well, now *he* was going to see one. He'd surely be able to make a deal with Luke, of that he was certain. Luke didn't have a decent buck on his whole plantation and surely Maxwell had plenty at Falconhurst to barter with. Besides, Falconhurst bucks had a reputation that was equal to that of Mandingos, although it was not quite as legendary. People could see and judge Falconhurst bucks, whereas Mandingos lay mostly in the realm of fancy and hearsay.

They sipped their drinks quietly without speaking. Each felt that he had made a good deal on the horse. Maxwell's place was overrun with saplings and one more or less did not make much difference. He'd got the horse he wanted at a low price with a saddle and bridle to boot. On the other hand, Luke was equally satisfied. He had a fair price for the horse and he would have a Falconhurst boy who would soon grow into a man and be an additional stud on his plantation. He wondered if he shouldn't make an offer to Maxwell to buy one or two adolescent wenches so that when the time came, the boy would be able to cover them.

Lucretia Borgia saw the silhouettes of two horsemen, black against the sunlight that streamed in the open barn doors. Even from their outlines it was easy to tell the old groom from the other rider, who sat straight and tall in his saddle. She heard the thud of the horses' shod hooves as they walked across the barn floor and saw the men dismounting. The hostler led the horses to a stall; the other came over to stand before Mr Luke.

211

She was entranced. She couldn't help moving. She walked from the shadows to stand by her master, who was so engrossed in the newcomer that he did not notice her. But no matter how occupied Maxwell might be with this man, Lucretia Borgia was even more excited. He was without a doubt the most beautiful man she had ever seen. Her eyes bulged from her head as she looked at him and she could feel the saliva gathering in her mouth and dribbling from the corners of her lips, so great was her desire for him.

He bowed before Luke and with his right hand touched his forehead and then his chest by way of greeting. Every movement that he made was easy, as though he was conscious of his own grace but realized he did not have to exert it. He wore a pair of osnaburg trousers and a ragged shirt but wound around his head was a turban, not unlike that which Lucretia Borgia wore, except that his was snowy white.

'Masta,' he said. His voice was low, powerful and musical.

'Yes, Omar,' Luke acknowledged his salaam. 'Mista Maxwell here a-wantin' to see yo'. Tol' him that you were Mandingo, 'n he never laid eyes on a Mandingo afore.'

'My father, he Arab,' Omar said, bowing slightly in Maxwell's direction and showing a flash of white teeth in a smile. 'My mother, she Mandingo.'

'Goddamn good combination.' Maxwell leaned forward in his chair. 'Mista Luke suh, would yo' be askin' this boy to shuck down. Wantin' to look at him.'

'Afore yore wench?' Luke pointed to Lucretia Borgia, now standing behind Maxwell's chair.

He turned quickly. 'Now what in hell yo' a-doin' here, Lucretia Borgia? Thought yo' was up at the house a-helpin' with the kitchen work.'

'Thinkin' mayhap yo' need me, so come down here.'

'Well, yo' kin jes' go back again. Skedaddle! Ain' no place for a wench nohow. No,' he reversed himself at once, 'don' go. Yo' knows near as much 'bout niggers as I do. Yo' seen plenty o' naked bucks in yore time, but never no Mandingo; if'n yo' keep yore big mouth shut, yo' kin stay.'

She kept silent. She would have done anything to see this

212

man stripped down, so great was her desire for him. Luke ordered Omar to shuck his clothes; with an easy movement, he unbuttoned his trousers and let them fall to the floor. He shrugged out of his frayed shirt just as effortlessly, to stand before them stark naked. He unwound his turban and let his hair fall to his shoulders. It was glossy black and wavy and except for his superb physique, would have given him an effeminate appearance.

Lucretia Borgia could not avoid an 'Oh' of admiration, but Maxwell gave her no heed. He was looking at one of the most perfect specimens he had ever seen. He beckoned for Omar to come to him.

Although he was a slave and technically a 'nigger', he was not negroid. His complexion was dark olive, and while he was tall and powerful, he was not large-muscled. There were no bulges on his body, where one muscle flowed into another, and yet there was the suggestion of great strength in the slender frame. Lucretia Borgia noted the width of his shoulders and the powerful chest on which the paps were emblazoned like copper pennies. Between them there was a thatch of black hair that flowed down his body to the triangular patch of hair in his crotch. This was long and silky instead of sparse as in a true Negro. Lucretia Borgia's gaze was riveted on his genitals. He was heavily endowed, but the first thing she noticed was that he had been circumcised, and the nakedness of the deep purple-black glans fascinated her. It was difficult to move her gaze upward to his face.

His head was supported on a strong, slender neck. He lacked the round cheeks of a Negro. Instead, his face was narrow and the high bones caused his cheeks to appear almost hollow. The nose was slightly aquiline and his fine nostrils dilated with each breath. Sooty arched eyebrows curved above his eyes, which were dark brown with nearly blue whites. His lashes were so long that they almost hid his eyes.

Lucretia Borgia saw Maxwell's misshapen hands delicately appraising the wonderful body, sliding down over the smooth, hairless skin of his arms and then losing themselves in the luxuriant growth of hair on his chest. His fingers prodded the hardness of the belly and then crept down into the pubic hairs. His hands lifted the man's testicles and weighed them, then encircled his prominent manhood and squeezed lightly.

'Bin cut, ain' he?' Maxwell observed.

'They a-tellin' me that all them Arabs git cut when they boys. Don' hurt their breedin' none. Matter of fact, some say it a-makin' them better breeders.'

'So I've heard tell; so I've heard tell.' Maxwell motioned for Omar to turn around so he could examine his back and spread his buttocks. He then motioned for him to turn around and kneel before him so that he might run his fingers around inside the man's mouth.

'Got all his teeth. Ain' more'n twenty-two or twenty-three, would yo' say?'

Maxwell did not go through the usual procedure of throwing a stick to see the man's coordination in retrieving it. It was unnecessary. He was well aware of the perfect musculature and coordination of this superb body. He signalled to Omar that he was through with his examination and the fellow returned to slip into his clothes.

'I want that nigger,' Maxwell stated unequivocally. 'I'm goin' to have him one way or 'nother. Bin wantin' a Mandingo all my life 'n this one's the nearest I'll ever git. Yo' a-wantin' to sell him?'

Lucretia Borgia held her breath while she waited for Luke to answer.

'Ain' had it in mind,' he finally said, 'but always open to an offer. Bought him for two reasons. First, he knows all about horses. Got a hand with 'em, he has. Second, bought him to stud my four wenches. Got to raise me a new herd. Most of the niggers we got here were heired by either Miz Luke or me 'n they all a-gittin' old. Stock a-runnin' out. Figured I'd git some good suckers out-a him.'

'Any good buck kin git good suckers,' said Maxwell. 'We got some at Falconhurst that are prime – yes sir-ee, prime! Better'n him in many ways. He kinda slim, not too well

214

muscled out. Yo' should see some o' the boys we got. Powerful bucks what kin work all day in the field 'n pester the wenches all night.'

Luke nodded his head. 'Know about yore niggers, Mr Maxwell. Finest niggers in the South. But too expensive for me.' He paused a moment. 'How come if'n yo' got so many fine ones, yo' a-wantin' this one?'

Maxwell shrugged his shoulders. 'Jes' a notion o' mine. Bin aimin' for a Mandingo buck for twenty years 'n this the nearest I ever come to it. Figures this boy would bring 'bout three thousand dollars on the New Orleans market particularly if'n he sold as a fancy.'

Luke's eyes opened with surprise. He had traded three horses – fine ones to be sure – for the man, but at the most that would make about twelve hundred dollars.

'Three thousand, yo' say?'

'Give or take a few hundred.' Maxwell could not take his eyes from the man, nor, for that matter, could Lucretia Borgia. Now that he had his pants on, she gazed in wonderment at the heavy bulge in his crotch. He became conscious of the concentration of her gaze and responded, so that the thin cotton of his trousers clearly outlined his excitement. Maxwell noticed it too. 'Goddam quick on the trigger, ain' he? Even an old wench like'n Lucretia Borgia gits him rared up.'

'He bin a-coverin' one of my wenches 'n she say he mighty forceful. Kin keep on goin' all night. Guess he got plenty o' sap 'n some to waste.'

'Ain' no sap ever wasted at Falconhurst,' Maxwell affirmed. Both men lapsed into a silence which to Lucretia Borgia seemed interminable.

Finally Maxwell said, 'How 'bout a trade? I'll give yo' two o' my finest bucks for this one. My boys bring two to three thousand at private sale. Tha's four thousand at least for this one buck. Mighty costly, but tooken a notion to him 'n want him. That'll give yo' two fine Falconhurst studs, both o' 'em better for raising field hands than this one. He too fancy for a field hand, 'n I'm takin' it that's what yo' want.'

Luke could scarcely find the words to answer him. To be the owner of two Falconhurst bucks was beyond anything he had ever dreamed. Except that this Omar had a knowledge of horses and was a young and potent male, he had no particular attachment to him. The fact that he was part Mandingo meant nothing more to Luke than if he had been part Ashanti or Ibo. So, if Maxwell was fool enough to offer him two Falconhurst bucks for this one, he'd never be so lucky again. He could visualize the pride with which he would show them off. *Two* Falconhurst bucks! Man alive! That was something to make a man proud.

'Agreed,' Luke finally found the word. 'We'll shake hands on this one too.'

'Give yo' a bill o' sale, I will.' In his enthusiasm, Maxwell forgot entirely to ask for anything to boot. 'It always better to have a bill o' sale when dealin' with niggers, 'case anythin' comes up.' They shook hands and Luke made an appointment to drive over to Falconhurst and pick out his bucks and his sapling. The formalities over, the whole matter adjusted to mutual satisfaction, the old hostler hitched up Tom Patch to the surrey, and Luke helped Maxwell into the back seat. Lucretia Borgia climbed up in front but left the driver's seat vacant for Omar, who understood from Mr Luke that he had been sold to Maxwell. He seemed undisturbed by the news and asked only that he be allowed to fetch something that belonged to him. When he returned, he had a leather-bound book under his arm. He got in the surrey and took up the reins.

They cantered down the long avenue of trees with Starfire hitched to the back of the surrey. Soon Maxwell was fast asleep, his head nodding with the motion of the wagon. Lucretia Borgia caught Omar's eye and he smiled. She returned his smile and watched as he stretched out his legs as far as the cramped quarters of the surrey would allow. It was a direct invitation for Lucretia Borgia to place her hand on his thigh. She could feel the warmth of his flesh through the thin material of his trousers. Slowly she inched her hand up

216

his leg. He peered straight ahead through lash-veiled eyes, his body quivering.

Her hand encountered the throbbing hardness of his flesh and she fumbled at the button of his trousers but before she had a chance to undo it, Maxwell awoke. 'Don' forget to stop at the tavern for my corn!'

Lucretia Borgia replied with a disappointed 'No, Masta Warren suh,' and although she hoped he would drop off to sleep again, frequent glances told her that he was awake. They reached the tavern and Maxwell sent Omar in to get the keg of whisky.

When they were nearly home, Lucretia Borgia turned in her seat. It took a moment to summon the courage to speak. 'Masta Maxwell suh?'

'What yo' a-wantin' now Lucretia Borgia? We got us a horse for Ham 'n a nigger too. What more yo' want?'

'Ain' askin' yo' many times for somethin' for myself, Masta Warren suh, but if'n I kin, would like to ask yo' for somethin'. Kin I?'

'Ain' a-sayin' as how yo' a-goin' to git it, but go ahead 'n ask anyway.'

'Masta Warren suh, kin I have this Omar boy for myself, Masta suh? Have him bed down with me in the kitchen? Mem he ain' no good no more 'n I shore do cotton to this boy.'

Maxwell harrumphed with disdain. 'Answer's no, Lucretia Borgia. Yo' think I'm a-goin' to waste this boy's sap on an old wench like'n yo'? Not by a damn sight! If'n I cotch yo' a-foolin' round with him, yo're a-goin' to git the skin waled right off'n yore ass. Mean it, I do, so be careful 'n don' fool round with him. I know yo' too well, Lucretia Borgia, I know yo' man-crazy; but this boy's one yo' ain' goin' to have. Tha's *final*, 'n yo' remember it or yo' goin' to git whopped. Don' hold with whoppin' wenches, but promise yo' I'll whop yo' if'n yo' so much as touch him.'

She sighed and turned around in her seat. 'Yes suh, Masta Warren suh. I 'members.'

217

Had they not arrived home long after dusk that night, they could not have put the horse and the new slave into the barn without Ham's knowledge. He would have insisted on trying out the new horse and examining the new slave at once. Probably the slave would have come before the steed; as much as he might be interested in a horse of his own, it would have been the magic word Mandingo that intrigued him the most.

But they arrived after dark and Hammond, bored with sitting alone, had gone to bed. It was far more interesting being in bed with the willing Dite than it was being alone downstairs. He had dallied vigorously with her, not once but twice, and was asleep from utter exhaustion when they arrived.

Lucretia Borgia helped Maxwell out at the steps of the gallery and got him into the house while Omar waited in the surrey. Maxwell told her to show Omar how to get to the barn, and unhitch the horses, and stable them; she asked permission to do it a little later. Despite Maxwell's threats, she knew that she had to have a few moments alone with this paragon of slaves before she came back to sleep in the kitchen beside Mem.

'Thinkin' yo' better have a bite to eat afore yo' go to bed, seein' yo' ain' had no supper.' She flew to get it for him. A stoneware plate with some fried chicken was in the Dutch oven keeping warm, and a pot of coffee was on the trivet by the hearth. With a plate of chicken in one hand and a coffee cup in the other, she went back into the sitting room.

'Ain' much but 'nuff to keep yo' from starvin'. I'll go out in the barn later 'n tell that Omar boy whereat he kin put the horses 'n where he a-goin' to bed himself down.'

Maxwell looked up at her and smiled a knowing grin. 'Won' take yo' more'n a quarter of an hour to do it all, Lucretia Borgia, yo' black Jezebel, 'n if'n yo' more'n that,

I'll know yo're a-pesterin' with Omar. Know yo' cain' wait to spread yore legs for him, but if'n yo' do, I'll whop yo' myself. Ain' havin' him waste no sap on yo'. Yo' hear me?'

'What wench yo' a-goin' to have him cover?' She thought it best to divert his thoughts to another channel.

'Ain' none o' yore damned business, Lucretia Borgia. Have him cover any wench I wants 'cept yo'.' He answered between bites of a chicken leg.

She delayed a moment before answering him. 'Was a-thinkin' that Queenie wench be a good one for him. She part human 'n got straight hair. Shore, she bin a-busted, but that don' matter. Better she has, 'cause he shore hung heavy. She's had two suckers already so's she cotch all right. Give us a fine sucker, seein' as how they both good-lookin'.'

He sucked the bone clean and laid it back on the plate. 'Yo' jes' keep yore nose out'n my affairs. Tha's all I'm askin' from yo'. Bin a-thinkin' 'bout Queenie myself, but ask Ham's opinion first.' He changed the subject again. 'How we a-goin' to surprise Ham tomorrow mornin' with his new horse?'

'Got it all worked out, Masta Warren suh. A-goin' to git up afore daybreak 'n git things started. Askin' yo' now, kin I git some clean clothes for that Omar boy. He ain' got nothin' but them rags yo' bought him in, 'n he don' look too pert in 'em. Wantin' him to look special when Masta Ham a-seein' him first.'

Maxwell nodded assent, and asked her to help him upstairs before she went out in the barn. More than anything else he wanted to get into bed.

She did as she was told, first dashing to the door to bid Omar wait a little longer. With her assistance Maxwell got up the stairs and onto his bed. She pulled his socks and trousers off, divested him of shirt and stock and left him in his underwear. All the time she was helping him she was conscious of Omar sitting in the surrey, not knowing where to go or what to do. Now, with Maxwell in bed, she was free to go. She lit a tallow dip and put it in the lantern in the kitchen, put some of the warm food on a plate, and went out the kitchen door.

He was still in the surrey, his head nodding in sleep. She got up beside him and headed the horses toward the barn. He awoke there and got down to untie Starfire, removing the bridle and saddle and putting him in the vacant stall that Lucretia Borgia pointed out to him. With the noise the other boys that slept in the barn awoke, and Lucretia Borgia had them unharness Tom Patch and pull the carriage back into its space, with the thills roped up so that they hung from the ceiling.

This done, she sent them all back to the straw on which they were sleeping, but beckoned Omar to follow her. They both went out of the barn, guided by the circle of light from the lantern, down towards the sewing and weaving shed where she knew new shirts and trousers were kept for the men. Once inside, she closed the door quickly, then cast the rays of the lantern around the room to make sure that nobody was sleeping there for the night. She went to a pile of finished men's shirts and took out two or three. Holding them against his broad shoulders, she found one that fitted him. Then she tackled a pile of trousers, all the same osnaburg that he was wearing, but new and clean.

Instead of holding up the trousers to see if they fitted, she bade him take off the ragged ones he was wearing and try on several pairs to see which would fit him the best. He slipped out of his pants and, conscious of Lucretia Borgia's intent gaze, responded with an erection.

Unabashedly she stared down at it, her eyes riveted on it, watching it become more and more rampant. She looked up into his eyes, saw the invitation there, and was almost tempted to yield to it when she bethought herself of Maxwell's threat. To be sure, she *was* Lucretia Borgia and she *was* a factotum at Falconhurst, but she could not forget the threat of a whipping, for she knew that he would keep his word if she disobeyed him. She had never been whipped in her life and the very thought of it made her cringe.

Well, she had been forbidden to sleep with Omar, but that

220

was the only thing she had been forbidden. There were other acts that could be done and although they would not satisfy her, they would satisfy Omar, and she would experience a vicarious thrill. At least it would give her desiring fingers a contact with that warm hard flesh, which attracted her more than any she had seen before. Perhaps it was because she had never before seen a man who had been cut.

She moved closer. Her fingers touched his face, outlined his lips, crept down his chin to touch his throat and over his chest through the fine hair. They proceeded down, to lose themselves in the long, silky hair of the groin, so different from anything she had seen or felt on a man before. Her fingers grasped and squeezed and she could feel his body quiver and arch under the impact of her strong fingers. She was not gentle in her manipulations; she sensed he did not want gentleness, but force. Her hand moved, clutching strongly and forcefully, and then, as she increased the tempo of her movements, his arm came around her shoulders. He was breathing hard and she realized he was near to spending himself, so she stopped but did not relax her hold.

'No.' He was hoarse. 'No, no, no!' His words were scarcely audible. He sucked in his breath. 'More! Hard!'

She resumed her movements, clutching him with an iron fist, her hand moving fast. She was aware of the approach of his ecstasy as soon as he was, and she could not halt the motion of her hand. It happened. The candlelight showed the long arc of the hot fluid, but still she did not release him until he had completely spent himself. Then she reluctantly let him go and felt his weight against her as though he needed her for support.

'Is good,' he finally managed to mumble.

'Well, yo' keep yore mouth shet about it,' she warned. 'Promised Masta Warren I wouldn't let yo' pester me, 'n I haven't; but he be mighty riled if'n he know yo' wasted your sap all over the sewing room floor.' She gave him a scrap of tow linen to clean himself with and then picked up a pair of pants which she thought might fit him.

'Here, try these on.'

He slipped into the trousers. They fitted well and she took them, along with the shirt, and slung them over her arm, bidding him put on the old trousers and shirt which he had worn. She led him back to the barn, pointed to an empty stall where there was fresh straw, and told him to sleep there but to awaken early in the morning, wash at the watering trough, dress in his new clothes and await her there.

She took up the lantern and returned to the kitchen. She saw that Mem had returned. He was stretched out on his back on the shakedown, snoring loudly. The embers of the fire had not died out and he had thrown off the blanket they used to cover them. Although he was still wearing his shirt, he had taken off his black trousers and except for the shirt he was nude. She lifted the lantern the better to look at him.

Mem was still a good-looking fellow and fully as potent as the boy she had just been with. A little surge of her old feeling for Mem welled up in her and she blew out the tallow dip in the lantern and undressed by the dying light of the fire. Ascertaining that the twins were all right, she knelt on the floor and crawled in beside Mem. Her hands moved over his body and she felt him becoming tense while he struggled between sleep and wakefulness.

She snuggled up to him and his arm came around her. 'That yo', Lucretia Borgia?' he asked sleepily.

'Yes, Mem, I'se here.'

His lips sought hers and she was surprised at their ardency. 'Shore bin a-missin' yo' 'round here today, Lucretia Borgia. Somehow this place awful empty 'thout'n yo' a-bustlin' round 'n Masta askin' for his toddies. Quiet as a grave, it was.'

'Glad yo' missed me, Mem.' Her hand for the second time that night discovered male rigidity.

He was fully awake now. He eased her over onto her back and mounted her. He seemed like the old Mem, the one she had been in love with when she first came to Falconhurst.

'Les' take it slow 'n easy tonight, Lucretia Borgia. Ain' had me no lovin' – no real lovin' – for a long time. Them wenches fine for a quick pesterin' in the weeds but they ain''

222

like'n yo'. Mayhap if'n we take it slow 'n easy we git Masta 'nother set o' twins tonight.'

'Slow 'n easy it is, Mem.' She clutched at him. 'Shore like to git Masta 'nother set o' twins. He be mighty proud.'

Their bodies moved in unison. The last smouldering embers flickered out and the room was in darkness. There was only the sound of their movements, of Mem's strained breathing and Lucretia Borgia's whimpers of encouragement. Then, after a while, there was silence.

'Thinkin' that shore a-goin' to bring Masta 'nother set o' twins,' Lucretia Borgia whispered finally.

Mem did not answer. He was already fast asleep.

CHAPTER TWENTY-FOUR

The next morning, Lucretia Borgia was up before dawn. Shivering, she took some shavings, fat pine knots and one or two substantial sticks, and arranged them in the fireplace. She struck a light from the old tinderbox, blew it into a flame and applied it to the shavings. The kettle on the crane was already full of water and while she waited for it to heat, she stepped outside.

She heard a twittering of birds in the live oak tree behind the house. In the dim light of early morning, Lucretia Borgia descended the gallery steps and walked across the grass, her bare feet wet with the heavy dew. Since Mrs Maxwell's death there had been little attention paid to the flower garden, which had once done much to offset the drabness of the big house. Unlike cotton or slaves, flowers did not contribute to the prosperity of the plantation, and although she might have a passing glance of admiration for a rose or a geranium, Lucretia Borgia would never think of picking one or cultivating it so that it might produce more blooms.

Many of the plants, however, which Mrs Maxwell had so carefully tended had managed to survive, choked though they were by weeds and grass. These Lucretia Borgia descended upon ruthlessly, and plucked every bloom until she had a big mound of dew-drenched flowers on the gallery before the kitchen door.

Inside she heard the lid of the big iron teakettle rising and falling with the steam and she went inside. Grabbing a rag so as not to burn her hands, she tilted the kettle to pour some of the hot water into a basin, diluted it with cold, took off her dress and with a rag and some soft soap went over her body, drying herself on a well-bleached flour sack. Once again she donned her dress, went over and nudged Mem with her toe until he got up. She decided to let the twins sleep a while longer so that they would not be underfoot. There remained an hour before she had to prepare breakfast for the Maxwells. She went back onto the gallery and moving the heap of flowers over to the steps, she sat down to work on them. With painstaking effort, she wove them into two garlands, one considerably larger than the other. There was the scarlet of geraniums, the purple of heliotrope, the waxen white of tuberoses, the magenta of petunias. They were a riot of colour against the weatherbeaten boards of the gallery, and she was satisfied with her work.

She heaved herself up and carried the garlands into the kitchen, hiding them under the big kitchen table. Then Alicia having arrived to help her, she set about to prepare a more elaborate breakfast than usual with ham and waffles – how Alicia hated to hold the heavy long-handled waffle iron over the coals! Instead of frying the eggs, she made them into an omelette, delicate and crusty brown around the edges.

When she heard Maxwell descending the stairs, she went to help him, seated him in his chair in the dining room, and whispered to him. 'Don' be surprised, Masta Maxwell suh, if'n yo' hears the bell a-ringin' when yo' 'n Masta Ham finishes breakfast. Wantin' all the folks to come up to the house to wish Masta Ham a happy birthday.'

'Ring all the damn bells yo' want to, Lucretia Borgia. Jes' so long as Ham a-goin' to like that horse.'

'He shore a-goin' to like it, 'n he a-goin' to like that Omar boy too.'

'That ain' rightly a birthday present,' Maxwell grumbled, helping himself to the delicately brown waffles that Mem brought in.

'But why don' yo' give it to him anyway?'

Maxwell considered for a moment, hearing Ham approach. 'Kin do,' he whispered to Lucretia Borgia, who disappeared into the kitchen. No sooner had Ham entered the dining room and commenced on his breakfast than the plantation bell pealed out.

The cabins, barn, and sheds erupted streams of plantation folk all shouting at the top of their lungs. They gathered in a wide semicircle around the gallery steps that led to the kitchen door.

'What's a-happenin'?' Hammond was alarmed at the clamour.

Maxwell smiled, reaching his gnarled hand out to Hammond. 'Nothin', son, 'ceptin' it yore birthday 'n all the folks are wantin' to wish yo' a happy birthday, jes' like I do. Happy birthday, son.' Maxwell's handclasp was firm and affectionate.

' 'N me too!' Lucretia Borgia, panting for breath, was back in the dining room. She went to Ham and embraced him. 'Happy birthday, Masta Ham suh, happy birthday to yo'.'

' 'N another happy birthday.' Mem came in from the kitchen with the twins. Each held a posy of flowers tied with twine. They ran and presented them to him, then clung to his legs and tried to scramble into his lap.

Ham could not sit still to finish his breakfast, despite the special care Lucretia Borgia had taken with it. He extricated himself from the twins, jumped up and ran around the table to embrace his father, then hugged Lucretia Borgia and kissed her soundly on the cheek before he ran onto the gallery to accept the best wishes of the Negroes. His father

225

hobbled after him, then Lucretia Borgia came to stand behind him.

'Happy birthday, Masta Ham suh!' A chorus of voices arose to greet him. 'Happy birthday to our Masta Ham.'

They heard the booming of a big drum, which one of the men had made from long-ago memories of drums in Africa, and the barn doors opened wide. All the blacks made a wide path from the barn to the house. Out dashed a horse, resplendent with a wreath of flowers around his neck, ridden by a black man who, in addition to the wreath of flowers around his own neck, sported a snowy white turban. In the short distance between the barn and the house, he forced the horse into a gallop, stopping and wheeling so abruptly at the steps that it seemed they would both crash headlong. The rider gave a long ululating shriek, turned the horse to face Hammond, and slowly dismounted to stalk up the steps, making a low salaam before Hammond, and present him with the reins. He uttered a few words in a strange language, accompanied by a smile and a flash of white teeth.

'Happy birthday, son!' Maxwell clapped his hand on Ham's shoulder. 'Hope yo' a-goin' to like this new horse o' yourn. He called Starfire, 'n he the best I could find. He's gelded, but that better for a boy like'n yo'. Yo' don' want no randy stallion what's too hard to handle.'

Hammond turned and kissed his father.

'Thank yo', papa. Shore is a scrumptious horse. But who that nigger a-ridin' him? Ain' never seen him afore. He new?'

'Jes' 'nother birthday present, son.' Maxwell beamed. 'What do yo' know, this buck's half Mandingo. Yes siree, son! Half purentee Mandingo! Bin lookin' all my life for a real Mandingo, but this one's half, 'n that better'n nothin'. He half Mandingo 'n half Arab: his dam Mandingo 'n his sire Arab. Bought him from Mista Luke yesterday, when I bought the horse. Mista Luke bought him in N'Orleans, 'n he ain' bin here long. Cain' talk too good, but understands mos' everything yo' say to him.'

Ham descended the steps to pat Starfire on the neck; but as much as he admired the horse, he could not take his eyes

226

off the man. His interest, however, was diverted by the shouts from the Falconhurst blacks. Mr Maxwell's birthday wishes had cued them again and now from all sides came an even louder roar of good wishes. 'Happy birthday, Masta Ham, happy birthday!' He waved his hand and stepped back onto the gallery. Looking behind his father, he saw Lucretia Borgia, now resplendent in a stiffly starched white apron.

'Lucretia Borgia,' he had to talk loud to make himself heard above the crowd. 'We got any o' them lemon drops 'n hoarhound drops from las' Christmas?'

She nodded her head. 'Still got a lot left.'

'Then git 'em 'n have all the folks line up 'n give one to each o' them.' He hushed the throng. 'Thank yo' all for yore good wishes. I'm sixteen now, 'n reckon I kin take over more of the work here 'n help my father. Yo' all good niggers 'n a credit to Falconhurst and . . .' He hesitated, could think of nothing more to say, but stood looking down on them and smiling. Finally words came to him and he gestured to the steps. 'If'n yo' all lines up, Lucretia Borgia she a-goin' to pass out lemon 'n hoarhound drops for all o' yo'. Don' wan' no pushin' nor shovin'. Everyone a-goin' to get his. Then yo' all go back to work.'

Acknowledging all the well wishes with a wave of his hand, he turned to his father and helped him down the gallery steps. 'Le's go out to the barn, papa. Kin yo' make it?'

'Shore kin, boy.' Maxwell straightened up and made an effort to keep in step beside his son.

Hammond beckoned for Omar to follow, and he led Starfire at a slow pace behind the two. In the barn, Hammond placed a splint-bottomed chair in the sunny doorway for his father, stood momentarily admiring his birthday present, then went up and patted the smooth sleekness of Starfire's neck.

'Yo' shore a beautiful horse, Starfire.' His words gentled the spirited animal. 'Yo' 'n me goin' to be good friends.' He turned to his father. 'Goin' to ride him down to the road, papa, jes' to git the feel o' him.' He swung his leg up over the saddle and motioned to Omar to hand him the reins. He

227

walked the horse out, and then trotted slowly past the line of slaves, to whom Lucretia was doling out lemon and hoarhound drops. Once past them, he slapped the horse's rump, causing him to break into a gallop. Horse and rider sped down to the road, then turned to trot back to the barn. He handed the reins to Omar again.

'He a bit skittish, papa.' Ham's underlip protruded in some doubt, 'but mayhap jes' because he nervy with a new rider. Think I kin calm him down, 'n thinkin' he likes me already.'

'Mayhap it them damn posies 'round his neck what makin' him skittish. Horse ain' used to doo-dads like'n that.' Maxwell pointed to Lucretia Borgia's wilting heliotrope and roses.

'Then take 'em off,' Ham commanded Omar, ' 'n take them off yore own neck too. Ain' much sense for man or beast to be a-wearin' flowers.'

'It Lucretia Borgia's idea,' Maxwell chuckled, 'she all up in the air about yore birthday. Wantin' yo' to have this horse 'n now she a-sayin' that I give yo' this nigger for a birthday present too. Ain' much sense in that – he yourn anyway.'

'Like to think o' him as a birthday present, though, papa. Yo' a-sayin' that he half Mandingo.'

'Sayin' jes' that.'

'Calls himself Omar?'

'Right. Damn funny name, but that what Mista Luke a-sayin' it is.'

Ham dragged another chair across the floor to stand it beside his father's.

'Bin a-itchin' to finger him, papa.'

'Don' blame yo'; I was too.'

'Yo', Omar!' Ham called. 'Come over here.' He pointed to the floor in front of his chair. 'Take off them flowers what yo' got strung 'round yore neck 'n take off that white cloth yo' got wound 'round yore head.' Ham was impatient. 'Then shuck down.'

At the man's look of incomprehension Ham shouted,

'Take off yore clothes. Want to finger yo' like my papa did. Cain' do it with yore clothes on.'

With a look of inquiry to see if he were doing the right thing, Omar removed the circlet of flowers and then unwound his muslin turban. Ham noticed that he folded it carefully, as he also did the clean shirt and trousers he was wearing. Then naked, his hand shielding his genitals, he came over to stand before Hammond and his father.

'Take yore hand away. What yo' tryin' to hide?' Ham pushed the shielding fingers aside. 'If'n we wants to look at yo', we looks at all of yo'.' Ham stared at him for a long minute, during which he appraised Omar from head to foot, then bade him turn around. He nodded to his father.

'He's good, but he ain' so hefty as I'd like him.'

'He got good lines,' Maxwell countered. 'He like'n a race horse. Don' need no bulgin' muscles. He strong 'n well set-up.'

Ham shrugged his shoulders in half-agreement. Then he got up and ran his hands over Omar's back, turning him around to do the same on his chest, then down to his calves and his feet.

'Don' fancy so much hair on a nigger.' Ham seemed bound to find some fault with the man, although he was actually pleased with him.

'Tha's cause he's no regular nigger. He part Arab, yo' know.'

'Well, he ain' got a blemish on him,' Ham finally admitted proudly, ' 'n he damned good-lookin' too.'

' 'N he hung heavy; going to make a good breeder, that boy is.'

'But he cut.' There was a slight objection in Ham's voice.

'All the better, they say. Make better breeders when they cut.'

Ham went on with his examination. As he had not been with his father when the man was purchased, he felt that he had to raise some objections, although he was proud and pleased that his father had bought him. Now he was more thorough. When he had finished, he pointed to a sack of middlings leaning against the feed box.

'Heist that,' he ordered.

Omar walked over and picked up the sack, which weighed about a hundred pounds, swung it up and over his shoulder. He carried it easily across the barn floor, then waited for Ham's orders to put it down. Ham nodded and the sack slipped to the floor.

'He good 'n strong,' Ham admitted. 'Lookin' like'n we got us a good stud, papa.'

' 'N half Mandingo,' the old man beamed.

'Yo' a-thinkin' it all right to mate him up with our wenches? Heard yo' say a hundred times that it bad to cross a Mandingo with another breed.'

'*He* bin crossed: he nigh onto perfect, ain' he?'

Ham nodded. 'Who yo' a-thinkin' o' havin' him cover?'

'Bin a-thinkin' o' Queenie. She light-skinned, got straight hair, 'n pretty's a picture.'

'What kinda work we put him to? 'Pears like'n he too good for a field hand. Cain' see him a-choppin' cotton.'

'He's an expert with horses.' Maxwell remembered Luke's statement. 'Bin around horses all his life. Goin' to have him here in the barn to work, 'n he kin bed down in Leul's cabin with Queenie. Who a-coverin' her now?'

'Noah, but she ain' cotched yet.'

'We ain' never got no sucker out'n Noah yet. Bin a-thinkin' he sterile,' Maxwell said thoughtfully. 'Take Noah away from her. If'n yo' helps me back to the house, I'll tell Lucretia Borgia to take him down to Leul's cabin.'

Hammond, after seeing that his father was ensconced in the rocking chair in the living room, went out to the kitchen. 'Right nice birthday presents I got, Lucretia Borgia.' Ham smiled at her and then put his arms around her. 'Yo' 'n papa shore picked out some nice things for me. A horse *and* a nigger, 'n both o' 'em the best.'

She grinned. 'Yore papa did it. I didn't have a word to say, but thinkin' he did pretty good. Now yo' git out'n here, Masta Ham suh. Ol' Lucretia Borgia she a-stirrin' up a pound cake for yore birthday dinner 'n if'n yo' keep botherin' her, she a-goin' to forget somethin'.'

He laughed loud and heartily. 'Ain' never a-goin' to come the time when Lucretia Borgia she forgettin' nothin'.' He departed for the barn. She was happy. She knew that he had the two things he had been wanting – a horse and a Mandingo, or at least a half-Mandingo. She hoped some day he would have a purentee Mandingo. My! If a half-Mandingo was as handsome as this Omar, what would a purentee Mandingo be like?

CHAPTER TWENTY-FIVE

Lucretia Borgia had rarely suffered from the pangs of jealousy. Tonight, however, when supper was finished and Maxwell gave her instructions to take Omar down to Leul's cabin and have him cover Queenie, she experienced an unfamiliar emotion. Yes, she had to admit to herself that she was jealous. She wanted to take Queenie's place. True, she had been denied Omar, and had been threatened with a whipping if she let him pester her. Although she felt secure in her position, and knew that Maxwell would never have her whipped, still it was the first time in her life that she had ever been threatened. She dreaded the actual pain of the whipping itself – she had seen often enough what it had done to others – more than anything except the diminution of her prestige at Falconhurst. That, indeed, would be far worse than the actual pain. But now, at the command to take Omar down and introduce him to Queenie, she could scarcely bear the jealousy. She did not, however, allow her feelings to show on her face; her only response was a bobbing of her head and a murmured, 'Yes suh, Masta Warren suh.'

Having supervised the clearing up and assured herself that

Alicia was working satisfactorily, she went out to the barn in the fading daylight. She regretted now that she had suggested Queenie; she could have bitten her tongue off. She was, she realized now, all too quick to offer suggestions just because she wanted to run everything. It would have been several days before Maxwell or Ham came up with the right wench with whom to pair Omar off. 'Damn it!' she said.

When she reached the barn, she entered through the big open doors to see a most unusual sight. The men and boys who lived in the barn were all standing around in a mute semicircle, watching Omar, who was babbling in some incoherent tongue which she could not understand and alternately kneeling and prostrating himself on a dirty sack spread out on the floor. It did not seem right to interrupt him, so she, along with the others in the barn, stood mutely regarding the spectacle.

She was relieved when he had finished with his gymnastics and babbling. He stood up, took the croker sack and folded it carefully, placed it on one of the feed bins and then turned to face her, ignoring the others.

'Whaffor yo' a-doin' that?' she questioned. 'A-jumpin' up 'n down on that old sack?'

Haltingly, in strangely accented words, he said, 'I pray to Allah. It is my evening prayer. Like all true believers, I pray four times a day.'

'Allah?' She pursed her lips and shrugged her shoulders in a gesture of non-understanding. 'Who he?'

'There is no God but Allah, and Mohammed is his Prophet,' he answered, the English words repeated as if by rote.

'Yo' mean that yo' a-prayin' to God?' she asked with raised eyebrows and open mouth. 'Time was, when Miz Maxwell she alive, we all pray. Miz Maxwell she had a chapel 'n we went there every Sunday, but since she died, we don' pray no more. Masta Maxwell he a-sayin' it ain' no use for servants to have religion, 'counta we ain' human, so he turn the chapel into a sleepin' place for the boys 'n any bucks which ain' mated up.'

232

Omar answered only, 'Yes, I pray to God.'

'Well, it a good thing yore prayin' over, 'cause I come to take yo' someplace else. We a-goin' to Leul's cabin. They's a wench there what Masta Maxwell he a-wantin' for yo' to cover.'

'What do you mean – wanting me to cover?'

A giggle followed by loud and raucous laughter came from the men and boys who were still standing around.

'He don' know what it mean to cover a wench!'

'He right soon a-goin' to fin' out.'

'Masta a-wantin' yo' to pester her.'

Lucretia Borgia quieted the others with a wave of her hand. 'Yes, he a-wantin' yo' to pester her. Bed yo'self down with her. He a-wantin' yo' to git her knocked up; he anxious to get a good sucker out'n yo'.'

'Sucker?'

'Yes suh, a baby.'

Omar nodded in understanding.

'Whaffor yo' think he went 'n bought yo'? Jes' to have yo' 'round to take care o' the horses? Lands sake! We got us 'nuff hostlers 'n grooms 'n stable boys now. Place fair overrun with 'em. He not give a damn if'n yo' good with horses or not. He a-wantin' yo' cause yo' half Mandingo, wantin' to git some Mandingo suckers out'n yo'.'

True, Omar did not understand all that Lucretia Borgia was saying, but he caught the general idea. He responded with a single word. 'Woman?'

Lucretia Borgia nodded her head. 'Tha's what Falconhurst for,' she tried to explain. 'This ain' no place for raisin' cotton, horses, nothin' like that. Here we raise niggers – best niggers anywhere 'round – 'n Masta Warren 'n even young Masta Ham, they right particular who a buck covers. That's why they picked out a good wench for yo'.'

He surveyed her for a moment, remembering her fingering him the night before. 'You?'

She shook her head. 'Shore a-wishin' it was, but Masta Maxwell he a-thinkin' I too big 'n black for yo'. He say yo' jes' waste sap on me. He got his mind set on a younger

233

wench, one what pretty 'n got straight hair. Yo' a good-lookin' boy, Omar, 'n he a-thinkin' he git a fine fancy sucker out'n yo' 'n a wench named Queenie. Where'd yo' put yore trogs what yo' brought from Mista Luke's? Better git 'em 'n come along. Yo' cain' wear them new trogs for workin' – save 'em for Sundays. Come along, yo' ain' a-goin' to sleep here in the barn no more.'

'But I like *you*, Lucretia Borgia. I like to have sucker with you.'

She was flattered. To think that he wanted the same thing that she did was almost unbelievable. But he had not yet seen Queenie, and when he did he would probably forget all about a fat old wench like herself.

He disappeared for a moment, going to the stall where he had spent the previous night, and returned with his few garments and the leather-covered book that he had brought from Luke's.

'Whaffor yo' got a book?' Lucretia Borgia had seen few books in her life but she recognized it as one. (The big house had two books, a Bible and a copy of Bullfinch's *Mythology*, which were principally used as a source of names for the slaves.)

'It is book I read often,' he answered. 'It is the Koran – the holy book.'

' 'N yo' kin *read*?' There was overwhelming amazement in her voice. Never before had she known a slave who could read.

He nodded. 'In my language, not yours. Every day I read book. I take it from Africa and it never leave me.'

She wanted to inspect it but she did not dare ask him, because it seemed such a thing of reverence to him. Together they walked out into the dusk which now was deepening into night. Creatures of the darkness were making a cacophony of sounds all about them as they went down the path to the street of cabins. There was only a sliver of a moon, but with the stars it gave enough light for them to see. They passed under the black shadow of the big live oak tree. Lucretia Borgia came closer to Omar and took his arm. They stopped.

For a long moment, during which they listened to the night noises, nothing was said. Lucretia Borgia had too much to say and she didn't know where to begin. Then she whispered, 'Yo' a-sayin' yo' likes me. Whaffor yo' like a fat wench like'n me? I ain' pretty 'n I ain' so young neither, but young enough to give Masta a set of twins 'n young enough to make him other good suckers if'n he let me have a buck what kin give 'em to me.'

'I like you,' he whispered in reply. 'Yes, I like you, Lucretia Borgia, because you are big.' His hand crept down the neck of her dress and fondled one of her huge melon-like breasts, his fingers pinching the large, hard nipple. 'In my father's country, men like big women. A man wants a real woman, not a thin little girl. That is why we feed our women and make them eat much; the fatter a woman, the more beautiful she is. The men of my father's race must be thin, strong, great riders of horses, but the women must be big, fat. Those we think beautiful.'

'My, oh my!' She pressed herself closer to him, 'I'm shore glad I'm a fat wench if'n that what yo' like. Ain' too fat though. I'm titted out big 'n big-assed too, but I ain' got no fat belly. No siree! Work too hard, I do, to get fat on my belly.'

He disengaged his hand from her breast and leaned over to kiss it. 'I like you.'

' 'N I like yo' too, Omar. Thinkin' someday we kin do somethin' about it. Know yo' a-wantin' to do it right now, but ain' a good time. Kin feel yo' all hard 'n throbbin', but Masta Maxwell he right particular. He say for me to take yo' down to Queenie 'n he a-meanin' it. If'n I don' take yo' down to Leul's cabin 'n git back to the house, he a-goin' to raise hell.' She pushed him away from her and buttoned up her dress.

She waited a moment for him to adjust his trousers and then took him by the arm. The cabins were all dark but one. Candles were a luxury that slaves could seldom have and the occasional one was always saved for a festive occasion. Besides, what need had they for candles? They did not read;

there was nothing that they could do at night that necessitated a light. Instead they were all outside, sitting on benches in front of their cabins, or walking back and forth in the dusty roadway to call on friends, to talk and sing with them. Each cabin had a bench in front which was filled with people, and other men hunkered down on the ground. It was their own time of day. It was their one period of relaxation. Now there was nobody to tell them what to do or how to do it. No white man stood over them. For this little space they were free. Then, when it came time for them to go to bed, there was always a warm and ardent bedfellow. Perhaps it was this reason more than any other which caused them to go to bed early. Slaves had few pleasures: fornication was one of them.

Even in the darkness, Lucretia Borgia could recognize the various women who were mistresses of their own cabins. She called out greetings to them as she and Omar passed. 'How yo-all, Kate?'

'We all fine here, Miz Lucretia Borgia ma'am.'

' 'N yo', Clemmie?'

'Jes' fine, Miz Lucretia Borgia ma'am. Jes' a-waitin' for the breeze to cool the cabin off 'fore we beds down.'

'Miz Lucretia Borgia ma'am,' a dark figure walked out of the night to stand in front of her, 'how long it goin' to be afore Masta Maxwell he a-goin' to give me back to Queenie?'

'Who yo'?' Lucretia Borgia halted Omar with a restraining hand and peered into the darkness, catching only the faint light of white teeth in a black face.

'I'se Noah, Miz Lucretia Borgia ma'am.' His voice had undertones of pleading. 'Jes' a li'l while ago, come in from the fields 'n Leul a-tellin' me I ain' goin' to sleep here no more, 'n for me to go down to the chapel. She a-tellin' me I ain' goin' to cover Queenie no more. How come, Miz Lucretia Borgia ma'am? How come Leul she a-kickin' me out?'

'Yo' a right pretty boy,' Lucretia Borgia recognized whom she was talking with now. 'Yas suh, a right pretty boy; but

I'm a-thinkin' yo' ain' got no sap. Yo' bin a-coverin' Queenie for nigh onto three months now 'n yo' ain' got her knocked up yet. Masta Maxwell he a-sayin' that this new boy he a-goin' to cover her.'

Noah's voice caught in his throat and had it been lighter she would have seen tears in his eyes. 'But I love Queenie, Miz Lucretia Borgia ma'am. It ain' jes' a-coverin' her 'tween us. Fair goin' to break my heart if'n I cain' bed down with her. She a-lovin' me too.'

Lucretia Borgia pushed him aside and although her gesture was rough and peremptory it was not without a tiny bit of tenderness. 'Ain' makin' no nevermids, Noah, if'n yo' a-lovin' her or she a-lovin' yo'. Yo' a nigger 'n I'm a nigger 'n ain' no real lovin' for niggers. Masta Maxwell he a-sayin' yo' go back to the chapel to sleep, 'n I'm a-sayin' it, 'n yo' a-knowin' it. 'N yo' a-knowin' that boys from the chapel ain' got no business a-wanderin' 'round the cabins at night. Yo' shore as hell a-goin' to git a whoppin' if'n I tell Masta Maxwell 'bout yo' a-moonin' roun' here like'n a sick calf.'

'Don' tell him, Miz Lucretia Borgia ma'am. Don' tell him. Don' want no whoppin'. I'se a good boy. Yo' knows I am.'

She knew that Noah had never caused any trouble and was meek, obedient, and willing. Her voice softened. 'Won' tell him if'n yo' scurry back to the chapel quick-like so's yo' be there when I come to lock up in a few minutes. Cain' have no randy bucks like'n yo' a-wanderin' loose at night.'

He disappeared in the darkness. She sighed. Just as she wanted Omar, so he wanted Queenie. But she tried hard to convince herself that that was a lot of poppycock. Niggers had no business falling in love. Not, of course, that she was in love with Omar, but she sure as hell wanted him, just as Noah wanted Queenie. Lucretia Borgia took Omar's arm again and walked with him until they came to the only cabin that was lighted.

She gestured to the open door. 'Queenie she live here with Leul.' They stood for a moment in the doorway. A candle stub in a cracked saucer gave off a dim yellowish light, sufficient to show four primitive roped bedsteads with straw

237

ticks and pieced quilts over them. Seven people were in the cabin – three couples, each couple sitting on a bed, with the fourth bed holding only one girl. Even in the dim light it could be seen that she was far prettier than the others. She was small-boned, with a heart-shaped face and long wavy hair that fell to her shoulders. Her age might have been between sixteen and eighteen.

Lucretia Borgia surveyed the cabin, to see if it met the standards of neatness and cleanliness that she demanded. It did, at least as much as she could see in the dim light. The beds were smoothly made, the hearth swept clean, the people neatly dressed. She nodded her head in the direction of a tall, strapping wench of about twenty-five.

'Evenin', Leul. How yo-all?'

'We jes' fine, Miz Lucretia Borgia ma'am. Bin havin' a li'l trouble with that Noah boy. He a-comin' here for supper 'n I fed him, but Masta Maxwell a-sayin' that Noah not to bed down here any more. Masta got a new buck for Queenie.'

At the mention of her name the girl stood up from the bed, then leaned over to smooth the quilt where she had been sitting.

'Evenin', Queenie.' Lucretia Borgia's greeting was short. She was far too jealous of the girl to be overly pleasant to her. 'This here's Omar. He a-goin' to cover yo' from now on. See to it that yo' cotches quick, 'cause Masta Maxwell he right anxious to git a sucker out'n this boy. He special, this boy Omar. He half Mandingo.'

Queenie appraised Omar. She smiled wanly at him and then at Lucretia Borgia.

' 'N if'n I gits knocked up 'n gives Masta Maxwell a good sucker, kin I go back to Noah? We in love, Miz Lucretia Borgia ma'am.'

'Tish, tush,' Lucretia Borgia levelled an indignant glance at the girl. 'What any nigger know 'bout being in love? Ain' no such thing for nobody but white folks. They gits in love 'n gits married by a preacher 'n has to stay together all their lives. Tha's it; tha's all. Tha's why all white women so peaked-lookin'. Nigger wench she gits knocked up 'n gives her masta a sucker. Masta gives her a silver dollar all for herself. 'N then she gits another buck 'n gits knocked up all over 'gain. Never has to stay with one buck all her life. 'Sides, this Omar boy he much better'n Noah.'

Queenie sniffed. True, this new man with the white turban was attractive and she certainly was not repelled by him, but she had an affection for Noah and it was hard to forget him. He was sentimental, Noah was, and they had a whole vocabulary of little words and phrases that meant nothing to anyone but themselves. She had, of course, no choice in the matter. She bowed her head, hiding the tears in her eyes.

Lucretia Borgia pushed Omar forward. 'Yo' sit down on the bed with her. That mean yo're her man now, like'n these.' She gestured to the other three couples in the room. She waited until Omar sat down, then cupped Queenie's chin in her hand and lifted her head.

'Better yo' forgits about Noah, Queenie. He ain' no good. Ain' got no sap in him. Bin pesterin' yo' for three months 'n no good comes o' it.'

'But I love him, Miz Lucretia Borgia ma'am. Love him, I do.'

Wanting Omar as she did, Lucretia Borgia could sympathize with Queenie's desire for Noah. For a brief instant and for the first time in her life, she realized what it must be like to be white; to be in love with a man, to be married to him, to know that he would never be sold away from her and that she would never be separated from him. But as quickly as the thought entered her head she dismissed it. Be white? Pshaw! What would she want to be white for? She thought of the white women she had seen and the white men they were mated to. She wouldn't trade places with any of those women, faced with the dreary prospect of the same man night after night, year after year. Not by a damn sight!

She turned swiftly and cuffed Queenie on the cheek. It was a resounding slap and all the others in the cabin sat up straight and stared at Lucretia Borgia. She had drawn back

her hand to give Queenie another slap, then, thinking better
of it, she allowed her hand to fall at her side.

'No more o' this foolishment, yo' ungrateful wench. Here
Masta Maxwell done give yo' the finest buck he got, 'n yo'
sit here a-cry-babyin' for that worthless Noah. 'Sides, it ain'
a-goin' to do yo' no good nohow. Noah, he a-goin' to be
sold off in the next coffle. I know, 'cause I hear Masta
Warren a-talkin' 'bout it with Masta Ham.' She turned with
a swish of her apron and stopped by Leul's bed a moment.

'Yo' stay awake tonight, Leul, after I go, 'n after yo' 'n
Sol git through. Want yo' to listen to them bed ropes 'n hear
if'n they a-squeakin'. 'N if'n they ain', yo' better see to it
that they do. If'n this Omar boy he too heavy hung for
Queenie, yo' give him some bacon rind. I 'members that
Noah boy ain' too big. Understand?'

Leul bowed her head in acknowledgement as Lucretia
Borgia left the cabin. She stopped for a moment in the cool
darkness, then set her face towards the big house. Most of
the folks had gone inside now and the street was practically
deserted. It was not until she came to the big live oak tree
that she stopped and let the tears come. She sobbed, but only
for a moment.

'Yo' a damn fool, Lucretia Borgia,' she said out loud to
herself. 'Whaffor yo' a-wantin' that Omar boy? He ain' so
much-a-much. Yo' had better'n him.'

She dried her tears on a corner of her apron and resumed
her walk towards the big house. She realized that no matter
what she said she could not convince herself that she did not
want Omar instead of Mem, who was probably in the kitchen
now waiting for her. Well, Mem was better than nothing.
Perhaps he'd give her another set of twins for her Masta
Warren and Masta Ham. Another set of twins! Well, she'd
try again.

She reached the house. Now all she had to do was to re-
port to her master that everything had been arranged between Omar and Queenie. As she hoisted her big body up the
kitchen steps, she wondered if Maxwell would really keep his
promise of whipping her if she pestered with Omar. No, of

course not! It was silly to even think of it. If she were to be whipped and couldn't cook for a day, who'd get their meals for them?

She was Lucretia Borgia. More than that, to all the folks she was 'Miz Lucretia Borgia ma'am.' Master Warren would never whop her, no matter what she did. Never! Young Masta Ham wouldn't let him.

CHAPTER TWENTY-SIX

One sun-spattered day followed another, and all of them possessed an agreeable sameness for Lucretia Borgia. She was always busy and her interest extended to everything that happened in her domain, yes, hers: let Warren and Hammond Maxwell think that they ran Falconhurst. She knew that they couldn't do it without her, because she had a big black finger in every pie; those that were baked in the kitchen and those that affected the life of the plantation.

There was nothing that went on that she did not know about and influence in one way or another. Her pressure was subtle and she never forced her opinions on her white masters, but she had a way of making suggestions so artfully that in the end both Maxwell and his son felt sure they had thought of the whole idea themselves and congratulated each other, not realizing that it had been Lucretia Borgia who had gently nudged them into their opinions. True, she did not always get the credit for her suggestions, but the fact that they were accepted and carried out was sufficient reward for her; although occasionally when some really big event took place which she had manoeuvred, she saw to it that the glory came to her.

'Shore glad I thought 'bout that, Masta Warren suh,' she purred over him one morning while he finished his breakfast by wiping his plate clean of egg yolk with a piece of bread. 'Shore glad it came to my mind.' She was referring to a suggestion she had made a few days before, which had just been carried out.

'What do yo' mean *yo'* thought 'bout it?' he asked. 'Ham's idea it was, right from the start, 'n yo' knows it.' He shook a misshapen finger at her. 'I declare, Lucretia Borgia, you always takin' credit for everythin' done around this place.'

'Yes suh, Masta Warren suh.' She thought it better to change the subject because she had a favour to ask. 'Mem he a-comin' with a toddy if'n he ain' forgotten.' Lucretia Borgia bustled into the sitting room to pump the bellows; despite the promise of a hot day, the fire always felt good to Maxwell's rheumatic limbs in the cool of a morning. With his chair well-upholstered with bed pillows, she fetched him and lowered him into it, fussing over him to give the impression that his comfort was of paramount importance to her; as indeed it was, because the more comfortable he was, the less irritable he would be.

'Got us some good news this morning,' she beamed, folding a coverlet around his shoulder.

'Mus' be somethin' bad, else yo' not a-hoverin' over me like'n a settin' hen with one egg. What's gone wrong now, Lucretia Borgia?' The twinges of pain as he settled into his chair caused him to be even more petulant than usual.

She grinned. 'Why, ain' nothin' wrong, Masta Warren suh. It news that shore a-goin' to make yo' happy.' She added a reassuring pat on his shoulder and then encircled him with an affectionate arm.

He shrugged her arm off, his lips forming a half-pout so that, despite his years, he looked like a spanked baby. 'Whereat that Mem 'n my toddy?' he demanded.

'He a-comin' if'n he ain' forgot it.' Lucretia Borgia hoped that Mem would delay a little longer; she wanted her master's ear for herself.

He glared up at her. 'Well, if'n it such goddamn good news yo' has, how come yo' don' tell me instead o' standin' there like'n a lump on a log 'n lettin' yore big mouth blather away?

242

Tell it, damn it! Git it out'n yore head once 'n for all, 'stead o' jes' talkin' 'bout it. Come on, le's *hear* it!'

She straightened up and took a long breath, her hands on her hips, her turban glowing red in the sunlight which came through the small-paned window.

'Yas suh, Masta Warren suh, we shore got good news, we have. Queenie's cotched. She knocked up higher'n a kite, she is.'

He regarded her blankly.

'Queenie,' she prompted him. 'Yo' knows Queenie, what down in Leul's cabin.'

''Course I do.' He was trying to recollect just who Queenie might be. 'Well, she got herself knocked up, 'n why's that so important to me? What's good news about that? Wenches a-gittin' knocked up every day, 'n all of a sudden yo' comes a-screechin' in here 'bout some goddamn Queenie. Jes' 'nother wench, ain' she?'

'Queenie's a right particular wench, 'n it good news that she's cotched. That Omar boy, *he* bin a-coverin' her. A' knowin' how anxious yo' 'n Masta Ham are to git a pup out'n that Mandingo boy, Omar.'

It dawned on Maxwell what all the to-do was about. In the weeks since Omar's purchase, Maxwell had completely forgotten the name of the wench he was covering. He was indeed delighted, but would not for the world let Lucretia Borgia know that the girl's name had momentarily escaped him.

'What yo' a-botherin' me with all that drivel for? Ham already a-knowin' all 'bout it. Tol' me at breakfast, he did.' This was a lie and Lucretia Borgia knew it. 'Shore I'm right happy. Hopes she births a boy, I do. Should be a right fancy buck when he grow up. Glad that Omar boy fertile.'

Lucretia Borgia looked around as Mem came in. She crossed to take the toddy from his hands and bring it to Maxwell. 'Now yo' jes' drink this.' Her words were sweet and dripping with unction. 'Got to git me down to Leul's cabin 'n tell her yo' ain' a-wantin' Omar a-sleepin' there no more. Knows yo' 'bout to tell me to do that, Masta suh.'

He sipped the toddy. 'Jes' 'bout to say so,' he admitted.

' 'N then I'm a-goin' down to the barn where Omar he a-workin' 'n tell him that for a spell he to bed hisself down in the barn.' She stood waiting for confirmation of her words.

Maxwell was lulled by the fire, the comfort of his chair, and the toddy into accepting almost anything that Lucretia Borgia might mention at that particular moment.

'Till Ham 'n me picks out 'nother wench for him.' He nodded his head in time to his words as though to emphasize each syllable. 'Give him a li'l rest between wenches. Musta bin pluggin' that wench mighty hard to git her knocked up so soon. Don' want him a-wastin' his sap. Yo' kin tell him that.'

'Masta Warren suh?'

He had closed both eyes, but he opened one and looked up at her. 'Ain' yo' gone yet, Lucretia Borgia? Thought yo' was a-goin' down to Leul's cabin 'n the barn.'

She had to wet her lips before she could speak; her mouth had suddenly become so dry with anxiety. 'Yes suh, Masta Warren, but afore I go, thought I'd talk over somethin' with yo'.'

'What yo' got to talk 'bout? With that big tongue o' yourn a-waggin' day 'n night, a body would think yo'd be purely talked out. What is it?'

'It that Omar boy.'

'What 'bout him?'

'Jes' bin a-thinkin' it 'bout time I brung yo' 'nother sucker, Masta Warren suh. Ain' had none since I had them twins 'n tha's all of a coon's age ago. Somehow Mem he ain' got no good sap no more. Ain' a-doin' me no good 'cause he a-wastin' what little he got on any wench he kin find. Come time to bed hisself down, he jes' a-wantin' to go to sleep. All he kin do of a night is snore. Right tired of him, I am.'

'Yo' too old for suckers now,' Maxwell appraised her.

She shook her head violently. 'I ain' too old, Masta Warren suh! Yo' a-knowin' that. Ain' so old but what if'n I gits me a good man what kin rightly pester me I kin git yo' a *lot* more suckers. Kin git yo' one every year, 'n mayhap even more twins too.'

He stared at her, but she did not lower her gaze. Without dismissing her he sipped at his toddy and rocked in his chair. Finally he spoke, and with his words came a smile.

'Yo' shore are a connivin' wench, Lucretia Borgia. But,' he nodded, 'I'm onto yo', I am. Yo' bin a-wantin' that Omar boy ever since we bought him. Told me yo' wanted him, begged me to give him to yo'. Reckon it 'cause yo' saw how well hung he is. Wonder if'n yo' remembers what I told yo' when yo' asked for him then?'

She was caught in her own trap; she wondered how she was going to escape from it and get what she wanted.

'Remember, I do, Masta Warren suh.' She grinned back at him, though she felt far from elated. 'Remember yo' a-sayin' that I too old 'n fat for a fancy buck like'n Omar.'

'That ain' all, Lucretia Borgia. Said more'n that.'

She regarded him with blank-eyed astonishment. She was a fine actress, Lucretia Borgia was, otherwise her eyes could not have been so innocent-seeming. 'Cain' remember yo' sayin' more, Masta Warren suh.'

'Yo' knows damn well I said more.'

With her lips pressed tightly together as though trying hard to remember, she continued to shake her head. 'Disremembers, I do.'

Again his finger pointed at her. 'Well, I don't disremember, 'n yo' ain' disremembering neither, yo' black imp o' Satan. Said I was a-goin' to heist yo' up 'n strip yo' down if'n yo' so much as looked goggle-eyed at that Omar. Know yo' a-dyin' to have him pester yo', but this one time, Lucretia Borgia, when yo' ain' a-goin' to git what yo' wants no matter how much yo' finagles. Not by a damn sight! Don' care if'n I *never* gits another sucker out'n yo'. If Mem cain' knock yo' up, then yo' a-goin' to stay not knocked up. Ain' a-goin' to waste that Omar boy's sap on yo'. Don' hold with whoppin' wenches, but this time I'm shore a-threatenin' yo': start sweet-talkin' that Omar into beddin' with you 'n I peel the hide right off'n that fat ass o' yourn! Hear me?'

She nodded. This time Maxwell had had the last word, and she realized there was no benefit in her proceeding further.

' 'N don' think I don' mean it,' he snapped.

'Yes suh, Masta Warren suh.' She was contrite. 'Makes me sorrowful that yo' don' want 'nother sucker from me or mayhap twins, but if'n yo' say I cain' have Omar, reckon I cain'.' She took the empty toddy glass from his hand.

Once the kitchen door had closed behind her and she saw there was nobody in the kitchen she gave way to her feelings. She was not a weeper, yet she had to wipe the tears from her eyes, tears more of frustration than of sorrow. Her plans had gone awry and she did not take disappointments easily. She wanted Omar more than anything else in the world. His face had been before her night and day during the weeks he had spent in Leul's cabin, yet she had restrained herself and not approached him. Now that his mission there had been accomplished, she felt that she had a right to him. Surely it would not hurt anyone, least of all Omar, if he were to bed with her until the Maxwells had chosen another mate for him. Besides, it was all poppycock that a man had to rest up and guard his sap after he had knocked up one wench. She knew better. The more a man drained his sap, the more potent he was prone to be. Didn't do a man any good not to have a woman every night. Not any good at all!

Despite Maxwell's angry threat, it occurred to Lucretia Borgia that no wench had ever been whipped at Falconhurst. The most severe punishment any wench had ever had was to be shackled in a box stall in the barn and fed on bread and water for three days.

Three days! Bread and water for three days! She wouldn't mind that if she could have Omar. It would be a small price to pay for the joy of those sleek arms and legs, with his mouth on hers and nothing around them but the darkness of night. With her lips compressed in a straight line, and nodding her head in confirmation of her thoughts, she stood up straight and faced the door. A determined stride took her outside and led her along the path that went to the barn.

Bread and water! Huh!

Her starched apron swished around her legs as she made the short journey in the mid-morning sunlight. Inside the shadowy barn, she paused to adjust her eyes. Omar was there, directing two other boys while they cleaned out the stalls preparatory to putting down fresh straw in them. She beckoned to him to come over.

'Hear Queenie cotched.' She smiled at him, her head at a coquettish angle.

'So she a-tellin' me.' His English seemed to her to have improved since he had been at Falconhurst.

'So that means yo' no longer stayin' in Leul's cabin. Yo' a-goin' to bed yo'self down here in the barn, 'n yo' ain' havin' no wench till Masta Warren or Masta Ham picks one for yo'.'

He shook his head and shrugged his shoulders with a disconsolate little smile, moving closer to her so that the other two boys could not hear him. 'Wishin' I could bed me down with yo', Lucretia Borgia.' His eyes lingered on the voluptuous curves of her breasts.

'Wishin' that too.' She came closer in her turn, so that she could feel the heat from his body and smell the musk from him. They regarded each other and read the desire in each other's eyes.

It was Lucretia Borgia who spoke first. 'Shore hate to think o' yo' beddin' down alone out here in the barn,' she whispered, ' 'n especially with me in the kitchen with Mem. Might jes's well be alone so far's he's concerned. He ain' no good to me.'

'But I could be.' He laid a finger on her cheek, traced a line down to the fullness of her lips, then along her jaw until it came to rest on her ear.

'Yo' shore could, Omar boy.' She had an almost uncontrollable desire to reach out and touch him but she feared what it might do not only to him but to herself. He had never appeared more handsome, more attractive, and she wondered how she had withstood the temptation to be with

247

him for so long. Certainly it was more than she could bear any longer.

With her fingers on her lips, showing that her words were to be a secret, she again whispered to him. 'A-goin' to make shore you bedded down here 'stead of in the chapel. Boys in the chapel gits locked in every night, so's they don' go snoopin' 'round like a pack o' randy dogs. Boys here in the barn ain' never locked in.'

He nodded his head: he understood her so far.

'So,' she leaned closer to him while she whispered, 'yo' meet me tonight soon's it git dark. I'll be waitin' for yo' out in the old shed behind the sewin' house. It where we keeps the loomed goods, 'n it locked, 'n I has the key.'

'I be there,' he whispered, his finger again drawing a tender scroll on her face.

CHAPTER TWENTY-SEVEN

There was one thing that Lucretia Borgia could not do, even though she was able to handle most things with speedy efficiency. That was to carry a tune. To be sure, the tune was right there in her mind, yet when it came out of her mouth, the sound had no relation to the tune. It was a tuneless cater-wauling that could set nerves on edge. Of this, however, she was ignorant, and when she was happy she always sang, unaware that her off-key screeching was not in any way tuneful. Today she was happy, therefore she sang. It was a loud and exuberant paean of joy, about as musical as two tin pans banging together.

'La-de-da, la-de-da, la-de-da!' She was singing as she left Omar at the barn and went down to Leul's cabin to inform her with her usual pompous majesty that Queenie would be immediately transferred to the birthing house with the other pregnant wenches and that Omar would be temporarily confined to the barn. She promised Leul that she would provide a replacement for Queenie just as soon as she could get Maxwell or Ham to decide on a proper wench for Omar. It did not pay to have a bed cool off at Falconhurst. Each night that a bed was unoccupied by a coupling buck and wench meant one less chance of getting another sucker. Empty beds, like unploughed fields, were unproductive.

It was a wordless as well as a tuneless song that Lucretia Borgia sang as she went up the weed-grown path that led to the neatly whitewashed shed just behind the sewing house. This was one building on the plantation that was seldom used – at least it was not used every day, as all the others were. When a bolt of tow linen, rough osnaburg or hand-loomed butternut cloth had been woven, it was taken from the loom and stored in this cloth shed. Only Lucretia Borgia, not even the Maxwells, had a key to it, and now, as she hurried along the path, she reached for the key ring that hung from a chain in the voluminous folds of her apron. She inserted a key in the lock. The rasping sound as she turned it suggested that she should oil the lock, although it was extremely doubtful that anyone would hear her, for the cloth shed was some distance from the slave quarters. It was the most private and secure place on the plantation for a rendezvous.

She was still crooning to herself when she went into the shed. The one small glazed window did not let in much light, but she could see the bolts of cloth piled on the rough table. She contemplated the rough puncheon floor, the bolts of cloth, and the table. Certainly there was no comfortable place for a couple to bed down here. A simple pallet such as she and Mem shared in the kitchen was not the ideal solution either. For this coupling she needed something special, like a feather bed.

A feather bed! She stopped singing and pursed her lips in a quandary. A feather bed? Well, it might be done. Without locking the door, she departed, quickening her steps as she neared the big house. One glance in the kitchen assured her that everything was in order for the noonday meal. In the sitting room, she found Maxwell dozing in his rocker. Mem was nowhere to be seen. Plucking up her skirts, she opened the staircase door and ascended to the second floor, then down the hall to the slightly musty but sacrosanct splendour of the spare room, whose ugly Empire furniture was rarely used these days because Falconhurst had so few guests.

She threw back the candlewick coverlet and then the sheets, wondering as she did so when was the last time that the spare room had been used. It had been at least a year ago, and the immaculate sheets had not been disturbed since.

Stripping the bed, she folded the sheets and the counterpane carefully and set them aside. It was difficult to gather the billowy tick into her arms and as she did so she realized that it was filled with costly goose feathers. No chicken-feather bed for her and Omar! Nothing but the best for their nuptial night. She grabbed an embroidered towel from the washstand and took the bulky tick in her arms. She had some difficulty in getting it down the stairs; then opening the door at the foot was such a challenge that she made some noise in doing so. It roused Maxwell, who looked up at her with irritation for having been awakened from his dreams, in which there was no pain or distorted limbs and he was again a virile young man.

'What in tarnation yo' a-doin', Lucretia Borgia, a-trampin' roun'? Where yo' a-takin' that feather bed o' Miz Maxwell's? Declare to goodness, they ain' no time a man kin rest in his own home 'thought'n some nigger wench a-cartin' a feather bed through his settin' room! Whereat yo' a-goin' with it? Lookin' like it Sophie's best feather bed, which she heired from her papa and set such store by.'

' 'Tis.' Lucretia Borgia smiled at him over the striped billows. 'That jes' what 'tis. Needin' a new tickin', o' else needin' to sew up this 'un. Cleanin' the spare room t'other day 'n found some feathers on the floor. They a-comin' from this here bed, 'n anxious to fix it. It were Miz Sophie's pride

250

'n joy, 'cause she always a-sayin' that it goose-feather 'n that mighty hard to come by.'

Maxwell waved her on with a lethargic gesture, content to know that Lucretia Borgia was looking out for things at Falconhurst as always.

'A-takin' it down to the cloth shed in case I got to make new ticking for it.' She halted to gather up the towel, which had slipped from her grasp. 'Cain' have goose feathers all over the house.' She waited expectantly; then, knowing by his silence that she had received tacit permission, went out the front door and, once again, singing to high heaven, toted her burden down to the shed. Inside, she put it on the table while she swept a portion of the floor clean with a twig broom. This done, she spread the feather bed on the floor.

'M-m-m!' She regarded it with satisfaction; but something was lacking. 'Got to git me a sheet too. Cain' have that Omar boy a-shootin' off on this tickin'. Like new 'tis, 'n ain' goin' to take no chances on it. Sheet ain' no problem, kin hide it under my apron, but shore couldn't hide a feather bed. No sir-ee, couldn't do that no matter *how* fat I am. Good thing that Omar likes fat wenches. Should of been born in his country. M-m-m, wouldn't they all like me 'n my big tits!' She chuckled as she smoothed the tick on the floor, plumping it up into a full and rounded appearance. 'Uh-huh, jes' bet that Omar boy never slept on a feather bed afore, but he ain' a-goin' to git no sleep here. No sir-ee, not the way I plans to work him out, he ain'.'

Her high-rising laughter was as musical as her tuneless singing was not. Everything so far had been arranged exactly as she wanted it. By first dark, she and Omar would be together. She envisaged the sleekness of his limbs and the stone-hardness of his manhood, and even the thoughts gave her an insatiable itch for him. She hoped that the feather bed would see many nights of occupancy, and told herself that she was not going to suggest to either Maxwell or Hammond that a mate be found for Omar. Let them attend to it in their own time; every day that they put it off would mean another night that she could enjoy Omar. Surely she had more to offer him than some spindle-shanked young virgin who had never been broken to the saddle. Even Mem had told her that she knew more tricks to satisfy a man than any other wench on the plantation. The only thing Omar could possibly want from her that she could not give him was the chance to break her in, and that she couldn't do because she could hardly remember how long ago she had been busted.

Regardless of how she could please Mem, he seldom let her because he was obsessed with only one thing, busting young girls. Bah! She didn't want to think about Mem now. Let him chase after every filly he could find. Someday she was going to tell on him. But not now! She'd have to sweet-talk him so that if he came back to the house in the early morning and found their pallet unoccupied, he wouldn't run and tattle on her to Maxwell. Probably he wouldn't anyway, because he didn't want to be found out himself, but that was something she didn't have to worry about now. Night was coming and there was a feather bed, a locked door, and Omar to think about. Surely she had enough to anticipate to keep any wench happy – to make her sing praise to high heaven just as she was now going to do.

Ham was not coming to the big house for his midday meal, so she decided to fix up something rather special for Warren Maxwell just to keep him happy and in a good frame of mind. The men had finished slaughtering and she decided on some succulent fried pork chops for him, tenderly brown and with the fat curling around the edges the way he liked them. She'd have rice and some beans which she had been soaking. Then when Ham came in from the fields, they would have a real supper. She was so happy, she wanted to express her happiness in good food for her masters. Let them be happy too, even if it was over a minor thing like food. She had a major fact to be happy over. Omar! How she wanted that boy – the taste of him, the smell of him, the sight of him and the feel of him, as well as the sound of his words of love in her ears.

'Omar.' She spoke the name aloud just for the joy of hearing it.

At last the evening meal was over and the time arrived when Hammond escorted his father to bed. Mem had put in an appearance and served supper and was now waiting upstairs to take off his master's boots and undress him. It was not quite dark and Lucretia Borgia sat out on the gallery by the kitchen door, scanning the sky. There was an afterglow of gold and orange and heliotrope that faded at dusk. She waited until it was wholly dark with the stars showing before she ventured out. With both Maxwells upstairs, there was nobody whom she had to advise of her departure, and she started out, walking softly. Her path led down by the stable; she wondered if Omar had left yet. It would be nice to find him waiting for her when she arrived at their tryst; it would signify that he was anxious as she was. Anxious? That was hardly the word; she ached for him.

There were no lights back in the big house nor in the street of cabins when she rounded the sewing house and came to the cloth shed. It was now too dark to distinguish anything, but she knew her way. When she came up the path by the cloth shed, she thought she heard some movement and stopped still in her tracks. She waited: the sound was that of somebody breathing. She hesitated for another moment until she dared to whisper, 'Who there?'

There was a gleam in the darkness, of lips smiling to disclose white teeth. 'It me, Lucretia Borgia,' the answer came in a husky voice. 'It me, Omar.'

She extended her arms, groping until her hands touched flesh. 'It yo', Omar?' There was really no need to ask the question, but she treasured the reassurance and the sound of his name. 'Omar?'

'It me, Lucretia Borgia.'

A lump was in her throat, she couldn't answer. She opened the padlock and kicked the door open. 'Yo' stand still, Omar boy, for a minute.' She located the feather bed with her slippered foot and sank down on her knees, reaching out to pull Omar to her. He came closer. She reached for his hands, covered them with kisses, placed them on her shoulders. He pulled her closer and she nuzzled her face against him until she could feel his throbbing turgescence through the thin trousers. It pressed against her cheek and seemed to have a special heat and life of its own. Her hand reached out, the button slipped from its hole, and the imprisoning cloth fell from his slim hips around his ankles.

She kissed him; the contact of her lips caused him to draw in his breath and she could feel a tremor run through his body. Although she was not a stranger to him, this time she gloried even more in the rigid evidence of his feeling for her. It rared up in almost frightening proportions beneath her fingers; she had forgotten how enormous it really was. After a moment of wondering and wonderful exploration, her fingers grasped it and manipulated it with the softness of her lips. He backed away from her. She released him and he leaned forward, his hands under her shoulders, and pulled her up to him so that his lips met hers.

'Not that way tonight, Lucretia Borgia. That fine when we not have much time and there are clothes between us, but tonight, my glorious full moon of the desert. . . .'

'Tonight?' She was as querulous as a girl with her first lover.

'Tonight there will be nothing between us. See,' he loosened the straps of her apron and his fingers sought out the small buttons of her bodice. 'See!' His big fingers managed the buttons and he drew one of her breasts from the taut cloth. 'This what I mean.' He bent, the cloth of his turban brushing her cheek as his lips encircled the blunt, up-standing nipple. His tongue encircled it and played with it until she felt she could not bear it another moment and pushed him away, throwing off her clothes and sinking to the downy softness of the feather bed. In a moment he was down beside her, his long muscular body stretched out against the curves of her own, his mouth seeking hers, his tongue discovering the tender secret places of her mouth, his hands stroking the velvet softness of her belly, finding her hands and forcing them down to that place where he throbbed with a special ecstasy at their touch. His mouth, now like some wet and parasitic bloom that sucked the life

254

from its host, opened and closed on her body until with each new place that his tongue traced a circle of wetness, she squirmed in voluptuous desire beneath him. His white teeth nipped at her black body and when all her nerves were wire-taut, she forced his head away from her body and loved him all over with the damp affection of her own lips. Time and place were gone; it was neither night nor day, summer nor winter, high noon or deep midnight. In all the world there were only two bodies writhing with desire for each other. Everything was lost in one great moment of fleshly torment and mental spiritualization, as one mind sought to blend with another through the fine instruments of two wholly receptive bodies twitching in a macabre dance of death, the outcome of which could only be life.

He groaned, the sound forced from him, then began to groan in utter bestial howls, interspersed with crude mouthings of her name and words that she had never heard before – words which seemed by their very barbaric strangeness to be more endearing and pulse-quickening than understandable syllables. She twisted out from under his arms and forced her body out of the slippery sweatiness of his legs, rolling free onto her back and pulling him with her in her extreme exaction. He, quite beyond himself now, followed her movement and spraddle-legged himself onto her heaving body. His hands, losing their tenderness, spread open her legs and unconsciously she arched her body the better to accommodate him. Groping in the darkness, she found him, and guided him into her. He entered slowly at first but once having achieved entrance he plunged with brute force into her while she, far from virginal, uttered a low shriek as though she were being violated for the first time.

Securely pinioned, he lifted himself on his elbows. His eyes tried to distinguish her face in the darkness but he could not see. His lips descended to meet hers and his tongue was engulfed in the passion flower of her mouth while she, unable to speak, could only move her hips in anguished circles to take in more of him. Neither could remain still any longer. He abandoned her lips slowly, then raised up on his arms, nearly withdrawing, then plunged again, taking courage from her cries that urged him on.

The heaviness of her legs encircled him and she began to raise her body to meet his, babbling incoherently while he continued his thrusting, which became more rhythmic although he plunged as deeply as before. Again and again her body paroxysmed and each time that he sensed her extremity, he stilled his vigorous pistoning to give her time to recuperate and to relax the strain on his lungs. But, after each cessation, his wildness mounted and her hands, clawing at him, pulled him down deeper and deeper into her until some wild and unimaginable something exploded in both of them, sending streamers of coloured fire to wreathe in concentric circles in their brains. She babbled incoherently under him, repeating his name in spastic workings of her jaws. She could feel the liquid warmth of him within her body and then he slumped down onto her, gasping for breath. She too was panting and now the heavy weight of his body on hers seemed too much for her to bear and she felt trapped with a claustrophobic fear although she did not have either the desire or ability to rid herself of his pressing weight. He managed to get his breath and shifted himself a little, still embedded within her. With the gulp of a long breath, he covered her mouth again but this kiss was one of love and affection rather than of unrequited passion.

'Lucretia Borgia,' he murmured, and his voice was almost normal.

'Omar.' She found enough air in her lungs to speak his name.

Again he raised himself on his elbows, then on his arms and finally on his hands until he was kneeling over her. Gently he withdrew from her to hunker back on his haunches while she made the final effort and sat up, leaning against him. 'Never was like this before, Lucretia Borgia,' he confessed in the darkness.

'Never before for me neither,' she answered him.

She reached for the towel she had left there earlier in the day. Its soft cloth in her gentle hands scrubbed his still throbbing maleness and before she had finished she realized he was entirely in condition for another bout. As much as she wished for it herself, she was forced to listen to an inner voice of caution. Once was her good fortune; a second time might be fatal.

'Cain' do it again tonight, Omar boy.' She threw the towel down on the floor. 'Gotta save it for tomorrow.'

'Sometime the second time better'n the first,' he urged her.

'Nothin' ever could be better'n that. We gotta go. Yo' goes first. Yo'll find yore way now – moon comed up 'n give plenty o' light.'

'I kiss you good night.' He bent and kissed her lingeringly, then stood up and found his way to the door. The silver light of the risen moon came into the shed, striping her black body with metallic brilliance. He came back, leaned over her again, kissed her on the mouth and on the breasts, then left.

For a moment she remained in the darkness, collecting her thoughts as her hands reached out to grope for her garments. She donned them carelessly. Nobody would see her at this hour of the night. Dressed, she opened the door and stood for a moment in the moonlight, then remembered that she had forgotten the towel and the sheet and went back to retrieve them.

She raised the bundle of cloths to her face, anxious to sniff the alkaline male pungency of him once more. Then she strode out with them under her arms, snapped the padlock shut and started for the house.

Halfway there she stopped and looked towards the stable, etched in black silhouette against the light of the moon. Somewhere within that shadow, Omar was bedding himself down in clean straw. She ached to be with him; to repeat all that ecstasy; to relax beside him after they were both spent, and finally to fall asleep in his arms, his body pressed against hers. Always. But she knew she could not have everything. Already she had had more than was ever given to most women. She had had Omar, and whatever might happen to her in the future, she had this to remember; and nothing could ever be greater than this.

The sinister words of Maxwell's threat crossed her mind and the black silhouette of the barn took on a direful significance. It was in that very barn that Maxwell whipped. Then the thought was rejected. Warren Maxwell would never whip her, and if he wanted to punish her with bread and water, all well and good. She had that night tasted a man, a veritable man among men, and from now on it would take more than bread and water to frighten her. She had only to think of the taste of Omar and be satisfied. That was enough.

Mem was not in the kitchen when she arrived; for this she was grateful, and thanked whatever young wench had manoeuvred to keep him out so late. Truly everything had worked out for her tonight, and although the pallet on the floor was a far cry from the softness of the feather bed, she rolled onto it, finding peace in her heart. Tomorrow would be another day and tomorrow night would be another night. Thanks be to Omar's God!

CHAPTER TWENTY-EIGHT

It had always been Warren Maxwell's strong conviction that it was the right thing to do, for the sake of health and good production, to keep a stud in the barn or the chapel for a short period after he had successfully impregnated a wench. It gave him a chance to recoup himself, rest from his labours, and store up his sap, so Maxwell was in the habit of telling Ham; and Ham, always believing everything his father told him, was of the same firm opinion. This belief was not shared by other plantation owners, who kept their plantation studs busy in a continuous round of nightly and sometimes daily engagements. However, as Maxwell often said, 'Raising niggers ain't no hit-or-miss business at Falconhurst.'

This particular time, the longer Omar rested, the better for her, Lucretia Borgia felt. She knew it was all plumb foolishness: no man had to rest after getting a girl knocked up. Pshaw! Some beneficent human chemistry saw to it that a man always had plenty of sap, and Lucretia Borgia knew that there was no danger of Omar's sap ever being dried up. Wasn't he always anxious for a second bout just as soon as he had managed to catch his breath after the first one? In the brief periods she had spent with him on the feather bed, she had never come near to exhausting him. He was always begging for more. He seemed insatiable.

The days passed in idyllic happiness for her, with moments of wild tuneless singing as she went about her work. The nights came and went with her occupying the feather bed in the cloth house with Omar by her side. A whole week had passed now, seven nights of joyful bliss with Omar, and she was anticipating the far from likely possibility that both Maxwell and Ham had forgotten about him.

Yet, omniscient as Lucretia Borgia seemed to herself to be, she could not prepare for every contingency. There were a few things that had to be left to fate, and Maxwell's uncalculated calling for Mem one night was one of them. It was fortunate that Lucretia Borgia had left Omar rather early that night, returning to the kitchen and the loneliness of her pallet. As usual, Mem was not there, and as usual Lucretia Borgia was grateful that he had found entertainment elsewhere. Then, just as she was dozing off to sleep, mixing her daydreams with her coming night-dreams, she heard Maxwell's voice from the upstairs bedroom.

'Mem,' he was calling. 'Mem, yo' goddamn worthless son of a bitch, why don' yo' harken to me?' His calls awakened Ham, who cried anxiously, 'What's the matter, papa? Yo' sick?'

'Could be a-dyin' for all that Mem would care. Bin standin' here at the head o' the stairs a-bellerin' for him for an hour, 'n he ain' come yet.' He took a lungful of air and shouted 'Mem!' again.

259

'What yo' a-wantin', papa?' Ham's voice hit a falsetto note in his anxiety.

'Jes' a-wantin' me a bit o' saleratus in a glass o' water. Woke up in the night with sour stomach 'n heartburn. Think mayhap it those pork chops Lucretia Borgia cooked for supper. Too rich, with all that gravy. Bit o' saleratus best thing in the world for heartburn, but could be dyin' for all that shiftless Mem care. If'n he don' heist himself out'n his bed, why don' Lucretia Borgia come? Sure as hell *she* kin hear me, less'n they all gone deaf down there.'

She gathered the torn blanket about her and ran into the parlour. 'Yo' a-callin', Masta Warren suh?' she hollered up the staircase. 'Yo' a-callin', or I bin a-dreamin' that yo' called?'

'Sicker'n a mule, I am, 'n could be a-dyin' for all anyone cares. Callin' for Mem, I am. Want him now.' Maxwell belched his indignation.

' 'N tell him he edgin' up to a whoppin', he is,' Ham called.

'Want some saleratus.' Now that he had Lucretia Borgia for an audience, Maxwell lowered his voice to a whimper. 'It them damned pork chops yo' cooked for supper, givin' me the heartburn.'

'Pore Masta Warren!' Lucretia Borgia put the amount of sympathy into her voice that Maxwell was seeking. 'Yo' jes' hop back into bed 'n I bring up the saleratus soon's I git a candle lit to see what I'm a-doin'.'

She heard footsteps on the stairs and Hammond, naked, came down into the sitting room. He went to the kitchen and returned, meeting her in the dining room.

'Whereat that Mem, Lucretia Borgia?' he demanded. 'He ain' in yore bed in the kitchen where he supposed to be.'

'Don' rightly know, Masta Ham suh. He ain' bin in the house all night.'

He confronted her without making any move to cover his nudity while she struck a light from the tinder box on the mantle and lit a candle.

'Where he at?' he demanded again.

She pulled the blanket more closely about her and carried

260

the candle out into the kitchen. He followed on her heels. Opening one of the cupboard doors, she held the candle up and searched for the round wooden box of saleratus. Having found it, she shook an admonitory finger at Hammond, as much as to say, 'When we get your poor papa attended to, we'll talk about that.'

Carefully measuring out half a teaspoonful into a flint glass tumbler, she went to the water pail in the sink and added a little water, stirring it with a spoon. 'Yo' wants that I take this up to yore papa?'

'I'll fetch it to him.' Hammond reached out and took the tumbler from her hand. 'But yo' better slip on a dress 'n come up too. Papa, he madder'n a wet hen 'n a-goin' to be bellerin' for yo' jes' soon's he swallows this.'

'I'll be up,' she nodded in agreement, ' 'n yo' better git some trogs on if'n yo' a-goin' to be traipsin' round. Nekkid as a jaybird!'

'Yo' seen me nekkid afore, plenty times,' he half-grinned back at her.

'Shore have. A nekkid man no great shakes to me, but it ain' fittin' for yore papa to see yo' nekkid.' She waited for him to leave the kitchen before she dropped the enveloping blanket and slipped into her dress.

'Lucretia Borgia, where yo' at?' The summons came from above, as Ham had predicted.

'I'm a-comin', Masta Warren.' She went to where a ray of light shone down from the front staircase. 'Comin' right up.' She lifted her bulk laboriously up the stairs and waddled down the hall to Maxwell's room. He had returned to his bed and Hammond, now standing beside him, had slipped on his trousers.

'Yo' a-knowin' what time it is, Lucretia Borgia?'

She shook her head.

'It way past one o'clock.' Maxwell pointed to his big silver watch on the night table. ' 'N that Mem he ain' in the house yet. Yo' know whereat he might be?'

She shook her head, admitting for once her ignorance of a plantation matter. 'Shore don' know, Masta Warren suh.

He probably out tom-cattin' like'n he do every night. If'n they one thing Mem likes, it those pretty li'l pussycats with him tom-cattin' after them. He a-thinkin' he still a young buck with lots of sap in him.'

'He not a-goin' to have any sap left in him when I git through a-whoppin' him!'

'Yo' a-whoppin' him?' She walked over to the table and took the empty tumbler.

Maxwell looked at her with utter amazement at the stupidity of her question. 'Whoppin' him? Of course I'm whoppin' him. What kind o' niggers yo' think we a-goin' to raise here at Falconhurst if'n I let every goddamn buck on this plantation go round pesterin' any wench he take a notion to? Yo' knows, Lucretia Borgia, it a hard and fast rule here that I mate up the bucks 'n wenches. Plenty o' screwin' for everyone if'n a boy do like'n I say, but he got to wait till I say so.' He turned from her and beckoned to Ham. 'Yo' gits into yore trogs 'n see kin yo' find Mem. He not too far away – too damned lazy to walk far, so don' reckon he in the cabins.'

'He down in the weeds behind the barn, probably,' Lucretia Borgia interrupted. 'A-knowin' that he go there sometimes.'

'Take a lantern,' Maxwell advised Hammond. 'Findin' that black son of a bitch at night 'thout'n a lantern worser'n tryin' to tree a coon blindfolded. Take a bullwhip along too, 'n touch him up a little; though that ain' a-goin' to take the place o' the whoppin' I orders for him.'

'Thinkin' I go with Masta Hammond, Masta Warren suh. Mayhap I kin help him.'

'Yo' kin go to hell, Lucretia Borgia, for all I care. Gittin' goddamn sick o' niggers, I am. Treat 'em good, do everythin' yo' kin for them, 'n they turn on yo' like'n an adder. Mem he got the easiest job on the whole damn plantation 'n don' 'preciate it none. Shore, go with Ham 'n see if yo' kin spot him, bring him back 'n spancel him in the barn. Don' wake me up if'n yo' find him. First it's heartburn 'n then it's some worthless nigger what ain' here when I want him.' He sank back on the pillows and pointed to the candle for Lucretia Borgia to take with her.

She picked up the candlestick and followed Ham into his room, where she helped him on with his boots and waited while he put on his shirt. Together they went down the back stairway into the kitchen. The feeble rays of the candle showed that Mem had not returned; Hammond stared at the empty pallet, feeling his anger rise higher as he regarded the actual proof of Mem's insubordination. One of the twins, awakened by the light, sat up and started to cry, but Lucretia Borgia shut him up with a smart slap and he subsided into sniffles.

She lit a fat wax candle in the glass-sided lantern, put on her old carpet slippers, and opened the back door. They were both silent as they made their way through the darkness to the barn. Lucretia Borgia was praying silently that Omar had returned to the barn and was not still dozing on the feather bed in the cloth house. For a moment, fear shook her, because she realized that she and Omar were just as guilty as Mem, and for the same crime. The only difference was that Mem had been found out; she hadn't and didn't intend to be, because she knew she was far smarter than Mem. Although, and this she pondered with a rising fear, Warren Maxwell might have awakened an hour earlier and called for her instead of Mem. She would have been down in the cloth house with Omar and *she* would have been found out. She knew that regardless of the position she maintained and the influence she wielded at Falconhurst, she would be punished along with Omar. Maybe she would have to change her tactics because no one, not even herself, could predict when Maxwell might have another attack of heartburn. Caution would be the watchword from now on. Perhaps it would be better to forgo her pleasures with Omar for a while. It was something she must think about in the morning.

The lantern showed all in order in the horsebarn. Omar was sound asleep on a pallet in one of the box stalls and didn't even wake as they passed. She was grateful; she was safe again, even if by a narrow margin. Now she could devote her entire energy to the pursuit of Mem.

She and Ham traversed the horsebarn, going out the big double doors which were open to allow a breeze to sweep through. There was merely a short path behind the barn – just enough to allow the toting of the manure from the barn to the big pile at the back of it. Beyond the manure pile, the weeds grew rank and luxuriant. It was here that Lucretia Borgia pointed, her fingers on her lips to ensure silence from Ham. She whispered, 'A-thinkin' that's where he a-goin' to be at, Masta Ham suh. He got a l'il hidey-hole in there he once told me about. Sh-h-h!'

Silently and cautiously, they parted the thick growth and traversed a narrow beaten path through the weeds. Suddenly they heard a rustling of the verdure ahead. Lucretia Borgia held the lantern and nodded her head. Hammond jumped in front of her and in a moment was in the little packed-down clearing, the whip in his hand unleashed.

Lucretia Borgia raised her lantern over his shoulder. Its brassy rays disclosed a naked Mem and an indistinguishable black shape beneath him, their motions momentarily checked. The lantern picked out purple highlights on the entwined mass of flesh. Mem did not have time to get up before the lash whistled down, catching him across the buttocks.

'No, Masta Ham!' he cried out, raising one hand to ward off the blows. 'Don' hit me! Don'!' He lifted his head so that the rays of the lantern fell across it and his eyes were following the rise of the whip and its swift descent. 'Don', Masta Ham suh! Don' whip Mem! Ain' a-doin' nothin'.'

'Yo' ain' a-doin' nothin'?' Ham was so angry his voice cracked. 'Who that gal yo' got under yo'?' His booted foot caught Mem under the shoulder and rolled him off the girl. He reached down and fastened his fingers in the girl's hair, dragging her up.

'That Saphira,' Lucretia Borgia volunteered as soon as she had the lantern light on the girl's face. 'She supposed to be down in Minty's cabin. She ain' been busted yet.'

'She's shore as hell busted now.' Ham released the girl. 'Ain' she, Mem? An' yo' the one what busted her? Right?'

'We jes' a-talkin', Masta Ham suh. Tha's all.'

'Hell of a way to carry on a conversation.' Ham laughed but it was a far from pleasant laugh. 'Naked buck 'n wench down in the weeds at one o'clock in the mornin'; buck a-ridin' that gal like'n he ridin' a pony; 'n yo' tell me yo' jes' a-talkin'.' He raised the whip again but he did not bring it down because Mem had thrown himself at Hammond's feet.

'Cain' help it, Masta Ham suh. Jes' cain' help it. Man got to have his pesterin' o' he git so hot he die. Cain' git none from Lucretia Borgia no more.'

She interrupted him. 'Pshaw! Reason yo' cain' is 'cause yo' cain' git it up no more.'

'Kin too,' he answered her and then went on with his supplication of Hammond. 'Yo' a-knowin', Masta Ham suh, that a man gotta have his pesterin' – cain' live 'thout'n it. Cain' git me none from Lucretia Borgia, she ain' there nights.'

'Git into yore trogs.' Ham's boot pushed Mem away. He motioned for Lucretia Borgia to lower the lantern so that Mem could find his breeches and the girl her dress. He quickly moved the girl's face into the light of the lantern so that he could identify her himself. She was indeed the adolescent that Lucretia Borgia had proclaimed her to be.

' 'N yo' git yo'self down to Minty's cabin. Tell Minty I'll be seein' her in the mornin'. If'n she cain' keep track o' her girls, we damn soon find another what kin. Reckon yo' a-goin' to git a whoppin' too.'

'Oh, don' whop me, Masta Ham suh.' Her young voice was high-pitched and querulous. 'It all Mem's fault. He a-sayin' that yo' tellin' him to bust me so's I could git a sucker for yo' quick.'

Without replying to the girl, Ham waited for them to dress, which was not a lengthy process, and then pushed them before him. They came out of the weeds, skirted the manure pile, and entered the barn. As they neared the front doors, Hammond motioned for Lucretia Borgia to stop. She

265

waited, holding the lantern high while he went to the wall and took down a pair of spancels. He walked to one of the upright beams that supported the hayloft and motioned for Mem to come to him. Placing a spancel on one wrist, he drew the other arm around and fastened the second spancel so that Mem was chained upright to the beam, his hands in front of him.

'Cain' lie down, Masta Ham,' Mem whimpered.

'Yo' bin a-braggin' about how yo' so goddamned upstandin', won' do yo' no harm to stand up the rest o' the night.'

'Oh, Masta Ham suh . . .'

'Shut up! One more word 'n yo' gits a taste o' the whip right here 'n now.'

Mem subsided. Ham shoved the girl ahead of him into the night, pointing in the direction of the cabins. 'Go!' He tickled her legs with the whip and she started off, running as fast as she could go, the sound of her bare feet slapping against the dirt drowning out her sobs.

Hammond and Lucretia Borgia headed for the house. They entered through the kitchen door. Lucretia Borgia lifted one of the glass sides of the lantern and took out the candle, lighting a tallow dip from it for Ham to take to bed with him. He started for the back stairs, then turned suddenly. 'What Mem a-meanin' when he a-sayin' that yo' not here nights?'

She had the courage to laugh, although not very heartily. 'He ain' meanin' nothin', Masta Hammond suh. He jes' a-tryin' to git back at me. Yo' a-knowin' how Mem lies.' She shrugged her shoulders, trying to make light of the whole matter.

'He shore as hell lies.' Hammond took the candle from her. 'But yo' know somethin' funny, Lucretia Borgia?'

She shook her head.

'*Sometimes* he tells the truth.'

CHAPTER TWENTY-NINE

When Lucretia Borgia awoke the next morning, it was with a presentiment of something dire about to happen. She couldn't explain what it was that seemed so ominous, but the feeling was there and she couldn't deny it. She was aware of Mem's empty place on the pallet and she gave him a moment's thought, standing through the long night, spancelled to a beam in the barn. She did not feel any particular sympathy for him. Though she had been in love with him when she first came to Falconhurst, long familiarity and a knowledge of his selfish, lazy ways had turned that love into indifference. She really didn't care what happened to him. That was definitely not what was troubling her; but some unknown thing pressed down upon her like a heavy weight.

The feeling persisted throughout her preparations for breakfast. Both Ham and his father were a little late in coming down so she decided to prepare a special breakfast as a sop to their feelings. Along with the daily ham and eggs she stirred up batter for hot cakes and set the big iron griddle to heating over the coals. The coffee was ready, the twins up and underfoot, and the cakes waiting to be poured out onto the hot griddle when she heard Ham and his father coming down the front stairs into the living room. With Maxwell's illness of the night before in her thoughts, she went into the sitting room and stood there, waiting for Maxwell to speak to her so that she could enquire about his health. Finally he stopped his heated conversation with Ham on the subject of Mem. His night's rest had not calmed his temper and he glared at her.

'What in tarnation yo' a-wantin', Lucretia Borgia? Know yo' a-wantin' somethin' or yo' wouldn't be starin' at me with yore big mouth open 'n yore eyes a-poppin'.'

'Ain' a-wantin' nothin', Masta Warren suh, 'cept to ask how yo' be this mornin', since yo' was sick last night.'

'Sicker'n a dog I was, 'n it all yore fault a-servin' me those pork chops. Could've died 'n nobody payin' no 'tention to me.' His voice was irritable.

'Pore Masta Warren.' Her voice had the proper edge of sympathy. 'Got us ham 'n eggs 'n hot cakes for breakfast this mornin' but if'n yo' wants I could make yo' up some nice milk toast. Gentle for your stomach.'

'Milk toast! Pshaw! Ain' needin' no invalid's pap. Git out in the kitchen 'n git breakfast on the table. We got lots to do this mornin'.'

'Yassuh, Masta Warren suh.' She hesitated, knowing she had no right to ask the question in her mind; but her curiosity got the better of her. 'Yo' a-goin' to whop Mem this mornin'?'

'Don' be such a nosey female.' His anger flared up and he snarled at her. ' 'N after breakfast, wants yo' should do an errand for me.'

'Yassuh, Masta Warren suh.' She was properly obsequious. 'Anything yo' say.' She headed for the kitchen, busying herself with preparations for breakfast, which she herself served in the absence of Mem.

She hoped that she would catch some fragment of conversation that would tell her what they were talking about, but each time she came in, not a word was said that would give her a clue. She also tried listening at the door, but her duties in the kitchen and dining room gave her little opportunity. It was not until breakfast was over that Maxwell called her in.

'Wants yo' to heist yo'self down to Minty's cabin 'n fetch me that girl Saphira, 'n also wants yo' to bring Minty; 'n don' yo' *dare* ask me whaffor I wants them, 'cause I ain' a-tellin' yo'.'

It had been on the tip of her tongue to ask exactly that, but she knew better now. She waited until they had finished eating and gone out on the front gallery before she went down to the street of cabins. Without knocking on Minty's door, which was closed, she went in. Minty, a buxom wench of twenty-two or three, was sitting on the only chair in earnest conversation with Saphira. Lucretia Borgia was in time to hear the end of one of Minty's sentences.

'. . . 'n yo' know how 'ticular Masta Maxwell is 'bout his wenches matin' up 'thout'n he say so.'

Lucretia Borgia stood in the doorway, waiting to hear Saphira's reply.

'But Mem he a house servant, 'n he a-tellin' me that Masta Maxwell wantin' me to go with him so's I could git busted 'n git a sucker for him.'

'That Mem a liar like'n always,' Lucretia Borgia spoke from the doorway. 'He jes' a lyin' fool, that man. But he a-goin' to git his come-uppance today. Masta a-goin' to whop him till the meat come right off'n his bones.'

'Know what yo' means, Lucretia Borgia.' Minty shifted in the chair so that she could face Lucretia Borgia. 'He sweet-talked me once. But I too old for him now. He likes the young uns like'n Saphira here.'

'All this talk about Mem don' make me no neverminds nohow. Masta done sent me down here to fetch yo' 'n Saphira up to the big house. He a-wantin' to talk to yo' both, I reckon. So yo' better come along 'n don' waste no more time a-talkin' 'bout that worthless Mem. Masta he mightily riled up, 'n he ain' a patient man.' She shooed them out of the cabin and set a brisk pace for them to walk to the big house. When they arrived, she ushered Minty and Saphira up to the edge of the gallery where the white men could look down upon them, then mounted the steps to stand behind their chairs. Minty she knew was trembling with fear, and as for Saphira, she was so frightened that her face was the colour of ashes. It was a rare thing for any of the folk at Falconhurst to be so ushered into their master's presence.

Warren Maxwell regarded them. He pursed his lips, coughed once or twice, cleared his throat and then commenced to speak with the attitude of a judge sentencing a criminal.

'Yo' Minty, and yo' Saphira, what yo' two wenches got to

say for yo'self?' It was an empty question because he knew, and they knew, that whatever they said would amount to nothing.

'Don' rightly know what yo' means, Masta Maxwell suh,' Minty answered him, taking the prerogative of so doing because she was the eldest.

'Means what yo' got to say 'bout one of the wenches that livin' in yore cabin and what I entrusted to yo'? What she doin' a-sashayin' out in the night with Mem, a-pesterin' down in the weeds behind the barn?'

Minty wrung her hands, peering up at her master from under tear-bedewed eyelashes. She seemed helpless and woe-begone, as indeed she was. Finally she found courage to speak. 'All the wenches in my cabin on their pallets 'n sound asleep afore I went to sleep myself. Always wait until they get quiet afore I beds myself down. Didn't know nothin' 'bout this Saphira till she come a-stumblin' into the cabin at night, a-weepin' 'n wailin' 'n carryin' on. Said Mem told her that it yore orders he takes her down in the weeds. She a-sayin' that he tell her to sneak outa the cabin 'thout'n anyone a-knowin' 'bout it, when everyone asleep. She a-thinkin' yo' a-wantin' her to, 'cause Mem he a house servant like'n Lucretia Borgia. Sometimes yo' send a message to us by Lucretia Borgia or Mem. Saphira thinkin' she a-doin' the right thing.'

Maxwell stared down at her, his lips set in a grim line. 'We a-raisin' niggers here at Falconhurst what I aim to be the best goddamn niggers in the South. Tha's why I have cabins like'n yourn.' He pointed at Minty. ''N tha's why I put wenches in charge o' them that I reckon to be responsible. If'n they ain', 'n 'low their wenches to be traipsin' round after dark, then I ain' got no control over none of the wenches here. Ain' never had no complaints afore 'n don' intend to have any 'gain. Got to drive it into every burrhead on this plantation that a buck 'n a wench mates up when *I* say so, 'n not a minute afore. Understand?'

'Yes, Masta Maxwell suh.' Minty bowed her head and used the hem of her osnaburg dress to wipe her eyes. 'Ain' never a-goin' to happen 'gain, not whilst I'm in charge of the cabin it ain'.'

'Damn right it ain' a-goin' to happen 'gain.' Maxwell regarded her with scorn. ' 'Cause yo' ain' a-goin' to be here, Minty. Goin' to sell yo' off to the first slave trader what comes along a-draggin' a coffle o' miserable critters behind him.'

She started to sob in earnest and came to the gallery to clasp Maxwell's feet with her hands. 'Don' sell me, Masta Maxwell suh! Don'! Not to any slaver. Yo' only sells yore worthless slaves to a trader. Look at me! Brought yo' in four prime suckers, I did. . . .'

'So it's high time yo' were sold.' He kicked her hands away from his boots. ' 'N that ain' all. Cain' trust yo' no more. When I has a wench or a buck what I cain' trust, I gits myself shet o' them once 'n for all. But afore yo' go, yo's a-goin' to git whopped.'

She stood before him, her shoulders sloped in utter dejection. She knew that there was no reason to plead because the word of her white master was final, but it was only human to beg forgiveness, to ask for a change of mind on his part, to convince him that it was not really her fault. She realized that nothing she could say or do, no promises for the future or explanations of things past, could move him. He was omnipotent; she was a nonentity. Yet she tried.

'Ain' my fault, Masta Maxwell suh. It all Mem's fault, it is. He a-comin' to Saphira 'n a-tellin' her that yo' said it all right for her to go with him. He a-sayin' that yo' a-wantin' it. What *I* to do? How *I* know that Saphira she a-goin' to run out in the middle o' the night? She ain' never done it afore, 'n shore she ain' a-goin' to do it 'gain.'

'Not carin' whether yo' know or not. It yore fault a-lettin' Saphira go. Now we don' hold with whoppin' wenches here, 'n don' aim to scar yo' up afore sellin' yo', but yo' sure as hell a-goin' to git whopped. Yo' a-goin' to have five strokes. That's not many, but 'nuff to let yo' 'n all o' Falconhurst know yo' did wrong, 'n that they a-goin' to git worse if'n they go a-traipsin' round with anybody they likes. Got to

271

make an example out'n yo'. I'm a-goin' to give yo' five strokes 'n then sell yo'.' He turned from her, ignoring the pleading hands stretched out for mercy, to look down on Saphira.

' 'N yo', wench. Yo' got a mighty tender hide on yo', but yo' a-goin' to git whopped too. Ain' a-goin' to welt yo' up none 'cause jes' mayhap Mem he got yo' knocked up, 'n 'sides, ain' wantin' no wales on yore back 'cause I'm a-goin' to sell yo' too, once I git some suckers out'n yo'. Seven strokes for yo' 'cause yo' a damn sight more guilty than Minty.' He turned to Hammond, who was listening to his father with a sober face. 'Take these two out to the barn 'n spancel 'em. Ain' thinkin' that they run. Falconhurst folk ain' runners. But with a whoppin' ahead o' them, no telling what they do.' He waited for Hammond to take the two women and start for the barn, then he too, leisurely and with a mien as sombre as Hammond's, started up, but before he left the gallery, he motioned to Lucretia Borgia.

'Yo' come along with me, Lucretia Borgia. These the first two wenches ever whopped at Falconhurst, so it right fittin' that yo' do it. Somehow seems better – wench whoppin' a wench more proper than a buck standing there a-pourin' it on.'

He descended the gallery steps with Lucretia Borgia behind him and they headed for the barn. Although she realized that she was exceeding her prerogative, she walked beside him, matching her steps with his.

'I'll shore pore it on 'em,' she said.

'But yo' be careful,' he admonished, not conscious that she was beside and not behind him. 'Don' want these wenches all waled up. We a-usin' a paddle, not the whip. Paddle don' leave no wales but hurt worse 'n a whip. Wants that yo' hit 'em right fair 'n square on the ass. Five strokes ain' a-goin' to draw blood, but it a-goin' to make it right tender for 'em to sit down for a couple o' days.'

She fell a step behind him. 'Shore will pore it on, Masta Maxwell suh. Wenches a-goin' to be eatin' their meals off'n the mantelpiece for a few days.'

His only answer was a grunt and a quickening of his footsteps to catch up with Hammond and the two girls.

CHAPTER THIRTY

When they arrived at the barn, Ham had spancelled the two girls to an upright beam where they stood facing Mem. Immediately upon their entry, he set up a heart-rending wail of lamentation, caterwauling, begging for mercy, weeping, promising never to do a like thing again, pleading for a remission of the whipping.

'I'se yore boy, Masta Warren suh. Knows jes' what to do to please yo' all the times. Makes yore toddies for yo'; helps yo' git undressed 'n into bed. I'se yore Mem, Masta Warren suh. Sorry 'bout what I did, 'n promise I won't do it no more. Promise yo', Masta Warren suh, 'deed I do, jes' if'n yo' won' whip me this time. Unlock me, Masta suh, 'n yo'll see. Mem never be wicked or slothful 'gain. Jes' try me this once. Don' whop me. Cain' serve yo' so well if'n yo' do. Yo' a-knowin' that Mem he a good boy.'

Maxwell, outside of a perfunctory glance just once in Mem's direction, paid no further attention to his pleas. Instead he went about making preparations for the flogging, turning a deaf ear not only to Mem's wailings but to the sobs and entreaties from the two girls. Finally he could stand it no longer, and walked over to where the three were stanchioned.

'One more sound out'n any of yo' varmints and I'll give each of yo' five extry strokes. Now, if'n yo' wants to git off light, keep yore mouths shut from now on. Plenty o' time for takin' on after yo' gits whopped; then yo'll have something to take on about.'

His words calmed the three suddenly. Not one of them

wanted five more strokes, although, to be sure, Mem did not know of what his punishment was to consist. Maxwell himself took down the perforated oxhide paddle which hung on the wall from a couple of nails. It had not been used in a long time. He swished it through the air a couple of times, noting the stiffness of the leather. Going to a cupboard on the barn wall, he took out a brown glass bottle, then called Omar to him.

'This is what we use for whoppin',' he explained to Omar, ' 'n look like'n yo're a-goin' to do some whoppin' here to-day. Yo' big 'nuff, strong 'nuff to do it. So whilst we a-gittin' ready, yo' oil this paddle so's it not so stiff-like.' He regarded Omar, who did not seem to understand all that he had said, and then pulled the cork out of the bottle and poured a little neat's-foot oil onto the leather. He rubbed and kneaded it in with his fingers, making sure that Omar followed all his movements, then gave the paddle to Omar, who continued with the work.

'Ham,' Warren Maxwell called out to his son, who was still standing before Mem and the sniffling girls. 'Better start the bell a-ringin' so's the folks will be a-comin' in. Wants every buck 'n wench on this plantation to see what a-happenin' to anyone what goes 'round pesterin' 'thout'n my say-so.' He motioned to the big bell atop a pole outside the barn. Its unmusical clanging could be heard all over the plantation, and its tocsin always foretold something of special importance at the big house and demanded that all the folk come in from the fields. Ham was a little peevish about his father's ordering him to do such menial work, so he in turn delegated the job to Lucretia Borgia. She went out, always pleased to be the centre of attention, and with willing hands pulled at the rope so violently that the bell turned over and over, clanging a metallic alarum that betokened something unusual. To be sure, the bell was rung every morning to waken the people, and again at evening to summon them from the fields; but when it sounded at other times, it was a dire warning for everyone.

The boys in the barn gathered around Mem and the two

274

girls, open-mouthed with excitement. Here was Mem, who in that special hierarchy of house servants, was next to the masters themselves in importance, spancelled to a beam and a picture of abject woe. It hardly seemed possible that such a high and mighty personage as Mem could be the object of his master's wrath. Yet he was, and it took only a little of putting two and two together to make four that the preparations Omar was making on the leather paddle presaged a whipping for Mem and probably for the two girls likewise. The boys muttered amongst themselves, speaking in whispers because they knew by the look on Maxwell's face – which was mirrored on Ham's – that one untoward word and they would be the recipient of the paddle along with these three. It was not good to tempt the patience of a white master when he was in this mood. Potential danger was present for every black boy and girl on the plantation. Step softly and speak quietly was the watchword.

Maxwell hailed two of them and made them come over and draw up a pair of splint-bottomed chairs for himself and Ham. He showed where they should be placed so that he could get a full view of the proceedings. Once settled to his satisfaction, he had the same two boys lower the ropes on wooden pulleys at each side of the big barn doors. The pulleys screeched as the ropes were pulled down; to test these, Maxwell had the boys pull on them with all their weight so he could be confident that they would not break. Whippings were such a rarity at Falconhurst that the equipment became rusty between uses.

By the time the boys had tested the ropes and Omar had restored some degree of resiliency to the paddle, the folk began congregating. They had hurried in from the fields and from their work in the various buildings, and now there was a crowd of them before the barn doors. Children ran naked between the rows of adults, playing their interminable games and totally innocent of what would happen to them when they grew up. The Falconhurst herd was unique, and probably could not be duplicated by any other plantation in the South. Among the entire assembly there was not a single sign of age. There was not a buck over the age of twenty-two or three, and the wenches were nearly all younger than that. Falconhurst was a plantation of youth, of well-muscled bodies, of handsome and intelligent faces, of large-bosomed pretty women. There was not a grey hair to be seen except for those that silvered Maxwell's locks. Youth was a precious commodity at Falconhurst. Other plantations might have the old, the crippled and the infirm, but not Falconhurst. Everyone was sold at the peak of his strength or the apex of her child-bearing productivity.

'They all here, Ham?' Maxwell viewed the crowd with a practised eye, and at the sound of his voice the whispers and murmurs ceased.

'Thinkin' they are,' Ham answered, 'all 'cept that gang from the north woodlot 'n they a-comin' now.' He pointed to a group of men who were dog-trotting towards the barn, fearful that they might miss something if they did not make haste.

Maxwell waited another few moments then beckoned for Ham to stand beside him. Looking around for Lucretia Borgia, his eyes discovered her and he motioned for her to stand behind Ham and himself. His upraised hand quieted the crowd until there was absolute silence. In a loud voice, so that even those in the back could hear, he started to speak.

'Call yo-all in here this mornin' 'cause I got somethin' extra special for yo-all to see. Wants that it should teach yo' a lesson. Wants that yo-all remember somethin'. This a very special plantation. Ain' a cotton plantation. Not by a damn sight! We a-raisin' niggers here at Falconhurst, 'n we aim to raise the best goddamn niggers in the South.

'Now, there ain' nothin' very difficult 'bout raisin' niggers. Soon's yo' git old 'nuff yo-all know how to do it. Puts a buck to a wench; she spreads her legs 'n the buck pesters her. He kin pester her twenty times a night if'n he able.' He waited momentarily for a deal of snickering to die out and for the first time his expression was changed by the ghost of a smile. 'Tha's how we raise niggers. But it important that the right buck is pesterin' the right wench. Cain' have no brothers

276

a-pesterin' no sisters, or no bucks a-pesterin' their dams. T'ain' right. Well! I gits a sucker out'n that good pesterin', 'n lets the sucker grow up. Then I sells him. He a Falconhurst buck or she a Falconhurst wench. Best goddamn niggers in the whole country. A-goin' to sell yo'-all when the time comes, but it ain' no regular sale that I sells yo' at. I sells yo' special in N'Orleans or Natchez. Ain' a-sellin' yo' off as field hands 'n cotton choppers. Sellin' yo' bucks as studs, yo' wenches as dams, so's yo' have special treatment where I sells yo'. How yo'-all like to be studs 'n breed-dams on some of the best plantations in the South?'

He stopped and smiled at them again, hearing their comments with satisfaction.

'We like that, Masta suh.'

'Shore fine, Masta suh.'

'Shore git us a lot o' pesterin' that way.'

'Keep right on a-givin' yo' suckers if'n yo' lets me stay here.'

He nodded his head in approbation and even went further in his acclaim by stepping outside the barn and patting some of the bucks and wenches on the arm as a public approbation of their strength and fitness. But when he returned to the doorway, the smile had vanished and he was stern again.

'Now, yo' bucks 'n wenches a-knowin' that I give yo'-all plenty o' chance for pesterin'. Mos' every buck has his wench 'n he a-workin' mighty hard every night to git me all the suckers he kin. Tha's fine. But remember one thing. I'm the one to say when a buck pesters a wench, 'n what wench he beddin' down with. Aimin' to mate yo' up for the best results. 'N that why I made it a rule not to let no buck or wench go round a-pickin' out their own mates. That ain' the way I does it. If'n I let yo'-all do that, pretty soon we be comin' up with a bunch o' runty suckers which ain' worth a damn when they grows up.

'So, it a hard 'n fast rule here that I does the pickin' 'n choosin', 'n then the buck 'n wench I picks 'n chooses, they go to work. Best work in the world. Ain' no other place in the country gives bucks 'n wenches such fine work.'

277

'Yes suh, Masta Maxwell suh. Yes suh, we know that.' The replies were enthusiastic.

He nodded and continued. 'But when a buck takes it into his mind that he wants to pester some other wench than the one I picks for him, trouble starts. Tha's somethin' I ain' a-goin' to have. Ain' a-goin' to have it; if'n I catches a buck 'n wench together what I ain' mated up myself, they a-goin' to pay for it. Jes' catched myself one pair last night. That Mem,' he gestured to the slavering Mem, still spancelled to the beam, 'he a house servant 'n he should of known better. 'N that wench,' he pointed to Saphira, 'I ain' blamin' too much 'cause Mem sweet-talked her, 'n she a-reckonin' that with Mem bein' a house servant, he a-knowin' what he a-talkin' 'bout; but she guilty none the less. 'N so's that wench Minty what I put in charge of a cabin o' young wenches to see they don't get busted till I wants 'em busted.'

There was a doleful shaking of heads and a general condemnation from the black audience.

'So,' Maxwell brought the fist of his right hand down into the palm of his left with a resounding smack, 'I'm makin' an example. Minty she a-goin' to git five strokes o' the paddle. That'll teach her 'n the other wenches in charge o' cabins to keep watch better. 'N that Saphira,' he turned and pointed to the girl, 'she a-goin' to get seven strokes. Next time she a-spreadin' her legs for any buck I don' already have the say-so for, she a-goin' to remember how her ass sting this time. 'N as for Mem, I'm a-goin' to give him twenty.'

A wail from Mem, louder than before, echoed inside the barn.

'Now I don' hold with whoppin's,' Maxwell had lowered his voice. 'Ain' much need for them here at Falconhurst, but I shore as hell a-goin' to whop today. These the furst wenches what ever been whopped here, 'n Lucretia Borgia she a-goin' to whop 'em at my orders. The new boy I jes' got, that Mandingo,' he pointed to Omar who held the paddle in his hands, 'he a-goin' to whop Mem. Now, I want yo'-all to watch what's a-goin' on, 'n figure out that if'n yo' goes out a-pesterin' in the weeds, yo' a-goin' to git the same,

278

be it buck or wench! Every time that paddle comes down, a-wantin' yo' to feel it on yore own ass, so's yo' won't think yo' kin do jes's yo' damn please. Yo're niggers 'n servants for life, 'n yo' do as I say 'n yo' won't be sorry, but if'n yo' take things into yore own hands, yo're shore as hell a-goin' to feel the sting o' that paddle on yore own black ass.' He stared down at them, catching first one pair of eyes and then another. '*Understand?*'

There was a strained silence for a second and then one of the big lads in the rear spoke out. 'We understands, Masta Maxwell suh. We ain' never a-goin' to do nothin' less'n yo' tells us.'

The remainder of the crowd was silent, although there was a bobbing of heads to assure Maxwell that they had all understood.

CHAPTER THIRTY-ONE

Maxwell seated himself rather pompously and indicated that Ham was to sit beside him. He turned around to Lucretia Borgia.

'Aimin' to whop them two wenches first, but afore we starts, I want a toddy. Hustle up to the house 'n git me one.' Looking at Ham, whose face was unnaturally pale and drawn, he said, 'Better fetch two, Lucretia Borgia. Ham a-lookin' mighty peaked this mornin'. He takes after his mama's folks. Cain' stand whoppin's. Toddy might do him good.'

'Water all hot in the teakettle. Won't take me a minute.' Despite her size, Lucretia Borgia could move fast; now, afraid she might miss something, she ran up the path to the big house.

Maxwell sat back, his eyes straying from Mem to the two girls. He knew that Mem would have liked to start his pleading again, but was deterred by the fear of those five extra strokes. The two girls were still sobbing under their breath. During the minutes that Lucretia Borgia was gone, Maxwell did not speak. Suspense grew, and so did the importance of the event in everyone's eyes.

From the time Lucretia Borgia reappeared, walking sedately now so as not to spill the toddies she carried on a japanned tray, all eyes were upon her; she sensed the dramatic scene and her own important role in it. With a lifting of her head and a straightening of her back, she strode down the weed-grown path – a veritable queen, not only recognizing but emphasizing her importance at Falconhurst. For this moment she was the centre of the stage. She presented the two toddies to Maxwell and Ham with a flourish.

'Yo' both takes care,' she warned. 'Toddies mighty hot 'n don' want yo' to burn yore tongues on 'em.' With a regal gaze at the upturned sea of black faces, she flounced around and once more stood behind Maxwell and Ham. But she was not destined to remain long in that position, for a far more authoritative one awaited her.

Maxwell beckoned to Omar who, back in the shadows of the barn, was still kneading the paddle with his fingers. Reaching up, he took the paddle from him and turning in his chair, placed it in Lucretia Borgia's hands.

'It right fittin' 'n proper that yo' whops these two gals, Lucretia Borgia,' he said portentously. 'Yo' a-knowin' how to do it?'

She came to stand in front of him, grasping the paddle by its thick hickory handle. 'Saw yo' whop Rasmus long time ago,' she nodded, ' 'n thinkin' I know how.'

'Jes' be shore yo' hits 'em square on the ass. Ain' a-goin' to leave no scar there if'n yo' careful, 'n five or seven strokes ain' a-goin' to draw blood or scar 'em up nohow. But yo' got to wait for 'em to swing toward yo'. Hittin' 'em on the back swing ain' a-goin' to do 'em no good. Wait till they right near yo' 'n swing it good 'n proper.' With a sweeping gesture

280

of his hand, he indicated for her to take her place just inside the barn door.

'Which one yo' aimin' for me to whop first, Masta Warren suh?' There was a note of pride in her voice – pride that she had been chosen for this important task.

'Whop Minty first off. She only git five strokes, so yo' kin practise up on her.' He called a big fellow by the name of Demon to him.

'Yo' bin at whoppin's afore, Deem. Yo' a knowin' what to do.'

'First we fastens their legs to the rope 'n heists 'em up. That what yo' a-wantin', Masta Maxwell suh?'

'That's it, boys yo' show this Omar boy how yo' does it.'

Lucretia Borgia watched Omar and Demon as they unlocked the spancels from Minty's wrists and half-carried her to a spot on the floor in the centre of the big doorway. They forced her to lie prone on the floor, her face pressed against the dirty boards. With leather thongs they bound her ankles, one to each of the ropes that hung down from the pulleys. When they had tested the ropes to make sure they were securely fastened, they each took one and pulled on it. Minty's body slid across the splintery floor and although she tried to ease herself along with her hands, she scraped most of the way across, screaming as the splinters from the floor penetrated her thin dress. The men continued pulling on the ropes, lifting her legs and finally her whole body so that her fingertips barely touched the floor. Vainly she tried to straighten her head up and now her screams were subdued by her inability to force much air out of her lungs.

'Time yo' started, Lucretia Borgia,' Maxwell's voice boomed in the silence.

Lucretia Borgia waited until Minty's body stopped swinging. The girl's single garment had now fallen down over her head, exposing her brown legs and thighs and her back as far as her armpits. When she had stopped swinging, Lucretia Borgia took careful aim and with a powerful stroke of the paddle landed it expertly on Minty's rear. Minty found enough air to scream and as her body swung back towards

281

Lucretia Borgia, she aimed again, making contact with the paddle slightly lower than she had on the first stroke.

Maxwell kept an account of the strokes, his voice rising above Minty's strangled screams. When he reached five, he bade Lucretia Borgia cease, and walked over to the dangling girl. His expert fingers traced a path over her reddened rump and he nodded his head in approbation. He gestured with his thumb to the two boys and they slowly lowered the ropes until Minty's body was again on the floor. They freed her ankles and she crept across the floor on her hands and knees to a pile of feed sacks in the corner of the barn. All the time she was whimpering like an animal in pain.

Now it was time for Saphira and despite her more violent struggles, she was strung up. Once again Maxwell timed Lucretia Borgia's strokes. Although Saphira screamed louder than Minty, Maxwell was able to make himself heard above her wails. Lucretia Borgia missed the sixth stroke as Saphira swung away from her in the increasing arc that the blows caused, and she had to make an additional attempt to achieve the total of seven strokes. Consequently the seventh stroke was ill-placed for the first time. Lucretia Borgia saw a trickle of blood appear on Saphira where the stroke had landed on skin made tender by a previous blow. Maxwell was quick in his censure of Lucretia Borgia for not being more careful, and when he examined Saphira's hanging body, his fingers were red with blood, which he wiped on her dress. Saphira was let down quickly and she too crept away to the same pile of feed sacks where Minty had found refuge. The girls tried to comfort each other, their arms entwined, their sobs interspersed with soothing words.

Lucretia Borgia's job was over. She was sorry indeed that she had had to be censured before all the folks, but this, she felt, was a small matter compared with the immense stature she had received by doing the whipping. She scrubbed at the paddle with a dirty wad of cotton which she had picked up from the barn floor, removing the blood from it before returning it to Maxwell. Once again, her work through, she took up her position behind Maxwell's chair. She had noticed a peculiar paleness in Ham's face and she leaned over worriedly to ask him if he felt all right. He answered with an affirmative nod. She saw that he had not taken any of his toddy; she picked up the glass and handed it to him.

'Better yo' take a good swig, Masta Ham suh,' she whispered. He turned up his head to meet her eyes. A wry smile appeared and he followed her advice, downing the now-cool toddy in quick gulps before he settled back in his chair.

Maxwell went over to where the two girls were stretched out on the pile of sacks. 'Bet yore asses sort of stingy-like,' he said, not unkindly. 'Thinkin' though that yo' kin both walk.'

They answered with doleful nods.

'Then better heist yo'selves 'n git down to yore cabin. Ain' no need for yo'-all to stay here 'n watch Mem a-gittin' whopped. Wash yo'selves in warm water 'n put some mutton taller on yore behinds to ease the pain. 'N Minty,' his voice was now friendly, 'yo 'n Saphira kin be excused from work the next couple days, but hopin' that what yo' got today been a lesson to yo' both.'

Minty struggled to her feet and reached a hand to Saphira to help her up. 'Ain' never a-goin' to do it 'gain, Masta Maxwell suh.' She seemed to harbour no resentment. 'A-goin' to watch my wenches like'n a mother hen does her chicks.'

' 'N I too, Masta Maxwell suh.' Saphira stopped sobbing long enough to speak. 'Ain' never a-goin' to listen to that Mem or no other buck less'n yo' tells me.'

He patted them both affectionately on the shoulders. The strokes of the lash had erased his anger towards them. They hobbled out of the barn together. With a glance at Mem, he returned to his chair. A restless movement crept through the crowd outside. They shuffled their feet uneasily and gestured towards the barn. They had enjoyed seeing Minty and Saphira whipped but they knew that these punishments were merely curtain-raisers. The big show of the day would be Mem's whipping. The crowd had no sympathy for him; instead they were looking forward to seeing him receive his twenty strokes. That was a lot to get at one time; he'd probably howl something awful. Well, the louder he howled the more interesting it would be. It would be something to talk about for days to come.

Maxwell sent Ham to unlock Mem's spancels. Mem stumbled across the floor to throw himself at his master's feet, begging once more for mercy; after a disdainful glance at him, Maxwell merely shrugged his shoulders and called Omar and Demon over to strip off Mem's clothes and take him away.

But Mem was not through. Regardless of the fact that he was disobeying Maxwell, he brushed his two captors aside and stood up, facing his master. 'Why yo' a-blamin' only me for all this, Masta suh? Ain' all rightly *my* fault.' He took a long breath and pointing an accusing finger at Lucretia Borgia, said, 'It rightly *hers*.'

'Shut yore big mouth, Mem, 'n take yore punishment.' Maxwell was stern. ' 'N don' forget your manners. *Masta Maxwell suh*, or I give yo' five more strokes for forgettin' how to 'dress me.'

But at this point five more strokes meant nothing to Mem. 'A-goin' to tell yo' somethin', Masta Warren suh. I mean it. It all Lucretia Borgia's fault. She ain' never in her bed no more so's I kin pester her. She out gallivantin' around of a night, 'n that's why I got to find my pesterin' somewheres else. If'n she stay in her bed, it be all right. But,' he stopped for a moment and pointed the accusing finger at Omar, 'he the one she been a-pesterin' with! He jes' as much to blame as me, so why don' yo' have him whopped instead o' me? Why don' yo', Masta Warren suh?'

Lucretia Borgia did not wait for Maxwell to answer.

'He a-lyin', Masta Warren suh. He always a-lyin'! Yo' knowin' that, Masta Warren suh. He jes' a lyin' snake in the grass like'n he always was.'

'Hush yore big mouth, Lucretia Borgia!' Maxwell rose from his chair and turned to confront her, his face scarlet with anger. 'Know that Mem he a liar, but wantin' to know if'n he a-lyin' *now*. Yo' been a-beddin' yo'self with this

Omar? Know yo' tooken a mighty big likin' to him, 'n want to know the truth. 'N yo' better *tell* me the truth. Yo' ain' so goddamn necessary to this plantation but what I could sell yo' to the first slave peddler what come along. Cain' stand no lyin' wench in my household. Better think good on that, if'n yo' don' want to git sold.'

She hesitated so long in answering him that he continued his questioning. His choler was so profound that he could scarcely speak. 'Yore face the colour o' wet ashes, Lucretia Borgia. Yo' been out pesterin' with this Omar?'

'Lucretia Borgia ain' a-doin' anything like'n that.' Ham stood up and confronted her also. He involuntarily started to stretch out his hands to take her in his arms, but the look on his father's face restrained him. 'Be yo', Lucretia Borgia?'

'Want the truth out'n yo', I do.' Maxwell pressed his question. 'If'n yo' lie to me, yo' a-goin' to be the worst off of all these damn folks bein' punished today. Cain' stand a lyin' nigger.' He turned to Mem. 'Yo' a-lyin', Mem, or a-tellin' the truth?'

Mem sensed that there might be a chance of mitigating his punishment. Maxwell's voice was not quite as harsh when he addressed him. 'It's the truth, Masta Warren, suh,' said Mem desperately. 'It's the honest truth. Kin tell yo' all 'bout it 'cause I followed her one night. She a-beddin' down with that Omar in the cloth shed. Tooken a feather bed out there, she did. They spreads it on the floor 'n pesters till it nigh come daylight. Ask her, Masta Warren suh, or ask him,' he pointed to Omar who, by this time, had understood that he too was being accused.

'Well, what 'bout it, Lucretia Borgia?' Maxwell's lips settled in a grim line. 'Yo' bin a-lyin' to me 'n throwin' the lie right in my face?'

'She not a-lyin', Papa.' Ham was near to tears. 'She good, Lucretia Borgia is, 'n she not a-lyin'.'

Except for a brief scornful glance at his son for being so gullible, Maxwell paid no attention to Ham.

'Want the truth, Lucretia Borgia,' he demanded. In the

285

tense silence that followed his last question, there was not a sound save Mem's continued whimpering.

Lucretia Borgia took a step towards her master, inhaled a long breath, squared her shoulders, and looked Maxwell in the eye. There was nothing abject or fawning about her manner. She was not even particularly fearful now – she was Lucretia Borgia.

'Yes, Masta Warren suh, I tell the truth. I ain'a liar, like'n yo' knows. Yes, I bin with Omar. Yo' didn't tell him to cover no wench, so not thinkin' that I a-doin' anything wrong. Shore, I bin with him. Him 'n me been together down in the cloth house like'n that dirty, spyin' skunk of a Mem a-sayin'. Ain' a-goin' to lie to yo'.'

For the first time her composure cracked and the first tear appeared in her eyes. She knew that now she was going to be punished. What that punishment would be, she had no idea, but she did not think she would be whipped. Still, she did not know.

'So, yo're finally tellin' the truth. Yo', Lucretia Borgia, of all people to do a thing like'n that.' Utter disappointment superseded his anger. 'Put my trust in yo', I did, 'n now yo' sneakin' off like any itchy wench jes' 'cause some new buck come here 'n yo' a-wantin' him to do some gallopin' on yo'. Tha's it, ain' it? Yo' jes' curious 'bout this new buck, tha's all.'

'Asked yo', Masta Warren suh, if'n I could have him.'

'That yo' did, 'n what did I say? Said "no". That a-makin' it all the worse for yo'. Lucretia Borgia, goin' to make an example o' yo' too. Yo' jes' as bad and a whole lot worser'n that Saphira gal. She didn't know. Yo' sure as hell did.' He sank down in his chair, trembling from his disappointment in her as well as his anger.

'Ain' a-goin' to whop Mem this time. Not that he not as guilty as hell, but a-goin' to whop yo' instead. Mem's a-goin' to git his come-uppance some day soon, but jes' now wantin' someone 'round the house to take care of us, 'n Mem he got to do it. Was a-goin' to give him twenty lashes, Lucretia

286

Borgia, but now a-goin' to give 'em to *yo*'. 'N a-goin' to give that new boy a taste too.'

'It my fault, Masta Warren suh.' She felt like sinking to her knees, the better to plead with him. 'Whop me if'n yo' wants, but don' whop Omar.'

'You a-tellin' me what to do, Lucretia Borgia?'

'Jes' a-beggin' yo' what not to do.'

'Aimin' to give yo' twenty strokes, Lucretia Borgia. Goin' to use a whip. Not usin' a paddle on yo', but usin' it on Omar; ain' aimin' to have him waled up, but don' make me no neverminds if'n yo' waled up or not. Ain' a-goin' to sell yo' nohow. Yo' too old 'n worthless to bring any money, so don' make no difference if'n yo' got wales on yore back or not. Ain' no one goin' to look at it. 'N no matter what yo' say, Lucretia Borgia, a-goin' to whop that Omar too.'

She stood silent before him. She knew that no amount of begging or entreaties would cause him to change his mind. She also realized her guilt and somewhere in the back of her mind she was glad that the whipping would wipe it out. She turned and took one long look at the sea of black faces which had hitherto regarded her as the most important person on the plantation after the white masters. More than the pain of the whipping she dreaded losing the esteem she had built up so gradually over the years. But nothing would help now. She bowed her head which she had been carrying so proudly all the morning.

'Yes suh, Masta Warren suh,' she said meekly.

Maxwell did not answer her. With an effort Ham stood up. He would have liked to put his arms around Lucretia Borgia to console her, but that he could not do. 'Yo' really a-goin' to whop her?'

'Shore as hell am goin' to. Don' yo' think she deserves it?'

'Yes, Papa, but a-wishin' yo' didn' have to.'

'So do I, son,' Maxwell's words lacked bitterness. 'But we a-goin' to, 'n we both a-goin' to watch it. Yo'll learn sometime that with a passel o' blacks on yore hands, yo' got to do a lot of things yo' don' want to do.'

CHAPTER THIRTY-TWO

The crowd was getting impatient; a restless rustle of movement crept through it, a shifting of feet and a press for better positions. They had been anticipating Mem's whipping and that, indeed, was something to anticipate. He was a house servant and far above any of them in the hierarchy of Falconhurst. A house servant being whipped was something they had never imagined could happen, because house servants were a privileged class. This fortunate group had daily contact with their masters, they ate the same food, dressed in decent clothes, and actually lived in the big house alongside the white people. They were as far removed from the ordinary field hands as the white masters were from the house servants.

This was an unprecedented happening and it was going to be something to see; that is why they were all anxious to get in the front row. But now, instead of Mem being whipped, they heard it was to be Lucretia Borgia. Yes, *Lucretia Borgia* was to be whipped. She had always moved in an orbit far above them, and now it seemed she was no better than the least of them. She was going to be punished, punished like any ordinary black wench who chopped cotton when she wasn't birthing a sucker. Lucretia Borgia! Well, she certainly had it coming to her for all her uppity high-and-mightiness, lording it over everyone else. Lucretia Borgia whipped! Good enough for her. Wonder how loud *she* was going to squeal?

And ... twenty strokes! That was as much as a grown man could take. My oh my, wouldn't she be cut up? With a lash too, not a paddle! It would strip the meat right off her bones. Wonder who was going to whip her? Bet it would be Demon. He had whipped before and he knew just how to lay it on. Yes, Demon was surely the man to do it.

But it was not to be Demon. Maxwell had devised something far more cruel and subtle for Lucretia Borgia. He beckoned to Omar.

'I'm a-goin' to whop yo', boy.' Maxwell punctuated his words with solemn nods of his head. 'There's some mastas as might think I should skip a-whoppin' yo' 'cause yo're new here, but yo' did somethin' 'gainst the rules and that means yo' git punished jes' like'n anyone else. But afore I whops yo', I'm a-goin' to have yo' do a little work. Yes, a-goin' to have yo' exercise those muscles o' yourn. How'd yo' like to be my whoppin' boy for a spell? Thinkin' perhaps I'll make yo' jes' that. Reckon as how I'm a-goin' to have yo' whop Lucretia Borgia. Seems right fittin' that yo' should do it, seein' as how yo' knows her so well 'n so well acquainted with that body o' hers.'

Omar stood before him alongside Lucretia Borgia and Maxwell eyed them both, making a slow visual inventory of them.

'Quite a pair yo' two are,' he finally spoke. 'If'n Lucretia Borgia younger 'n able to git a sucker from yo', it shore as hell a-goin' to be a right lively sucker. But she ain' a-birthin' nothin' no more, 'n nothin' she does birth a-goin' to be much good 'cause she past her prime.' He shifted his gaze to stare directly at Omar. 'Well, how 'bout it, boy? Yo' ready to whop her? Lookin' like'n yo' done yore ridin' 'thout'n a whip; now it time to put the whip to this old mare.'

Omar understood little of what Maxwell was saying, only enough to know that he too was destined for the whip. He shrank from it after seeing how it had hurt Minty and Saphira, but even more than the lash, which he knew he must endure, he abhorred having to whip Lucretia Borgia whom he really loved. To put the whip to that flesh which he had so ardently fondled would be punishment indeed – even worse than the pain the paddle-blows could cause his own body. He stood silent before Maxwell, not knowing what to say.

'Decided I'm only a-goin' to give yo' ten strokes,' Maxwell said. 'It not yore fault so much's it is Mem's 'n Lucretia

Borgia's 'cause, after all, yo' new here 'n don' know all the rules 'n regulations o' Falconhurst. Thinkin' that ten strokes a-goin' to teach yo' a lesson. Be a long time afore yo' starts pesterin' 'nother wench 'thout'n my say-so.'

He surveyed the two of them again – Lucretia Borgia and Omar – and his anger was somewhat mollified by the pride he took in them. He was forced to admire Lucretia Borgia. She had not begged for mercy, but had accepted her sentence. Once again she was holding herself proudly. She was a statuesque queen and Omar was a fitting consort. Too bad she was getting old, otherwise he would have been glad to mate her with Omar. He took a deep breath, wishing now that he had not already passed sentence on them. But now it was right that they should be punished. His eyes shifted to Ham, who was still sitting in his chair.

'Yo' mighty peaked-lookin',' Maxwell addressed his son. 'Shore yo' all right?'

'Yes, papa,' Ham nodded, but his eyes did not meet those of his father.

'Then git up 'n do somethin'. Yo' lookin' like'n yo' aim to puke up yore breakfast. Git over there 'n see 'bout gittin' them ropes round Lucretia Borgia's ankles. This Omar ain' a-goin' to be no good. He a-shakin' like'n a leaf, but when it come to whoppin' he got to lay 'em on good.' He turned to Omar. 'Hear that, boy? Don' think yo' kin let Lucretia Borgia off easy by not hittin' hard. Yo' jes' a-goin' to make it worse for her. If'n I think yo' ain' hittin' hard 'nuff, yo' got to do it over so 'stead o' gittin' only twenty strokes she a-goin' to end up with a lot more. Cain' cheat in front o' me. Not by a damn sight.'

He coughed, perhaps a little uncomfortably. 'Might's well shuck yo'self down, Lucretia Borgia,' he advised her, 'ain' no sense t'all to yore gitting yore clothes all bloodied up. 'Sides it worse to git whopped with clothes on. Lash cuts 'em right down into the flesh 'n makes the welts harder to heal. Best yo' strip 'em all off.'

Her eyes went to the crowd of blacks facing her and then back to Maxwell. He read her thoughts and for the first time smiled. 'Ain' none o' them what hasn't seen a black wench nekkid,' he said. 'Shuck yo'self down.'

Slowly she untied the starched white bow of her apron. Reluctantly she took it off and handed it to Hammond; it was her cherished badge of authority. Under the apron she was clad only in a frayed and patched black-and-grey calico dress, but it boasted mother-of-pearl buttons, which were a mark of distinction compared with the hand-made wooden buttons on the dresses of the other wenches. Now she unbuttoned each slowly and when that was done she took her dress off over her head. Now she stood before them naked – no, not quite naked, because Maxwell had not ordered her to take off her turban. She would have been ashamed for the folks to know that she had such short, wiry, kinky hair.

Now, standing before them naked, she felt ashamed. Even when she had been sold at auction she had not had to stand naked for so many eyes to see, and she wondered if this awful moment would ever pass. All the folks would be talking about her and even now she fancied she could hear them whispering among themselves. The great Lucretia Borgia reduced to a fat naked wench without her proud white apron and her calico dress. She wished the floor would open up and she would drop into it. But the one thing that shamed her most of all was that she had been forced to undress in front of Hammond. She felt like a mother to him and she knew that he had substituted her for his own mother. She wondered if she could ever look him in the eye again. Yet he was beside her, and gently took her arm and piloted her over to the middle of the barn floor.

'Best lay yo'self down, Lucretia Borgia.' Ham's voice was gentle and persuasive, not like his father's. She stretched belly-down on the floor, her nostrils inhaling the acrid dust. Now she could not see what was going on but she could judge by the sounds of activity. She felt the ropes being tied around her ankles and wondered who beside Demon was doing it. There was a moment of testing the knots and then she heard Maxwell's voice.

'She mighty heavy 'n solid, boys. Be shore them ropes a-goin' to hold her.'

'Yes suh, Masta Maxwell suh, they a-goin' to hold her all right.' It was Demon's voice. She wondered where Omar might be. With this punishment inflicted upon her, she realized she was no longer infatuated with Omar. She still admired him, but this was far too heavy a price to pay for him. It was his fault as much as hers, she reckoned, and it was unfair of Maxwell to give her double the punishment. She had a fleeting thought that she wished she might be the one chosen to give the strokes to Omar. No, she didn't. The sleekness of his flesh still held a pleasant memory for her and she did not want to harm it. Neither, she was sure, would he want to hurt her, but hurt her he must. She hoped he would not try to make the strokes easier for her. Maxwell would know and make him repeat them. God knows, twenty strokes were enough. That was a man's punishment, not a woman's. She hoped she could stand it.

'Heist her up, boys.' Maxwell was standing near her; by turning her head slightly she could see the shine on his boots. ' 'N heist her slow. She a-goin' to get 'nuff punishment on her backside 'thout draggin' her too fast across the floor.' He hunkered down beside her momentarily. 'Use yore hands, Lucretia Borgia. Ain' a-wantin' yo' to have to pick splinters out'n yore belly.'

The ropes tugged at her ankles and she felt her legs lifted. With the palms of her hands on the floor she eased her body up and, because Maxwell had ordered the boys to go slowly, she was able to support herself as the ropes pulled at her legs. Maxwell needn't have given her that little dole of kindness, but he had and for that she was grateful. She had once picked splinters out of a whipped slave's belly with a darning needle and she knew how painful that could be. Nothing, of course, compared with the actual whipping, but the splinters were an irritation when a person could lie only on his belly.

Now she was up in the air, her fingers not quite touching the floor. She could hear the ropes creak as they were wound

292

around the stanchions. She felt the blood rush to her head. In vain she tried to lift her head, but was able to do so for only a moment. What a spectacle she must make, strung up like a side of beef. Her full and pendulous breasts were hanging down and that would make her look even more ridiculous. She could see Maxwell's boots approaching her and feel his hand on her body as he gave her a push. She swung in an arc over the floor and as her body swung backwards, she felt the terrible sting of the lash as it snaked across her buttocks. It bit into her and burned as though she had been scorched with a red-hot iron. She had resolved not to cry out but the intense pain which bit into her like flame forced a scream from her; and she could hear herself screaming, although it sounded like someone else. Above the scream, she heard Maxwell's voice shout 'One.'

Only one, and nineteen more to go. She could never stand it. No human being could. Surely Maxwell would be merciful and let her down before the complete sentence was over.

'Two.' His voice rang out again and now with the swing of her body and the pain on her back she began to lose her senses. 'Three.' She could hear her own voice forming words that begged for mercy – something she had firmly made up her mind not to do. But she had never imagined such a hell as she was passing through. Resolves made under normal conditions did not apply now. Her body swung back. 'Four.' Her screams became so loud that she could not hear Maxwell's 'Five.'

She had entered into an animal world of pain and torture. She was no longer human. Existence had become a dizzying swing to more pain and each time she swung back the lash made contact and what was seemingly the utmost limit of pain was pushed back by one more number. She had lost track of the lashes now. There was nothing but a red haze in her mind, a pounding at her temples, and a torment in her back. Dimly, as though her ears belonged to another person, she heard the word 'twenty'. It meant nothing to her until she was aware that her body had stopped swinging and she was being lowered to the floor. Some instinct seemed to force her hands out to break her descent and she felt a certain relief, despite the pain, when her ankles were freed. Beyond that she realized nothing except the burning hell that raged in her body.

Boots approached. She managed to open one eye. 'It all over, Lucretia Borgia.' Maxwell's voice had lost its harshness. 'All over, Lucretia Borgia,' he repeated. 'Can yo' git yo'self up?'

The red mist was evaporating from her eyes and she could see better. 'Kin, Masta suh.'

'Demon will help yo'.'

A strong arm came to lift her and with difficulty she managed to stand. She remembered how Minty and Saphira had headed for the pile of sacking, and she too yearned for it – for any place to drop her body and hope that rest might ease the pain. Oh, how she ached, not only in her back but all over. The pain had taken roots in her body and was sending out tentacles along her nerves. It was no longer just something to be felt and endured, it was she herself – just one vast tabernacle of pain.

Again Maxwell spoke, but raised his voice so that all could hear. 'We ain' doin' no more whoppin' today. Mem, he got twenty strokes a-comin' 'n Omar he got ten, but we had enough whoppin' for today. Never whopped three wenches afore, so reckon that makes it a full day.' He took a few steps towards the open doorway and surveyed the assembled blacks.

'Yo' kin all git back to work now. A-hopin' this teach yo'-all a lesson 'n if'n it do, it worth it. No more pesterin' less'n I say so. Understand?'

'Yes suh, Masta Maxwell suh. Yes suh.'

'Shore ain' a-goin' to forget, Masta suh.'

He waited to watch them disperse and then walked out of the barn, but turned after a few steps and called back to Mem to help Lucretia Borgia to the house. For her it was a matter of putting one foot ahead of the other and praying that she could make it. She felt vaguely that somebody was missing – yes, Ham was nowhere to be seen. He should have been there. He would sympathize with her, and how she needed sympathy.

Painfully, step by slow step, Lucretia Borgia made her way to the house. She had donned her dress although it did not make much difference as all of Falconhurst had seen her naked, but she carried the white apron in her hand. She could feel the blood running down her back and the clammy feeling of her saturated dress. It seemed that she could feel every criss-cross welt on her back. Mem's supporting arm was welcome and he timed his footsteps to match her slow ones. She shrank from him. He was the cause of all her suffering. She hoped she would be well when the day came for him to be whipped so that she could see him suffer. No, she really did not want that, because when he was whipped, Omar would be too, and she did not want that glorious body to be in pain like her own. Even though he had been the cause of her suffering, she could not blame him. He had only followed out his master's commands.

The house was drawing nearer and now she could almost count the steps that it would take her to reach the gallery, ascend the steps, go in through the kitchen door and collapse face down on the blankets of her pallet. Now she was ascending the steps, now she was passing through the kitchen door, now she was on her knees before the bed, now she had slipped off the bloodied dress and had stretched her aching body out upon the bed, hoping that she might die in her misery and not suffer any longer.

She heard Mem at the sink, the sound of water being poured, and his footsteps traversing the kitchen floor. What was he doing? She gathered her strength to ask him. 'Whaffor yo' a-messin' round my kitchen, Mem?'

'Jes' a-hottin' up some water in the teakettle. A-goin' to wash yore back with warm water 'n then put some mutton taller on it. Takes out the sting. Yo' done it for me when I was whopped once, 'member?'

'Yo' a-doin' that for me, Mem?'

'Shore am, Lucretia Borgia. Sorry now I said what I did 'bout yo' 'n Omar.'

She didn't answer. In a few minutes there was the welcome sensation of her back being sponged with a soft cloth and then the strong muttony odour of the tallow. She imagined that she felt better. God knows she could not have felt worse.

Mem hunkered down. 'Yo' better, Lucretia Borgia?'

'Better,' she agreed.

The kitchen door opened and Maxwell came in. He was carrying a brown bottle in his hand. He went to the sink, filled a cup half full of water and then carefully measured out some of the bottle's liquid in a spoon.

'Here, Lucretia Borgia,' he squatted beside Mem, 'drink this.' He held the cup out to her. 'It laudanum, make yo' sleep. Yo'll feel better when yo' wakes up. Mem gits us something to eat this noon 'n I've sent for Millie to come up here 'n git supper. Yo' all right, Lucretia Borgia?' His last inquiry betrayed his anxiety.

'I'se fine, Masta Warren suh. Don' bother 'bout Millie. I'll git supper tonight.'

'Yo' shore are an ornery old buzzard, Lucretia Borgia!' His voice was kind although he spoke with authority. 'Yo' may think yo' are, but yo' ain' a-doin' a damn thing round here for two-three days. So jes' forget all 'bout it.'

'Yas suh, Masta Warren suh.' She raised her head enough to look at him. 'Thank yo'.'

His hand rested on her shoulder for a moment and then patted it. 'For strippin' the meat right off'n yore bones?'

She shook her head. 'No, Masta Warren suh, for being so good to me now.'

'Goin' to miss yo' while yo' laid up.' He straightened and walked to the gallery door. 'Where'd Ham go?' he asked Mem.

'Don' rightly know, Masta Warren suh. Didn't see him a-goin' nowhere.'

'Mighty funny he went 'thout'n tellin' me, but reckon he went somewhere to be sick. He more Hammond 'n Maxwell, 'n they mighty fine-haired, them Hammonds. They jes' cain' stand to see a nigger whopped. Always makes 'em puke.'

CHAPTER THIRTY-THREE

Although the laudanum did not obliterate the pain, it did ease it so that Lucretia Borgia drifted off into a somnolent state in which it did not really matter whether her body ached or not. It was almost as though the pain belonged to someone else, while she was safe and secure in her own bed in her own kitchen. Finally she dozed off, oblivious of everything – the pain, the stares of the other servants at her nakedness, the humiliation of being punished before them, the loss of her prestige among them. Nothing mattered now except the velvety black wings of oblivion that folded over her.

How long she slept she did not know, but something penetrated into the deep forgetfulness and roused her. She came back to consciousness and the awful realization that the pain was still with her. When she was finally able to open her eyes, she realized that a commotion in the kitchen had something to do with her awakening, but it took several minutes before she could orient herself and determine the cause of her awakening.

Millie, a buxom wench who had done some cooking for the hands from time to time, was at the stove and she was weeping. Also Mem was bustling about the kitchen fixing a hot toddy. Gradually, as she became attuned to her whereabouts, Lucretia Borgia was able to piece together the fragments of conversation that came to her, and struggled against the laudanum to wake up.

Gathering her strength, and ignoring the pain of her back which was not as strong as her curiosity, she lifted herself on one elbow and stared at the weeping Millie. She noticed that Mem too had tears in his eyes and now, fully awake, she was able to make sense out of what they were saying.

'Poor Masta Ham! He *such* a good boy. To think this had to happen to him.'

'Masta Maxwell he a-carryin' on somethin' awful. Oh,

woe be unto us! This not a good day for Falconhurst. Lucretia Borgia gittin' whopped in the mornin' 'n now this awful thing a-happenin' to pore Masta Hammond.' Millie wiped her eyes with the edge of her skirt and shuffled the pots on the hearth.

'Got to hurry up with this toddy.' Mem bustled around finding a tray for the steaming glass. 'Masta says he a-needin' it somethin' powerful.'

As much as it pained her, Lucretia Borgia sat up on the pallet, gathering the frayed blanket around her naked breasts.

'What a-happenin' here?' she demanded. 'What a-goin' on while I bin a-sleepin'? What happened to Masta Ham?'

'Ain' got no time to tell yo' now.' Mem carried the tray with the toddy on it importantly through the dining room door. 'Cain' keep Masta Warren a-waitin'.'

'What's all this mean, Millie?' Lucretia Borgia's agony was momentarily pushed far into the background. Something more important than mere physical pain had come up and she knew it demanded her attention.

'It Masta Ham, Lucretia Borgia.'

'I know that. Yo' 'n Mem a-squallin' like'n he's dead. He ain', is he?'

'Laws, no, Lucretia Borgia, but he might jes' as well be, he a-sufferin' so.'

'Then tell me 'bout it. I ain' so painful I cain' git up 'n clobber yo'.'

Millie backed away from the pallet. She knew the strength in Lucretia Borgia's uplifted hand.

'Well, it this-a-way. Masta Ham done lit out from the barn on that new horse o' his'n 'n off like'n a scalded cat down towards the river. Horse got scared at somethin' 'n threw Masta Ham off. No tellin' how long he lie there till Zolfo – he that big boy what's in Grace's cabin – he goes a-fishin' 'n comed along the river road 'n found Masta Ham a-lyin' there. Ain' no trace o' the horse so Zolfo he take Masta Ham on his back 'n brung him to the house. Masta Ham a-screamin' in pain 'n his leg jes' a-danglin'. Mem he comed down to my cabin 'n tell me I to go up to the kitchen in the big house, 'n here I am 'n tha's all I know.'

'Where Masta Ham now?' Lucretia Borgia looked towards the twins, who were quarrelling and about to burst into tears over some childish wrong.

'He up in Masta Maxwell's room a-lyin' on his papa's bed. Masta Maxwell he with him 'n he a-takin' on so's he cain' even think of what to do for pore Masta Ham.' She lifted the cover of one of the stew pans, stirred the contents with a big wooden spoon and cautiously tasted. 'Need more salt, it do.'

'Ain' nobody got no brains 'round this house?' Lucretia Borgia started to get up but her lacerated back impeded her. It took her three attempted trials before she managed to stand on her feet. She clutched the blanket around her. She had no desire to dress in front of Millie. 'Take them twins 'n git out'n here for a spell. Slap their bottoms good 'n give 'em something to cry for. Cain' be a-lyin' here whilst everything in an uproar. Got to stir myself 'n see what's a-goin' on. Masta Ham hurt 'n Masta Warren a-carryin' on. Someone got to take charge 'n reckon it's me.'

'But yo' ain' able to git up!' Millie shooed the twins over to the door. 'Yo' all cut up, Lucretia Borgia.'

'My white folks a-wantin' me 'n cain' let a little thing like'n a whoppin' keep me from 'em.'

Millie took one look at Lucretia Borgia, who, now that she was standing, needed the back of a chair for support. 'Yo' cain' make it, Lucretia Borgia,' she sniffled.

'Know I cain'. Cain' hardly stand. But I'm a-goin' to.' She made a menacing gesture with her fist and Millie and the twins disappeared through the door. She regarded her bloody dress on the floor beside her bed. It was impossible to put it on and it seemed a hundred miles to the cupboard over near the fireplace where she kept her other clothes. She stood erect, took a long breath and started to walk across the kitchen floor. Her back was worse than before; added to the pain was a constricting lameness that made any kind of movement nearly impossible. Yet step by step, using the

299

chair to help her, she propelled herself across the floor and opened the cupboard, and took down and unfolded a clean dress.

Now her real trouble started, in trying to get it over her head and down across her torn back. She was puffing and out of breath by the time she had finished, but using her muscles had somewhat decreased her lameness and she was able to get back across the kitchen without using the chair. She sat down to get her breath. If the trip to the cupboard had seemed far, it would be untold miles across the kitchen, into the dining room and through that, and into the sitting room and then up the stairs and down the hall to Maxwell's bedroom. But she had to go; neither physical pain nor the nausea which she felt rising in her stomach could restrain her. And if she were going to go, there was no time like this particular moment to start. Clutching at the big deal table in the kitchen, and then from chair to chair, she made her way to the dining room door. There she had to stop. She remembered how she had once prayed before, and she prayed for strength to see her through the ordeal that was before her.

The dining room was not quite as bad as the kitchen. She had the big table there for support and the dining room chairs around it but when she got to the vacant floor space in the sitting room she had to use all her will power to drag her feet across the room. She opened the door of the stairs and started to climb them but found it easier to sit down and hoist her heavy rump up backwards, one stair at a time. During this painful journey she could hear Hammond crying and his father's desperate and unsuccessful efforts to comfort him. When she neared the top of the stairs she could hear Hammond repeating her name between sobs.

'Where-at Lucretia Borgia?' he was crying. 'Want her, I do.'

'She cain' come,' his father answered. 'Don' yo' remember, we whopped her this mornin'?'

'Never should of done it. Lucretia Borgia she too good to be whopped,' Ham answered.

'Now, now, boy, yo' jes' rest easy. We a-goin' to get yo'

300

better soon. Don' know jes' what we a-goin' to do, but we shore as hell a-goin' to do somethin'.'

'Lucretia Borgia a-knowin' what to do. Whyn't yo' ask her?' Ham's voice was plaintive.

The fact that she was needed spurred Lucretia Borgia on. At the top step she hoisted her body up with her arms and stood up in the hall, leaning against the wall for a momentary rest. When her strength had come back she took a few painful steps and then, marshalling her resources, she threw her shoulders back and traversed the hall until she reached the door of Maxwell's room.

Ham was lying on the bed, fully dressed. His father was sitting in a straight chair beside the bed, holding his son's hand. Ham's head rolled from side to side with his sobs but his body did not move. His right leg was stretched out on the bed at an awkward angle.

'What's a-goin' on in here?' Lucretia Borgia spoke from the doorway, holding onto the door jamb for support. 'What's been a-happenin' to my baby?'

Hammond lifted his arms, voicing her name between sobs, and Maxwell turned in surprise. 'Yo' here, Lucretia Borgia? How come yo're here?'

'Jes' better be *somebody* here. What happened to my boy Ham?'

'He got thrown from that damn geldin' I bought him. A-goin' to shoot that damn horse with my own hand, I am. Never should of bought him a geldin'. They ain' to be trusted no more'n a gelded nigger.'

She dragged herself to Ham's bed, sat down on the mattress and took him in her arms, pressing him tight against her ample bosom. 'There, there,' she clucked. 'Lucretia Borgia's here 'n she a-goin' to make everything all right. Whereat yo' hurted, boy?'

His voice came muffled in her capacious bosom. 'It my leg. It painin' somethin' awful.'

'Know how yo' feels, boy.' She laid him back on the pillow and ran her fingers gently over the injured leg. 'No wonder it a-hurtin',' she said. 'Yo' done busted it. Now, ain'

301

that somethin'? My baby Hammond with a busted leg. But we a-goin' to fix it right quick. Kin do it myself but it better if'n we get someone else to do it.' She looked up from her examination of the leg and met Maxwell's gaze. 'Who'd yo' send for the doctor? Who a-ridin' for him?'

'Ain' sent no one yet, Lucretia Borgia. Been so upset over Ham, ain' had a chance to.'

'Well, godamighty, high time yo' did!' she shouted at him. 'Who yo' a-goin' to send? Mem, he the right one. He been to Benson a lot o' times 'n he know the way. Write him a pass so's the paddy-rollers won' pick him up. He a-knowin' where Dr Guthrie's house is at?'

'He a-knowin',' Maxwell said, 'but chances are the damn old fool is drunk, but I guess he better'n nothin', even if'n he ain' sober. Yo' stay with Ham whilst I go write the note 'n get Mem started.'

'If'n the old doctor ain' home, have Mem go to the tavern. Most likely he be there. Now, Masta Warren, yo' get out'n here! Got to make my baby as comfortable as I kin whilst we waitin' for the doctor.' For the second time that morning, she shooed someone out of a door, but this time it was her master, and he went meekly. She returned to the bed. Ham, grateful for her presence, had quieted down and his sobs were only quaverings of breath now.

'We a-goin' to get yo' undressed.' She smoothed back his hair. 'Goin' to get them clothes off'n yo' 'n make yo' comfortable. Shore glad I changed the sheets here yesterday. Everythin' lookin' nice 'n clean for the doctor to come – but probably he so dead drunk he not able to tell a clean sheet from a dirty one. Goin' in yore room to fetch a nightshirt. Be right back.'

It seemed to her that the hurt had almost disappeared and she walked quickly out of the room and down the hall, but when she stooped to open a bureau drawer in Ham's room, the pains informed her that they were still there. She shrugged them off. 'Ain' got no time for belly-achin' 'n complainin' today,' she whispered to herself, 'what with my baby sick in bed with a broken leg.'

She took the clean nightshirt and made her way back to Ham's room. She knew she could never get his trousers off the injured leg, so she went to the head of the back stairs and hollered down them to Millie. Fortunately Millie had returned to the kitchen; Lucretia Borgia bade her bring up the shears from the cutlery drawer. When Millie had done so, Lucretia Borgia started back to Ham.

He eyed the shears as she entered the room. 'Yo' a-goin' to cut my hair?' The only times he had ever seen Lucretia Borgia use the shears was in her attempts to barber him.

'A-goin' to cut them pants off'n yo'.'

'Yo' cain' see me nekkid,' he said.

'Shush,' she waved her hand as if to brush away such an inconsequential matter. 'Seen yo' nekkid every day when yo' jes' a shaver, 'n jes' last night yo' marchin' round here all bare ass, yo' forgit that? Don' make no neverminds, nohow. Yo' saw *me* nekkid this morning, a-swingin' back 'n forth. Now come on. Sit yo-self up so far's yo' kin 'n I'll git the shirt off'n yo'.'

She lifted him to brace him and slipped the shirt over his head. He, like the blacks, wore no undergarments and his trousers, although made of drill, were hardly better than the sleazy osnaburg clothing the servants wore. She unbuttoned the waist and then with the shears cut the trousers off the injured leg. She was horrified to see the broken white end of the bone piercing the skin. She shielded it with her body so he would not see it and become even more frightened. Easing the nightshirt on over his head, she straightened it out and then managed to get him under the sheet. Fluffing up the pillows, she propped them under his head. With Maxwell's comb and a liberal application of spit, she combed his hair. The exertions were almost too much for her and she wondered, for one moment when everything turned dim before her eyes, if she were going to faint. But this was no time for fainting. His injury was far worse than hers, and she realized that this, of all times, was when she was most needed. She couldn't allow herself the luxury of pain.

'It a-hurtin' somethin' awful, Lucretia Borgia,' he moaned.

'Shore do.' She smoothed the covers over him. 'Yo' 'n me both, Masta Ham. My pore back like ribbons, I reckon. We two pretty sick chickens, ain' we?'

'We shore are.' He managed to smile through his tears. 'Sorry papa whopped yo', Lucretia Borgia. Reckon as how that's why I'm here. Jes' couldn't hold my belly quiet after yo' got whopped. That's why I took a ride. Didn't want to puke in front o' everyone. Made that li'l old horse really gallop. Seemed to me the faster I got away from the barn, the better I liked it. Got down by the river road and puked my head off. Rode along the river road till I got feelin' better. Some varmint – a fox, I reckon – ran across the road 'n then all's I remember was flyin' through the air.'

'Reckon as how I learned me a lesson this mornin'.' Lucretia Borgia was meek. 'Don' blame yore papa for whoppin' me. He had to do it. But I ain' a-goin' to do nothin' 'gain to make me git whopped. Ain' worth it.'

She sat down on the bed, easing her body into the most comfortable position, and slipped her arm under him, propping him up. 'Feared to give yo' laudanum,' she whispered. 'We jes' have to wait like'n this till Mem come with the doctor.'

'Yo' ain' a-goin' to leave me?' He was plaintive.

'Leave my baby? 'Course not! Here yore papa now.' She glanced up as Maxwell entered. He nodded his head in approval of the smoothly made bed and Ham in his nightshirt.

'Mem, he off 'n not comin' till he fetch Dr Guthrie.' Then Maxwell did an unusual thing, probably one of the strangest he had ever done. He walked to the bed and laid his hand gently on Lucretia Borgia's shoulder. He was not a demonstrative man but there was, in this gesture, an expression of love and sympathy. 'Thank yo', Lucretia Borgia. Don' know how yo' managed it with yore back torn up 'n bleedin' so. Thankful, I am. Indebted to yo', 'n sometime I'm a-goin' to show yo'.'

'Tain' nothin',' she shrugged her shoulder, feeling the reassuring warmth of his hand. 'Ain' no use in yore a-settin here, Masta Warren suh. Yo' go 'n git Nathan 'n see if'n he got a small board in his carpenter shop. We a-goin' to need one, not too thick 'n not too long, for a splint for Masta Ham. Better have it ready when the doctor come, 'n see to it that it nice 'n smooth thout'n any splinters.'

'Never would of thought of it.' He left and she could hear his footsteps going down the stairs.

During the long wait for the doctor she scarcely moved from her position at the head of the bed, her arm around Hammond. Gradually he quieted, although she knew that his pain had not subsided any more than hers had. When Millie came upstairs to see if there was anything she could do, Lucretia Borgia sent her down for a bowl of milk toast, and this she fed to Ham with a big spoon. She kept her ears pricked, and it seemed an eternity before she heard Mem's horse and the scrunch of iron tyres on the gravel drive. She waited, and when Maxwell came up with the doctor she withdrew her arm from behind Ham, hoping that she could get back to the kitchen and lie down again.

But with the removal of her arm, Ham started to cry and begged her to stay. The doctor came over to the bed and started his examination. Lucretia Borgia realized that she resented his presence. She would have given anything to have handled it all herself, but she knew that this time she needed someone else. Somehow the doctor's whisky-laden breath and snuff-covered waistcoat made her distrust him. But, drunk or sober, he was the only doctor for miles around, and although she had once set a broken leg on one of the hands herself, she wanted a more experienced man to work on Ham.

After he had finished examining Ham, he took off his coat, removed his brassy cufflinks and rolled up his sleeves. He asked for a glass of water and she was amazed when Maxwell himself went down the stairs to get it. When he returned the doctor asked him bluntly, 'Whyn't yo' send this wench to fetch the water?'

305

Maxwell merely shrugged his shoulders. Far be it from him to tell the doctor he was saving Lucretia Borgia all the pain and trouble he could.

The doctor rummaged in his dilapidated bag and brought out a bottle. Removing the cork with his teeth, he poured out some white pills. With a dirty thumb and forefinger, he picked up two and put the rest back in the bottle. The two he gave to Ham, telling him to wash them down with water. He then pulled up a chair and settled back.

'Got to wait 'bout half an hour for them opium pills to take effect. Ain' a-goin' to stop all the pain, but do deaden it a little. Wonderin' if'n I might have a drink of corn while I'm a-waitin'?'

Maxwell went to the head of the stairs and called down to Mem to bring up two toddies – 'No, second thoughts, make it three.' Guthrie was surprised when the toddies arrived and Maxwell handed one to Lucretia Borgia, in a fine glass tumbler like the others. Guthrie glanced at it and frowned.

'Seems like'n yo' a-treatin' that nigger wench like'n she a white woman. Don' hold with sashayin' up to these goddam blacks 'n treatin' 'em like human beings. Only a-goin' to make trouble for all of us sooner or later.'

'This is my place, Doctor suh, 'n this my servant.' Maxwell was displeased at Guthrie's remark and showed it in his voice. 'Treats her the way I damn well wants.'

'No offence meant, Mista Maxwell. No offence 'tall.' Guthrie knew that he had overstepped and was apologetic. 'Kin see this wench she a special servant. My apologies, suh.'

Once again they sat, this time in silence. Hammond closed his eyes. It seemed that he was sound asleep.

But he wasn't. As soon as the old doctor started to manipulate his leg, Hammond awoke screaming. There was nothing Lucretia Borgia could do except try to hold him still with her own aching arms. Finally, at a motion from Guthrie, Maxwell went to the other side of the bed and helped to hold Ham. It seemed an eternity before it was over, but eventually Hammond's leg lay straight on the bed, the pine splint bound to it with a clean bandage torn from a sheet. Ham's face was as white as the bandage, but he was no longer screaming.

'We fixed it,' Guthrie mumbled, ' 'n how 'bout another sip o' corn afore I go back?'

Maxwell nodded and escorted him from the room. Hammond reached up his arms and encircled Lucretia Borgia's neck. His dry lips kissed hers and he fell back, comforted. The opium was taking effect again, and he snuggled his head against her bosom. Soon he was asleep. She tried to get up to soothe her own aching muscles, but every time she moved, he clung closer to her. She thought she was going to die of the pain in her back, but she did not move. Instead she stayed there throughout the long afternoon, brushing away the flies that buzzed around him. Every once in a while Maxwell tiptoed in, but each time she held up a warning finger so he would not disturb Ham.

The shadows were beginning to lengthen when Maxwell came up, accompanied by Mem with a tray. 'Millie fixed him some supper,' he said.

Lucretia Borgia took one look at the tray and then snorted. 'Ain' fit for a pig to eat.' She was indignant. 'Sick boy ain' a-goin' to eat burned pork chops 'n watery yams.' She felt Ham stirring in her arms. He opened his eyes.

'Yo' a-goin' to stay with me, Lucretia Borgia?' he whined. 'Don' leave me.'

She extricated her arm, which was practically dead. 'Got to go, boy. Got to fix yo' somethin' decent for supper. Ain' every day my baby break his leg, he got to have something special for supper. A-goin' downstairs 'n fix yo' some scrambled eggs so light they'll blow away off'n the plate. 'N a-goin' to fry yo' some ham 'n whilst that a-cookin', a-goin' to make yo' some biscuits.'

She stood up, every muscle in her body aching. With slow, careful steps, she started for the door, shooing Mem with his tray ahead of her.

Before she reached the door, Maxwell came up to her.

Gingerly, so as not to touch her lacerated back, he put his arms around her and he too, for the first time in his life, laid his head on her ample bosom.

'Obligated to yo', Lucretia Borgia, I am. Obligated, yes suh. Obligated more'n I can tell yo'.' Like Ham, he lifted his face and kissed her on the cheek. 'Obligated,' he repeated.

'Yes suh, Masta Warren suh. But ain' every day when our Masta Ham break his leg.'

'I'm a-goin' to make it up to yo', Lucretia Borgia.'

'Yo' already have, Masta Warren suh.'

He smiled at her. 'Goin' to do more'n that. Goin' to figure out somethin'.'

'Yo' jes' do that, Masta Warren suh, yo' jes' do that. I ain' worryin' my head over bein' made up to.'

He took his arms from her. Somehow all her pain had disappeared. She turned to wave a reassuring hand at Ham and walked slowly out the door. From the top of the stairs she called back. 'Won' be more'n a minute,' she promised. 'Know that my masta Ham he mighty hungry. Yore papa watch over yo' whilst I'm gone.'

Maxwell's voice came from the bedroom. 'That I will, Lucretia Borgia, and while yo' a-gettin' Ham's supper, fix some for me. Couldn't eat a damn thing that Millie cooked.'

She started down the stairs, smiling. Everything was all right again at Falconhurst. She knew that she occupied a unique place in her two masters' hearts. She was more than just a black slave, more than a mere chattel. She was a person. She was Lucretia Borgia of Falconhurst. They loved her, and what was even more, they depended on her.

EPILOGUE

When the plantation bell rang in mid-morning, a couple of weeks later, its toll did not predict a fateful happening to Lucretia Borgia. Instead, its reverberations seemed to her to foretell some happy event, although the slaves, hastily returning to the big house from the fields, did not immediately comprehend this. The whipping of Mem and Omar was foremost in their minds. However, whipping or not, they were happy. It meant that work would stop for an hour or so.

But Warren Maxwell himself had had enough of whippings for the time being and the punishment of Mem and Omar was pushed far back in his mind. Today was an occasion to honour a slave, not to demean one; to honour her as he had never honoured any slave before. Today was Lucretia Borgia's day; soon all the hands on Falconhurst would know it, but for the present even she had no idea of what was going to happen.

She had been up since early morning. The welts on her back had nearly healed and, although she was still lame, she was not in pain. With Hammond laid up in bed and with all the care of tending him in addition to her other work, she had had little time to nurse herself; but being a strong, healthy woman, her welts had healed with nothing more than the daily applications of mutton tallow which a contrite Mem had rubbed on her back.

Now she was dressed most resplendently. Mrs Maxwell's best black percale dress had been expanded to fit her, and though the gussets extending from under the arms to the hem were a muddy brown from her attempt to dye them black with walnut shells, she did not care, as their variance was completely eclipsed by the shiny mother-of-pearl buttons that decorated the front. The dress was further enhanced by a fichu of mended net, which gave it a festive appearance; and her turban of red calico was carefully wound and meticulously pleated around her head. She sat erect on a straight, splint-bottomed chair in the kitchen awaiting word from Maxwell, who had told her to be ready at ten, and meanwhile not to snoop.

She heard a commotion upstairs; and although she was tempted to go and see what it might be, she bided her time, unwilling to disobey her master's least order. She heard Mem and Maxwell and another male voice that must be one of the servants. Then there were steps on the stairs and a warning from Maxwell to take care. Her curiosity got the better of her (as it always would) and she tiptoed to the dining room door, in time to see Mem and one of the hands carrying Hammond down the stairs and across the sitting room. Nonplussed, she returned to her chair and listened to them carry him out the front door and down the gallery steps, accompanied by admonitions, curses, and warnings by Maxwell not to hurt him or hit his splinted leg.

She smiled to herself over the improvement in his condition that permitted him to be moved. She didn't dare go out on the gallery and see what might be happening. She had learned one lesson: to mind her master's orders. If he told her to stay in the kitchen until ten o'clock, there she would stay. At least the tolling of the bell did not presage another punishment; otherwise she would not have been told to make all the preparations that she had made. In addition to dressing in her new clothes, she had prepared a special dinner for the big house of fried chicken and beaten biscuits, as well as one of her famous pound cakes of which Hammond was so fond. Then she had supervised the making of a huge iron pot of Brunswick stew for the hands. It was succulent with squirrels, hog meat, and an opossum that one of the boys had shot. There was enough for all, along with chitlings, turnip greens, and black-eyed peas.

Her desire always to be in the centre of things caused her to fidget in her chair. There was no sound other than the lifting of the lid on the teakettle and the buzzing of a bluebottle fly that was unsuccessfully trying to penetrate a pane of glass. She wanted to know what was going on; why she was dressed up; why the bell was tolling; why Hammond had been carried out of the house; what it was all about, anyway! The hands of the big clock had ticked off another quarter of an hour before Maxwell entered the kitchen door and beckoned to her.

'Yo' all ready, Lucretia Borgia?'

' 'N all prettied up like'n yo' told me, Masta Maxwell suh.' She stood up and swept him a low curtsey.

'Well, if'n I do say so, yo' appear mighty fine, yes, mighty splendiferous. That dress o' Miz Maxwell's certainly do look good on yo'. Now come on, Lucretia Borgia. We a-goin' out to the barn.'

She followed a few feet behind him as they passed out onto the gallery. From there she could see the crowd of blacks standing in front of the barn and she was aware that the bell had stopped tolling. It began to look like another whipping after all, and she wondered how it could be that Mem was walking around and not shackled to a beam in the barn. She hoped it was not going to be Omar alone who was to be punished. She could not pick him out in the crowd.

All was quiet as she descended the steps of the gallery, but much to her surprise, as she neared the barn a shout arose from the crowd. She could even distinguish her own name.

'Mornin', Lucretia Borgia!'

'How yo' today, Lucretia Borgia?'

'Mighty happy to see yo' up 'n about!'

When they came closer, the crowd parted to let Maxwell through and she followed closely in his footsteps. She saw that the old horsehair couch had been carried from the sitting room, and Hammond was lying on it propped up with pillows. Beside him was the big rocking chair, also from the sitting room, and just behind these was Maxwell's splint-bottomed chair. Maxwell walked stiffly in front of her and sat down in the rocker; she obeyed the wave of his hand and sat in the chair just behind him. This, she realized, was an unprecedented honour; although she had twice sat in his presence at his bidding, she now felt absolutely glorified because everyone on Falconhurst could see her sitting in her master's presence.

311

Maxwell stood up and raised his hand for quiet. The shouting ceased and she could feel all eyes on her as she adjusted the folds of her voluminous skirt about her. Hammond reached out a hand and took one of hers for a moment. His smile told her that he was enjoying this as much as the grinning blacks who stood before her.

When the talking had ceased and there was only the shuffling of bare feet in the dust, Maxwell cleared his throat and started to speak.

'Glad to see all yo' bucks 'n wenches of Falconhurst here. Must say yo're a fine-lookin' bunch of niggers. Reckon they ain' so many good-lookin' niggers on any other plantation in the whole Territory of Alabama like'n I got here. Tha's my aim – good-lookin' niggers. I raises yo' 'n then I send yo' to the vendue table, but yo' *Falconhurst* niggers, 'n that a-meanin' yo' ain' a-goin' to be sold for no field hands. No siree! Yo'-all something special. When yo'-all go on the vendue table down in N'Orleans or up in Natchez, that mean yo' got a good life ahead o' yo'. All yo' bucks a-goin' to be stud boys on some fine plantation. Ain' a-goin' to do a lick o' work in the fields, 'cause all yo' got to do is pester the wenches every day 'n every night. Don' make no difference, though, how many wenches a Falconhurst buck pester, he always ready for the next one.'

He waited a moment for the cheers to die down and then continued. ' 'N yo' wenches, yo' a-goin' to be brood wenches, giving good strong suckers to yore masters. Ain' no heavin' 'n haulin' 'n cotton-choppin' for none of yo'. Not by a damned sight. Yo' a-goin' to be showpieces. Master of the plantation a-goin' to say to his company, "Want that yo' should see my Falconhurst stud. Shuck down, boy, so's the white folks can see what yo' got to make yo'self a champion stud." 'N when it come to the wenches, he a-goin' to say, "See this wench 'n this fine sucker she jes' birthed. Gives me a fine sucker like'n this every year, she do." Tha's 'cause yo'-all Falconhurst niggers. Ain' a blemish on nary a one o' yo'. Yo're all prime stock.'

312

He paused a moment, pursed his lips and nodded his head, waiting until the cheers and clapping were over.

'Now yo' know that we ain' never had us no overseer here at Falconhurst. I do the overseein' myself; ain' a-trustin' it to no drunken, no-good white trash. Most o' the time we git along pretty well here. Don' have many whoppin's, we don', but I'll tell yo' right here 'n now, if'n we'd had a white overseer here we'd of had whoppin's every day. Tha's why I keep track o' things myself, 'n what I don' do, my son Ham, he a-goin' to be doin' agin real soon. He a-gittin' better every day. Ain' goin' to be long afore he out again 'n seein' that yo'-all do like'n he tells yo'.'

'Pore Masta Ham.'

'Git well soon, Masta Ham suh.'

'We all a-missin' yo', Masta Ham suh.'

Hammond waved to the crowd and Maxwell waited for them to quiet down before he spoke again.

'Like'n I tol' yo', we ain' never had no overseer here, but I'm a-thinkin' it 'bout time we had one. I cain' be everywhere 'n now that Ham laid up, he cain' help me. Even when he all better, gittin' to be too many o' yo' for jes' two men. So I'm a-thinkin' we'd better have an overseer to take care o' the things me 'n Ham cain' handle. Been a-wonderin' who to get, racked my brain a-tryin' to think o' someone, when I realized that we got the best damn overseer in the world a-sittin' right here at Falconhurst.'

There was a movement of heads looking right and left, trying to figure out whom Maxwell might mean.

'Yes sir-ee! We shore got someone. But it ain' no pore white trash what knows more 'bout corn likker than he do 'bout plantin' 'n choppin' 'n gettin' new suckers into the world. Not by a damn sight. I'm a-talkin' 'bout Lucretia Borgia.'

He turned in the sudden hush and waved for her to stand up. 'Yes sir-ee, Lucretia Borgia's a-goin' to be our new overseer! That mean when she say anything to yo', yo' *jump*. 'Course she ain' a-goin' to say nothin' less'n I tells her to, so yo' can know that what she says, I tol' her to say. 'N now

313

I want to present yo' with Miz Lucretia Borgia. Yo' all knew her as Lucretia Borgia 'n that was fine, but from now on yo' a-goin' to call her *Miz* Lucretia Borgia *ma'am*. Yo' a-goin' to listen to me first, then to my son Ham, 'n then to Miz Lucretia Borgia. She yore new overseer.'

He stepped back, motioned for Lucretia Borgia to stand beside him, then actually waved her on so that for the first time in her life she stood a foot in front of her two masters. There was a great burst of cheers from the crowd.

'Miz Lucretia Borgia ma'am!'

'We yore boys, Miz Lucretia Borgia ma'am!'

' 'N we yore wenches too!'

It was an ovation such as she had never expected; for a moment she felt that she was going to cry with sheer gratitude, but she managed to control her tears. Ham reached out a hand and took hers and Maxwell placed his hand on her shoulder. It was almost more than she could bear. There were words in her throat that wanted to be spoken, but she could not find the ability to utter them.

'Miz Lucretia Borgia ma'am,' Hammond clasped her fingers and whispered to her. She felt Maxwell's hand grip her shoulder even more tightly and he too whispered in her ear.

It was a long moment before she could speak and when she did, her usually strong voice was weak and quivering with emotion; but after the first few words, her voice returned and she spoke so that all could hear her.

'Masta Warren Maxwell he jes' done give me my first order for yo'-all. He say that today a-goin' to be a holiday for all yo' folks. There's a big kettle o' Brunswick stew, 'n ain' no work this afternoon. Come evenin' yo'll do yore chores as usual, but Masta Warren say yo' kin have a Congo dance tonight 'n Masta Ham say he got a big bag o' lemon drops for yo'.'

Another tumultuous roar of applause resounded from the hands and they shuffled to form a line to pass by their three masters. Each sweaty palm clasped hers and then opened up for the lemon drop that Ham presented to them. It was a long procession and her arm ached from shaking hands, but it was a glorious moment for her. She was no longer merely Lucretia Borgia who reigned in the kitchen of the big house. She was Miz Lucretia ma'am of Falconhurst Plantation. Miz Lucretia Borgia ma'am! Yes, indeedy! Never before in all her life had she felt so happy. She was Miz Lucretia Borgia ma'am. There was no greater reward in all this life than being just that. *Miz Lucretia Borgia ma'am!*

Jaws 60p
Peter Benchley

Smashing together, they crush bones and flesh and organs into jelly.

The jaws of a giant killer shark that terrorizes a small holiday resort on Long Island.

Private feuds, lusts and jealousies take second place to a relentless duel almost unbearable in its suspense and danger ...

'As engrossing a tale as you're likely to encounter until Hailey's comet comes round again' *Chicago Sun-Times*

'Pick up *Jaws* before midnight, read the first five pages, and I guarantee you'll be putting it down, breathless and stunned – the final climax is even better than the beginning – as dawn is breaking the next day' *Daily Express*

Now a major film

If You Can't Be Good 45p
Ross Thomas

'Go-go thriller with absolutely smash finale' *Guardian*

'There were days when I went for an hour or more without even thinking about sex . . .'

Decatur Lucas had uncovered some nasty scandals working for the government. Now he was hired to dig the dirt on ex-Senator Ames.

It looked like easy money until the senator's daughter crumpled to the sidewalk in a big charred knot . . . until Homicide moved in . . . until he met Connie Mizelle . . .

'Along the line enters one of the bitchiest young women in contemporary mystery fiction . . . Thomas does not spare the punches . . . fast-paced, brightly observant' *New York Times*

'Hyper-compulsive' *Observer*

The Kappillan of Malta 75p
Nicholas Monsarrat

'A better novel than *The Cruel Sea*'
Sunday Times

'He gave us heart'

Heart was what the people needed during the long years of Malta's agony, 1940–42, and Father Salvatore was the man to provide it.

With superb immediacy and vivacity, Monsarrat retells the dramatic story of the fortress of the Middle Sea from its violent past to the days when enemy armadas swooped out of the blue skies to pound the island into dust.

Here are humour and compassion, bravery and devotion, and the tender love of a young Maltese girl for a Hurricane pilot . . .

'A blockbuster of a novel . . . in the figure of Salvatore who staunches the blood of the wounded and runs his own church in the ancient catacombs, Monsarrat has created one of the most memorable characters of postwar fiction' *Daily Express*

The Girl from Storyville 75p
Frank Yerby

Fanny Turner – a born wanton, dangerous and evil.

Her haunting, magnetic beauty brought degradation and
destruction to all who came under her spell.

In a gripping story of lust and passion, love and hate, set in the
red-light district of New Orleans amid the licence and elegance
which characterized the turn of the century, the graphic pen of a
master storyteller depicts the world of the *demi-mondaine* with
stark realism and compelling candour.

'A fine example of the romantic historical extravaganza here with
just a touch of pornography that Frank Yerby has made his own'
Sunday Times

These and other Pan books are obtainable from all booksellers
and newsagents. If you have any difficulty please send purchase
price plus 7p postage to

PO Box 11, Falmouth, Cornwall

While every effort is made to keep prices low, it is sometimes
necessary to increase prices at short notice. PAN books reserve
the right to show new retail prices on covers which may differ
from those previously advertised in the text or elsewhere